KU-661-181

A 358   5 ∅ 10
3 83   2 4. 6
40 9   6.

ued.

WITHDRAWN

THE INSTITUTE OF MARINE ENGINEERS	
DATE OF ACCESSION	11-8-89
PUBLISHED PRICE	—
CLASSIFICATION No.	93 (OR) *

8498/8N

LONGMANS' MODERN MATHEMATICAL SERIES

General Editors
P. ABBOTT, B.A., and
F. S. MACAULAY, M.A., D.Sc.

INTERMEDIATE MECHANICS

LONGMANS' MODERN MATHEMATICAL SERIES

Editor :

P. ABBOTT, B.A.

The Teaching of Algebra (including Trigonometry)
By T. PERCY NUNN, M.A., D.Sc. With Diagrams. Crown 8vo, 9s.

Exercises in Algebra (including Trigonometry)
By T. PERCY NUNN, M.A., D.Sc. With Diagrams. Crown 8vo.
Part I. Without Answers, 6s. 6d. With Answers, 7s. 6d.
Part I. Section I, 3s. ; Sections II and III, 4s.
Part II. Without Answers, 7s. 6d. With Answers, 8s. 6d.

Exercises in Arithmetic and Mensuration
By P. ABBOTT, B.A. With Diagrams. Crown 8vo.
Without Answers, 6s. With Answers, 6s. 6d. In Two Sections, 4s. each. Answers separately, 2s.
Also issued in Four Parts in Stout Paper Covers. Part I. Without Answers, 1s. 4d. With Answers, 1s. 6d.
Part II. Without Answers, 1s. 6d. With Answers, 1s. 9d.
Part III. Without Answers, 1s. 6d. With Answers, 1s. 9d.
Part IV. Without Answers, 1s. 9d. With Answers, 2s.

The Groundwork of Arithmetic
A Handbook for Teachers. By MARGARET PUNNETT, B.A. With Coloured and other Diagrams. Crown 8vo, 5s.

Exercises in the Groundwork of Arithmetic
By MARGARET PUNNETT, B.A. Crown 8vo. Book I, 8d. ; Book II, 1s. ; Book III, 1s.

Projective Geometry
By G. B. MATHEWS, M.A., F.R.S. With Diagrams. Crown 8vo, 6s.

A School Course in Geometry (including the Elements of Trigonometry and Mensuration and an Introduction to the Methods of Co-ordinate Geometry)
By W. J. DOBBS, M.A. With 361 Diagrams. Crown 8vo. Without Answers, 5s. With Answers, 6s. Answers separately, 6d.

Ruler and Compasses
By HILDA P. HUDSON, M.A., Sc.D. With 93 Diagrams. Crown 8vo, 6s. 6d. net.

Slide-Rule Notes
By Colonel H. C. DUNLOP and C. S. JACKSON, M.A. With Diagrams. Crown 8vo, 3s. 6d. net.

Infinitesimal Calculus
By F. S. CAREY, M.A. 8vo, 16s. net. In Two Sections. Section I, 7s. 6d. net. Section II, 10s. 6d. net.

Differential Equations
By H. BATEMAN, Ph.D., M.A. 8vo, 10s. 6d. net.

Numerical Trigonometry
By P. ABBOTT, B.A. With Diagrams. Crown 8vo, 3s. 6d.

Mathematical Tables and Formulæ
By P. ABBOTT, B.A. Crown 8vo, 2s.

Examples in Differential and Integral Calculus
By C. S. JACKSON, M.A. 8vo, 6s. net

A Companion to Elementary School Mathematics
By F. C. BOON, B.A. With Diagrams. 8vo, 14s. net

The Elements of Mechanics
By F. S. CAREY, M.A., and J. PROUDMAN, M.A., D.Sc., F.R.S. With Diagrams. 8vo, 8s. 6d.

Intermediate Mechanics
By D. HUMPHREY, B.A., B.SC. Vol. I Dynamics. With 159 Diagrams. 8vo, 10s. 6d. Vol. II. Statics and Hydrostatics. With 324 Diagrams. 8vo. 10s. 6d.

Longmans' Modern Mathematical Series

INTERMEDIATE MECHANICS

BY

D. HUMPHREY, B.A., B.Sc.

DIRECTOR OF EDUCATION, THE POLYTECHNIC, LONDON, W. I.
(FORMERLY HEAD OF THE DEPARTMENT OF MATHEMATICS AND PHYSICS).

DYNAMICS

WITH DIAGRAMS

LONGMANS, GREEN AND CO.
LONDON ◆ NEW YORK ◆ TORONTO
1933

LONGMANS, GREEN AND CO. LTD.
39 PATERNOSTER ROW, ·LONDON, E.C.4
6 OLD COURT HOUSE STREET, CALCUTTA
53 NICOL ROAD, BOMBAY
36A MOUNT ROAD, MADRAS

LONGMANS, GREEN AND CO.
55 FIFTH AVENUE, NEW YORK
221 EAST 20TH STREET, CHICAGO
88 TREMONT STREET, BOSTON

LONGMANS, GREEN AND CO.
480-486 UNIVERSITY AVENUE, TORONTO

First published July 1930
Reprinted by the Novographic
Process November 1933

Made in Great Britain

PREFACE.

WHILE engaged in teaching Mechanics to Senior Forms during a number of years, I have felt, especially in recent years, the need of a book dealing with harder applications of the principles of the subject, and filling the gap between the elementary book and the more advanced treatise written for degree students.

At the present time the standard required for the various Higher Certificate and University Scholarship Examinations is undoubtedly high, and the student is expected to be able to apply fundamental principles to problems which require considerable thought and skill without introducing any great mathematical difficulties.

To acquire the necessary skill necessitates a course of training which I feel is of considerable value in itself apart altogether from the question of examinations, and the object of the present book is to provide such a course. It is intended to meet the requirements of students working for Intermediate B.Sc., various Higher Certificate and University Scholarship Examinations. The book is not intended for beginners, but I have tried to make the earlier chapters in both volumes complete enough to enable them to be used by those who have done even a short course in the elements of the subject.

The methods of the Calculus have been used throughout. This subject is now taken in the Upper Forms of most schools, and the application to Mechanics can be used as a means of introducing and illustrating the fundamental ideas of the differential and integral calculus.

The contents of each chapter have been arranged to depend, as far as possible, on the same mechanical principle, the harder examples being placed at the end of the chapter so that they may be left to a second reading.

The present volume covers the subject of Dynamics to the standard already mentioned, and includes two chapters on the motion of a rigid body. Statics and Hydrostatics are dealt with in a second volume.

With such a large number of examples I can scarcely hope that there are no errors in the questions or answers, but shall be very grateful for any corrections, and also for any suggestions for improvement.

I wish to express my thanks to the Syndics of the Cambridge University Press, the University of London, certain of the Cambridge Colleges, the Oxford and Cambridge Schools Examination Board, the Joint Matriculation Board and the Central Welsh Board, for permission to use questions set in various examinations.

I am deeply indebted to Mr. F. J. Swan, B.A., for the very valuable assistance he has given me in correcting the proof-sheets and making a number of suggestions.

My thanks are also due to Mr. P. Abbott for much assistance and advice both with the manuscript and while the book has been in the press.

D. HUMPHREY.

THE POLYTECHNIC,
May, 1930.

CONTENTS.

CHAPTER I.

SPEED, VELOCITY AND ACCELERATION.

CHAPTER II.

FORCE, MOMENTUM, WORK AND ENERGY.

CONTENTS

CHAPTER III.

IMPULSIVE FORCES. IMPACT OF ELASTIC BODIES.

CHAPTER IV.

PROJECTILES.

CHAPTER V.

MOTION IN A CIRCLE.

CHAPTER VI.

SIMPLE HARMONIC MOTION.

CHAPTER VII.

MOTION OF A PARTICLE IN TWO DIMENSIONS.

CHAPTER VIII.

MOTION OF A RIGID BODY ABOUT A FIXED AXIS.

CHAPTER IX.

MOTION OF A RIGID BODY IN TWO DIMENSIONS.

The following abbreviations are used to denote the source from which examples are taken:—

B.Sc.   London University. B.Sc. Examination.
C.S.   College Scholarships. Cambridge University.
C.W.B.   Central Welsh Board. Higher Certificate.
Ex.   Exhibitions. London University.
H.C.   Oxford and Cambridge Higher Certificate.
H.S.C.   Higher Schools. Group C. London University.
H.S.D.   Higher Schools. Group D. London University.
I.A.   Intermediate Arts. London University.
I.C.   Imperial College. Entrance and Scholarship Examination.
I.E.   Intermediate Engineering. London University.
I.S.   Intermediate Science. London University.
M.T.   Mathematical Tripos. Part I. Cambridge.
N.U.   Joint Matriculation Board. Northern Universities. Higher Certificate.
Q.E.   Qualifying Examination. Mechanical Sciences Tripos, Cambridge.
S.   Scholarships Examination. London University.

CHAPTER I.

SPEED, VELOCITY AND ACCELERATION.

§ 1. When a point is changing its position it is said to be in motion, and the curve drawn through all the successive positions of the point is called its path.

§ 2. The *speed* of a moving point is the rate at which it describes its path. The speed expresses the rate of motion without reference to the direction of motion. Speed is therefore a quantity having magnitude only, and is expressed completely when we know this magnitude.

A quantity having magnitude and no direction is called a *Scalar quantity*, so that speed is a scalar.

Other examples of scalar quantities are mass and density.

§ 3. The speed of a point is said to be *Uniform* when it is moving through equal lengths of its path in equal times, however small these times may be.

When uniform, the speed of a point is measured by the distance moved through in unit time.

If s is the distance moved through in time t, then the speed v is given by

$$v = \frac{s}{t},$$

$$\therefore s = vt.$$

§ 4. When the speed is varying, its value at any instant is the distance the point would pass through in the next unit of time, if it continued to move with the speed which it has at that instant.

§ 5. The *average speed* of a moving point in any given interval of time is the speed with which it would have to move uniformly to describe the same distance in the same time. The average speed is obviously obtained by dividing the whole distance by the whole time. Now, if the interval of time is at all large, it is clear that the speed may have varied at different times during the interval. Hence we cannot obtain the speed *at any instant* from the distance travelled in an interval of time of any finite size.

§ 6. The speed at any instant is measured by the rate of motion during a very short interval of time including that instant, this interval being so short that the speed will not have time to change.

In the notation of the differential calculus, if δs is the length of path described in a very short interval of time δt, including the given instant, the limiting value of

$$\frac{\delta s}{\delta t} \text{ as } \delta t \to o, \text{ i.e. } \frac{ds}{dt},$$

is the speed of the point at the instant considered.

§ **7.** The unit of speed is the speed of a point which moves uniformly through unit distance in unit time.

The English units of length and time most frequently used in dynamics are the foot and the second, and the unit of mass is the pound. These units are often called the foot-pound-second system, abbreviated to F.P.S. system.

The metric units most commonly used are the centimetre, gram and second, and this is usually called the C.G.S. system.

The units of speed in these systems will be

1 foot per second, abbreviated to 1 ft./sec. or 1 ft. per sec., and
1 centimetre per second, abbreviated to 1 cm./sec. or
1 cm. per sec.

§ **8.** Speeds are, of course, often expressed in other units, such as miles per hour (abbreviated to m.p.h.), and the unit of speed used in navigation is the knot, a speed of 1 nautical mile (6080 ft.) per hour.

In most cases it is best to bring all speeds to feet per second (or centimetres per second) when working examples in dynamics, and it is convenient to remember that

$$60 \text{ m.p.h.} = 88 \text{ ft./sec.}$$

This relation is easily obtained as follows :—

$$60 \text{ m.p.h.} = 1 \text{ mile in } 1 \text{ minute,}$$

$$= \frac{1}{60} \text{ mile in } 1 \text{ second,}$$

$$= \frac{5280}{60} \text{ feet in } 1 \text{ second,}$$

$$= 88 \text{ feet in } 1 \text{ second.}$$

§ **9. Displacement.**

The displacement of a moving point is its change of position. Now we can fix the position of a point P in a plane in two ways, as follows :—

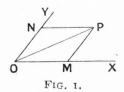

FIG. 1.

(i) Let OX, OY (Fig. 1) be two fixed straight lines in the plane, and let PM be drawn parallel to OY to meet OX in M, and let PN be drawn parallel to OX to meet OY in N. Then the lengths of PN and PM (or OM and ON) will determine the position of P.

These lengths are the Cartesian co-ordinates of P, referred to the axes OX, OY.

Usually the axes are taken at right angles to each other.

(ii) The position of P is also determined if we know the length of the line OP and the angle XOP.

These are the polar co-ordinates of P, referred to O as origin and OX as initial line.

§ 10. In the second method the position of the point relative to O is determined by the length and direction of a straight line. Any quantity which involves magnitude and direction in this way, and is therefore capable of being represented by a straight line of certain length drawn in a certain direction, is called a *vector quantity*.

The vector OP determines the position of P relative to O.

The notation $\overrightarrow{OP}$ is used to show that the direction of the vector is from O to P.

$$\overrightarrow{OP} = -\overrightarrow{PO},$$

§ 11. If P (Fig. 2) moves to Q, the position of Q with reference to O is represented by the vector $\overrightarrow{OQ}$, and the change of position or displacement of P is represented by the line (or vector) $\overrightarrow{PQ}$.

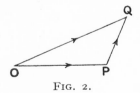

FIG. 2.

It is clear that to express completely the displacement of a point P in moving to another position Q we must state the magnitude and direction of the line joining P to Q.

By saying that the displacement is represented completely by the *vector* $\overrightarrow{PQ}$ we imply that the direction, as well as the length, of PQ is known.

We also see that if the positions of the points P and Q are represented by the vectors $\overrightarrow{OP}$, $\overrightarrow{OQ}$, the change in position, i.e. the difference between the vectors $\overrightarrow{OQ}$, $\overrightarrow{OP}$, is represented by the vector $\overrightarrow{PQ}$.

1 *

If P has moved to Q, the difference of the vectors $\overrightarrow{OP}$, $\overrightarrow{OQ}$ is $\overrightarrow{OQ} - \overrightarrow{OP}$, and this is equal to $\overrightarrow{PQ}$.

The difference $\overrightarrow{OP} - \overrightarrow{OQ}$ is equal to $\overrightarrow{QP}$.

§ **12.** If the point starts from O and moves to P, the displacement is $\overrightarrow{OP}$, and if it then moves to Q the further displacement is $\overrightarrow{PQ}$, the total displacement is $\overrightarrow{OQ}$,

$$\therefore \overrightarrow{OP} + \overrightarrow{PQ} = \overrightarrow{OQ}.$$

$\overrightarrow{OQ}$ is called the *vector sum* of $\overrightarrow{OP}$ and $\overrightarrow{PQ}$.

It is clear that OQ is equal and parallel to the diagonal of the parallelogram having OP and PQ as adjacent sides.

We thus obtain the parallelogram law for finding the resultant of two displacements.

§ **13.** If $\overrightarrow{AB}$, $\overrightarrow{AC}$ (Fig. 3) represent two displacements of a point, the resultant displacement is represented by the diagonal $\overrightarrow{AD}$ of the parallelogram ABDC.

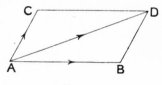

FIG. 3.

We have $\overrightarrow{AC} + \overrightarrow{AB} = \overrightarrow{AD}$,

and $\overrightarrow{BD} + \overrightarrow{DC} = \overrightarrow{BC}$,

but $\overrightarrow{BD} = \overrightarrow{AC}$, and $\overrightarrow{DC} = -\overrightarrow{AB}$,

i.e. $\overrightarrow{AC} - \overrightarrow{AB} = \overrightarrow{BC}$, the other diagonal.

§ 14. Velocity.

The velocity of a moving point at any time is the rate of its displacement. Velocity must therefore possess both magnitude and direction, and is a vector quantity.

The velocity of a point is said to be uniform or constant when it is moving in a constant direction with uniform speed.

When a point is moving in a straight line its velocity and speed are the same, otherwise they are not the same.

For example, suppose a point is describing a circle with uniform speed, then, since its *direction* of motion is continually changing, its *velocity* is *not* constant.

When uniform, the velocity of a moving point is measured by its displacement in unit time.

§ 15. When the velocity of a moving point is variable its velocity at any instant is understood to mean the displacement it would undergo in the next unit of time if it continued to move with the velocity which it had at the instant considered.

§ 16. Suppose a point P to move in a plane to the position Q, we have seen that the displacement is $\overrightarrow{PQ}$ and that this is denoted by $\overrightarrow{OQ} - \overrightarrow{OP}$.

If t is the time taken to go from P to Q, the average velocity during this interval is

$$\frac{\overrightarrow{OQ} - \overrightarrow{OP}}{t}, \text{ or } \frac{\overrightarrow{PQ}}{t}.$$

The velocity at P is given by taking the interval of time indefinitely small, so that the velocity at P is

$$\underset{t \to 0}{\text{Limit }} \frac{\overrightarrow{OQ} - \overrightarrow{OP}}{t}, \text{ or } \underset{t \to 0}{\text{Limit }} \frac{\overrightarrow{PQ}}{t}.$$

§ 17. The unit of velocity is the velocity of a point which undergoes a displacement equal to unit distance in unit time.

Numerically this is the same as the unit of speed, and the magnitude of the velocity of a point is the same as the magnitude of its speed. To express completely the velocity we must add a statement as to the direction of motion.

§ 18. A point or body may have several different velocities simultaneously, e.g. a person walking on the deck of a ship in motion. The single velocity which is equivalent to several other velocities is called their *resultant*, and the several velocities are called the *components* of this resultant.

Velocities, like all vector quantities, can be compounded by the parallelogram law, as shown in the case of displacements.

The resultant is the vector sum of the components.

It is, however, more satisfactory to give a formal proof for each kind of vector as we deal with it.

§ 19. The Parallelogram of Velocities.

If a moving point possess simultaneously velocities represented in magnitude and direction by the straight lines OA, OB, they are equivalent to a velocity represented by the diagonal OC of the parallelogram OACB.

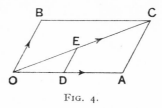

FIG. 4.

For, if OA (Fig. 4) represents a velocity of magnitude u, and OB a velocity of magnitude v, we may imagine the point to move along OA with speed u while the line OA moves parallel to itself so that its end O describes the line OB with speed v.   In unit time the point will have moved along OA to A, and the line OA will have moved into the position BC, so that the moving point will be at C.

At any intermediate time t the point will have moved a distance ut along OA to D, say, while the line OA will have moved a distance vt parallel to itself.

If DE is drawn parallel to AC to meet OC in E,

$$\frac{DE}{OD} = \frac{AC}{OA} = \frac{v}{u},$$

$$\therefore DE = OD \cdot \frac{v}{u} = ut\frac{v}{u} = vt,$$

∴ DE is the distance moved by the line OA,

∴ the point will be at E.

Hence OC is the path described by the point, and OC represents in magnitude and direction the velocity which is equivalent to OA, OB, i.e. it represents their resultant.

If the angle AOB = α,

$$OC^2 = OA^2 + AC^2 + 2OA \cdot AC \cos \alpha.$$

Hence, if the resultant OC is V,

$$V^2 = u^2 + v^2 + 2uv \cos \alpha.$$

If the component velocities u and v are at right angles,

$$V^2 = u^2 + v^2.$$

§ 20. Resolution of a Velocity.

We can use the parallelogram law to resolve a given velocity into two components.   It is obvious that this can be done in an infinite number of ways, for we can describe any number of parallelograms on a given straight line as diagonal.

In practice the directions of the components are given, and these directions are usually at right angles.

In the latter case the values of the component velocities are easily obtained as follows:—

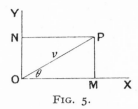

FIG. 5.

Let OP (Fig. 5) represent the given velocity v, and suppose we wish to resolve it into two components, one along OX, and the other in a perpendicular direction OY.

Draw PM perpendicular to OX and PN perpendicular to OY.

Then OM, ON represent the components along OX and OY.

If the angle XOP $= \theta$,

$$OM = v \cos \theta, \text{ and } ON = v \sin \theta.$$

Hence a velocity v is equivalent to a velocity $v \cos \theta$ along a line making an angle θ with its own direction, together with a velocity of $v \sin \theta$ perpendicular to the direction of the first component.

§ 21. If x, y are the co-ordinates of the point P at any instant referred to axes OX, OY, then OM $= x$, ON $= y$.

The component velocities parallel to the axes are the rates of change of OM and ON, i.e.

$$\frac{dx}{dt} \text{ and } \frac{dy}{dt}.$$

These are often denoted by $\dot{x}$ and $\dot{y}$, i.e. $\dot{x} = \frac{dx}{dt}$, $\dot{y} = \frac{dy}{dt}$. By considering both components, we automatically take into account changes in the direction of motion of P.

Changes in the values of x and y give us the change in position or displacement of P both in magnitude and direction, and the rates of change of x and y give us the rate of displacement of P.

This method of considering component velocities is of great importance when we have to deal with cases of motion where the path is not a straight line.

§ 22. When we speak of the component of a velocity in a given direction, it is understood that the other direction in which the velocity is to be resolved is perpendicular to this given direction.

If we do require the components of a velocity v in directions making angles α and β with it, they can be found as follows:—

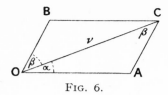

FIG. 6.

Let OC (Fig. 6) represent v. Draw OA and OB, making angles α and β with OC, and through C draw parallels to complete the parallelogram OACB.

Then OA and OB, or OA and AC represent the required components. Hence, from the triangle OAC,

$$\frac{OA}{\sin \beta} = \frac{OC}{\sin A} = \frac{OC}{\sin (\alpha + \beta)},$$

$$\therefore OA = \frac{v \sin \beta}{\sin (\alpha + \beta)}.$$

Similarly,

$$OB = \frac{v \sin \alpha}{\sin (\alpha + \beta)}.$$

EXAMPLES I.

1. Find the resultant of velocities of 8 ft./sec. and 6 ft./sec. at right angles.

2. Find the resultant of velocities of 8 ft./sec. and 6 ft./sec. inclined at an angle of 60°.

3. A railway carriage is travelling at 30 ft./sec., and a person rolls a ball across the floor of the carriage at right angles to the direction of motion of the train at 16 ft./sec. Find the resultant velocity of the ball.

4. A point is moving in a straight line with a velocity of 12 ft./sec.; find the component of its velocity in a direction inclined at an angle of 30° to its direction of motion.

5. A ball is moving at 60 ft./sec. in a direction inclined at 60° to the horizontal; find the horizontal and vertical components of its velocity.

§ 23. Triangle of Velocities.

If a moving point possess simultaneously velocities represented by the two sides AB, BC of a triangle taken in order, their resultant is represented by AC.

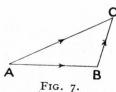

FIG. 7.

This follows at once from the parallelogram of velocities.

The resultant of $\overrightarrow{AB}$, $\overrightarrow{BC}$ (Fig. 7) is their vector sum, i.e. $\overrightarrow{AC}$.

§ 24. Polygon of Velocities.

If a moving point possess simultaneously velocities represented by the sides AB, BC, CD, . . . LM, of a polygon taken in order, their resultant is represented by AM.

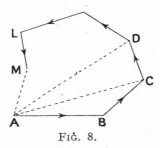

Fig. 8.

For, by the triangle of velocities, the resultant of AB and BC (Fig. 8) is represented by AC, the resultant of AC, CD is represented by AD, and so on ; the resultant of all the velocities is therefore represented by AM.

It is obvious that this result also holds if the sides of the polygon are not in one plane.

§ **25.** When a point possesses a number of given velocities we can find their resultant by resolving each of them in two fixed directions OX, OY at right angles, adding the components in each of these directions to obtain a single velocity along OX and another along OY, and then compounding these two perpendicular velocities into a single one.

EXAMPLE.

A point has velocities of 2, 4√2̄, 6, and 8 inclined at angles of 30°, 45°, 60°, and 120° respectively to a given direction. Find the magnitude and direction of their resultant.

Let OX (Fig. 9) be the given direction, and OY perpendicular to it. The components along OX are

$$2 \cos 30°, \ 4\sqrt{2} \cos 45°, \ 6 \cos 60°, \ 8 \cos 120°,$$

or, $\sqrt{3},$ 4,   3,   − 4,

and their sum is

$$\sqrt{3} + 3.$$

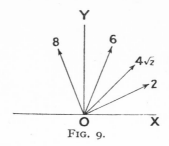

Fig. 9.

The components along OY are

$$2 \sin 30°, \quad 4\sqrt{2} \sin 45°, \quad 6 \sin 60°, \quad 8 \sin 120°,$$

or $\qquad$ 1, $\qquad$ 4, $\qquad$ $3\sqrt{3}$, $\qquad$ $4\sqrt{3}$,

and their sum is

$$5 + 7\sqrt{3}.$$

The velocities are therefore equivalent to a velocity of $3 + \sqrt{3}$ along OX and a velocity of $5 + 7\sqrt{3}$ along OY.

If V is the resultant,

$$V^2 = (3 + \sqrt{3})^2 + (5 + 7\sqrt{3})^2$$
$$= 315\cdot632.$$
$$\therefore V = 17\cdot76.$$

If θ is the angle made by this resultant with OX,

$$\tan \theta = \frac{5 + 7\sqrt{3}}{3 + \sqrt{3}} = \frac{17\cdot124}{4\cdot732} = 3\cdot618 ;$$

$$\therefore \theta = 74\tfrac{1}{2}° \text{ nearly.}$$

§ 26. EXAMPLE (i).

A boat is rowed with a velocity of 4 m.p.h. straight across a river which is flowing at 3 m.p.h. Find the magnitude and direction of the resultant velocity of the boat. If the breadth of the river is 400 feet, find how far down the river the boat will reach the opposite bank.

The component velocities of the boat are 4 m.p.h. and 3 m.p.h. at right angles. If v is the resultant velocity

$$v = \sqrt{3^2 + 4^2} \qquad = \sqrt{9 + 16} \qquad = 5 \text{ m.p.h.}$$

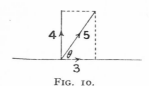

Fig. 10.

If θ (Fig. 10) is the angle the direction of this velocity makes with the bank,

$$\cos \theta = \tfrac{3}{5}, \text{ or } \theta = \cos^{-1}\tfrac{3}{5}.$$

To find how far down the river the boat reaches the opposite bank it is better to use the component velocities.

The time taken to get across the stream is not affected by the current as the man keeps rowing at right angles to the bank.

$$4 \text{ m.p.h.} = \frac{88 \times 4}{60} = \frac{88}{15} \text{ ft./sec.,}$$

$$\therefore \text{ the time taken to cross} = \frac{400 \times 15}{88} \text{ sec.,}$$

$$\text{The speed of the current is } \frac{88 \times 3}{60} = \frac{88}{20} \text{ ft./sec.,}$$

hence, in the time taken to cross, the boat will be carried down stream a distance of

$$\frac{88}{20} \times \frac{400 \times 15}{88} = 300 \text{ ft.}$$

EXAMPLE (ii).

A stream is running at 3 m.p.h., and its breadth is 440 feet. If a man can row a boat at 5 m.p.h., find the direction in which he must row in order to go straight across the stream, and the time it takes him to cross.

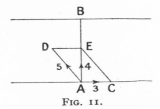

FIG. 11.

Let A (Fig. 11) be the point from which the man starts, and AB perpendicular to the banks.

Then the resultant of the stream's velocity of 3 m.p.h. in direction AC and the man's velocity of 5 m.p.h. has to be in the direction AB. If AC represents the velocity of the stream to scale, and AD the man's velocity to the same scale, then the diagonal AE of the parallelogram whose adjacent sides are AC and AD must lie along AB, and AE = $\sqrt{5^2 - 3^2} = 4$.

Cos DAE = $\tfrac{4}{5}$, i.e. he must row in a direction making an angle $\cos^{-1}\tfrac{4}{5}$ with AB.

Also his resultant velocity is 4 m.p.h. or $\tfrac{88}{15}$ ft./sec.,

$$\therefore \text{ the time to cross} = \frac{440 \times 15}{88} = \frac{40 \times 15}{8} = 75 \text{ sec.}$$

EXAMPLES II.

1. A boat is rowed with a velocity of 5 m.p.h. straight across a river flowing at 3 m.p.h. If the breadth of the river be 500 feet, find how far down the river the boat will reach the opposite bank.

2. A man wishes to go straight across a river ; if he can row his boat with three times the velocity of the current, find at what inclination to the current he must keep the boat pointed.

3. A boy is riding a bicycle at 10 m.p.h. ; in what direction must he throw a stone with a velocity of 22 ft./sec. so that 'its resultant motion may be at right angles to his own direction.

4. A boat is moored at a place where a current is flowing eastwards at $1\frac{1}{2}$ m.p.h. Two buoys are also moored, each 176 ft. from the boat, one due north, the other due east of it. Two equally fast swimmers, each capable of a speed of $2\frac{1}{2}$ m.p.h. in still water, start from the boat at the same time to swim one to each buoy and back to the boat. Which will reach the boat again first, and how much sooner ?

5. A point which has velocities represented by 8, 9, and 13 is at rest ; find the angle between the directions of the two smaller velocities.

6. A point has velocities of 3, 5, 4, and 6 in directions E., N.E., N., and N.W. respectively ; find the magnitude and direction of its resultant velocity.

7. A point has equal velocities in two given directions ; if one of these velocities be halved, the angle which the resultant makes with the other is halved also. Show that the angle between the velocities is 120°.

8. If a point has two velocities, u_1 and u_2 inclined at such an angle that the resultant velocity $V = u_1$, show that, if u_1 be doubled, the new resultant is at right angles to u_2.

9. A man who swims at 3 m.p.h. in still water wishes to cross a river 176 yards wide, flowing at 5 m.p.h. Indicate graphically the direction in which he should swim in order to reach the opposite bank (a) as soon as possible, (b) as little down stream as possible. How long will he take to cross, and how far will he be carried down stream in each case ?

10. A ship is steaming on a course 30° east of north at a speed of $12\frac{1}{2}$ knots, and a man walks backwards and forwards across the deck in a direction perpendicular to the ship's course at a speed of 5 ft./sec. Find the actual directions in which the man moves.

(H.C.)

§ 27. Relative Velocity.

When the distance between two points P and Q is altering, either in magnitude or direction, then either point is said to have a velocity relative to the other.

The relative velocity is the vector difference of the velocities of P and Q.

If the points are moving in parallel directions, this is the same as the algebraic difference of the velocities.

If $\overrightarrow{AB}$ (Fig. 12) of magnitude u, and $\overrightarrow{CD}$, of magnitude v, represent

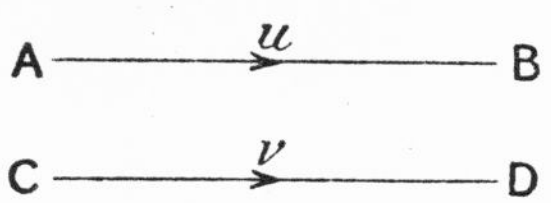

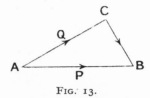

A $\xrightarrow{\quad u \quad}$ B

C $\xrightarrow{\quad v \quad}$ D

Fig. 12.

the velocities of P and Q, AB being parallel to CD, the velocity of P relative to Q is

$$u - v,$$

and that of Q relative to P is

$$v - u.$$

In each case this is the resultant of the velocity of one point and that of the other reversed.

Fig. 13.

If $\overrightarrow{AB}$, $\overrightarrow{AC}$ (Fig. 13) represent the velocities of P and Q, The velocity of P relative to Q is

$$\overrightarrow{AB} - \overrightarrow{AC} = \overrightarrow{CB},$$

The velocity of Q relative to P is

$$\overrightarrow{AC} - \overrightarrow{AB} = \overrightarrow{BC}.$$

Here, again, it is clear that the velocity of P relative to Q is the resultant of the velocity of P and the velocity of Q reversed. Similarly, in the second case.

Hence we may obtain the velocity of P relative to Q by compounding with the velocity of P a velocity equal and opposite to that of Q, and the point Q may then be regarded as at rest.

§ 28. This can be expressed in another way. It is clear that the relative velocity, which is the difference between the velocities, of two points, will not be affected by impressing on each of them equal (and parallel) velocities.

Hence, if we impress on both P and Q velocities equal and opposite to that of Q, the latter will be reduced to rest and the resultant velocity of P will be, as shown above, the velocity of P relative to Q.

We can find all about the *relative* motion of P and Q (such as the shortest distance between them) by considering P to move with this relative velocity while Q remains at rest.

Most problems on relative velocity can be solved by this method of reducing one of the points to rest, as illustrated in the following examples.

There are some, however (such as Example (iii), § 52), which require the use of the vector method.

The usual method is as follows :—

To find the velocity of P relative to Q, we compound with the velocity of P a velocity equal and opposite to that of Q by the parallelogram law.

EXAMPLE (i).

A ship is steaming due east at 15 m.p.h., and another ship is steaming due south at 20 m.p.h. ; find the velocity of the second ship relative to the first.

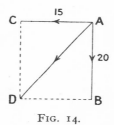

FIG. 14.

If AB (Fig. 14) represents the velocity of the second ship, we have to compound with it a velocity of 15 m.p.h. due west. If this is represented by AC, the relative velocity is represented by the diagonal AD of the rectangle ABDC.

$$AD^2 = AB^2 + DB^2 = 20^2 + 15^2 = 625,$$
$$\therefore AD = 25.$$

The relative velocity is therefore 25 m.p.h., and its direction makes an angle west of south whose tangent is $\frac{3}{4}$.

EXAMPLE (ii).

A train is travelling along a horizontal rail at 45 m.p.h., and rain is falling vertically with a velocity of 22 ft./sec. Find the apparent direction and velocity of the rain to a person travelling in the train.

The velocity of the train is 66 ft./sec.

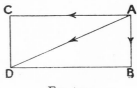

FIG. 15.

Let AB (Fig. 15) represent the actual velocity of the rain. Draw AC horizontal and opposite to the direction of the train to represent the magnitude of the velocity of the train to the same scale. Complete the parallelogram ABDC.

Then AD represents the relative or apparent velocity of the rain.

$$\tan BAD = \frac{DB}{AB} = \frac{66}{22} = 3.$$

The magnitude of the relative velocity is

$$\sqrt{66^2 + 22^2} = 22 \sqrt{9 + 1} = 22 \sqrt{10} \text{ ft./sec.}$$

EXAMPLE (iii).

A battleship which can steam at 15 knots sights an enemy cruiser at a distance of 8 nautical miles due east of her. If the cruiser steams due north at 20 knots, find what course the battleship must steer in order to get as close to her as possible, and show that when they are as close as possible, the battleship will have gone 6 nautical miles relatively to the cruiser.

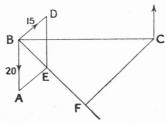

FIG. 16.

Let B, C (Fig. 16) be the initial positions of the battleship and cruiser respectively. Reduce C to rest by applying a velocity of 20 knots due south to each. Since the speed of B is only 15, it is obvious that its velocity relative to C, i.e. the resultant of 20 due S. and its own velocity of 15 must be in a direction south of BC. Now in order that B shall get as close as possible to C, its velocity relative to C must make as small an angle as possible with BC.

If BD represent the velocity of B, and BE the relative velocity, the angle EBC will be a minimum when the angle ABE is a maximum.

This is the case when AE (which equals BD) is perpendicular to BE, and then

$$\cos EBC = \sin ABE = \tfrac{15}{20} = \tfrac{3}{4}.$$

and $\sin CBD = \cos EBC = \tfrac{3}{4}$.

The required direction is therefore $\sin^{-1} \tfrac{3}{4}$ N. of E.

The shortest distance between B and C is CF where CF is perpendicular to BE.

$$BF = BC \cos EBC = 8 \times \tfrac{3}{4} = 6 \text{ miles,}$$

i.e. B has gone 6 miles relatively to C.

EXAMPLES III.

1. Two trains are travelling on lines which cross at right angles, one at 40, and the other at 50 m.p.h. Find the velocity of the second train relative to the first.

2. A passenger on the top of an omnibus feels a breeze which to him appears to blow directly across the bus at 10 m.p.h. If the omnibus is travelling at 15 m.p.h., what is the velocity of the wind ?

3. Raindrops are falling through the air with a velocity of 10 ft./sec. If a north wind blow at 12 m.p.h., find the direction in which the drops appear to fall to a person walking north at 3 m.p.h. With what velocity would they hit his umbrella ?

4. A steamship is travelling north at the rate of 10 m.p.h., and there is a north-east wind blowing at the rate of 20 m.p.h. In what direction will the smoke from the funnel appear to move to an observer on the ship ?

5. One ship is sailing due east at 12 m.p.h., and another ship is sailing due north at 16 m.p.h. ; find the velocity of the second ship relative to the first.

6. A steamer going N.E. at 14 m.p.h. observes at noon a cruiser 10 miles away and S.E. of her, which is going N.N.E. at 25 m.p.h. Draw a diagram of the cruiser's course as it appears from the steamer. At what time are the vessels nearest to one another, and how far are they then apart ?

7. Two ships are steaming in opposite directions at 20 and 25 knots respectively, and when they are directly abeam a shot is fired from one. If the gun at rest gives a muzzle velocity of 2660 ft./sec., find the direction in which it must be fired to hit the other ship, gravity being neglected. (A knot is 6080 ft./hour.)

8. Two roads cross at right angles at P ; a man A, walking along one of them at 3 m.p.h., sees another man B, walking on the other road at 4 m.p.h., at P when he is 100 yards off. Find the velocity of A relative to B, and show that they will be nearest together when A has walked 36 yards. (I.S.)

9. Two motor cars are proceeding, one on each road, towards the point of intersection of two roads which meet at an angle of 60°. If their speeds are 12½ and 20 m.p.h., and they are respectively 350 and 200 yards from the cross-roads, find their relative velocity, and the distances from the cross-roads when they are nearest together. (I.E.)

10. To an observer on a ship travelling due west at 16 m.p.h. another ship 1 mile due south appears to be travelling north-east at 12 m.p.h. Find the magnitude and direction of the true velocity of the second ship, and the distance apart of the two ships when nearest to each other. (I.S.)

11. A battleship is steaming 15 knots due N. ; a cruiser, which steams 25 knots, is 5 nautical miles S.W., and is ordered to line up 1 nautical mile astern. Find graphically, or otherwise, the course the cruiser should steer to line up as quickly as possible. (I.E.)

12. If a ship is moving N.E. at 15 knots, and a second ship appears to an observer on the first to be moving due, E. at 7 knots, determine the actual direction and magnitude of the velocity of the second. (I.S.)

13. From their point of intersection two straight roads lie respectively due E. and 60° N. of E. At the same instant that a motor travelling at 35 m.p.h. due E. is at the crossing, a second motor is 5 miles from it, and is travelling at 30 m.p.h. towards it from 60° N. of E. Find by a graphical construction (or by calculation) the relative velocity of the first to the second motor. Find also when they will be at their shortest distance apart. (I.E.)

14. Two ships are sailing at speeds of 10 and 12 m.p.h. along parallel lines in the same direction. When they are opposite one another and 2 miles apart, the faster ship turns its course through 30° in the direction of the other. Find how close they get to one another. (I.E.)

15. A ship A is steering S. at the rate of 8 m.p.h., and a ship B is steering E. at 10 m.p.h., the distance AB being 2000 yards and the line AB making an angle of 30° towards the west with the direction of motion of A. Calculate their relative velocity, and find how long it will be before they are closest together. (H.S.D.)

16. A man can swim at 2 m.p.h. in still water. Find the time he would take to swim between two directly opposite points on the banks of a river 250 yards wide flowing at 1 m.p.h. (H.S.D.)

17. A batsman is at the wicket W and a fieldsman is in the outfield at F. The batsman strikes the ball in a direction making 30° with the line WF with a speed $1\frac{1}{2}$ times that with which the fieldsman can run. If the fieldsman starts off at once, at top speed, so as to field the ball as soon as possible, determine, graphically or otherwise, the direction in which he must run ; and show that, if in doing this he has run 20 yards, he was standing about 39 yards from the wicket. (Assume that the ball travels along the ground with no diminution of speed.) (H.S.D.)

18. A destroyer, steaming N. 30° E. at 30 knots, observes at noon a steamer which is steaming due N. at 12 knots, and overtakes the steamer at 12.45 p.m. Find the distance and bearing of the steamer from the destroyer at noon. (H.C.)

19. Find the true course and the true speed of a steamer travelling through the water at 12 knots and steering due north by the compass through a current of 3 knots which sets south-east. Find also the direction in which the steamer should steer in order to make its true course due north, and the true speed on that course. (H.C.)

20. A cruiser which can steam at 30 knots receives a report that an enemy vessel, steaming due north at 20 knots, is 29 nautical miles away in a direction 30° north of east. Show (i) graphically, (ii) by calculation, that the cruiser can overtake the vessel in almost exactly 2 hours. (A knot is a speed of 1 nautical mile per hour.) (H.C.)

21. A ship leaves a certain port and steams N.E. at 15 knots ; 5 hours later another ship leaves the same port and steams due W. at 20 knots. Their wireless instruments can maintain communication up to 225 nautical miles ; find to the nearest nautical mile the distance of the ships from the port when communication ceases. (H.C.)

22. Two motor cars, A, B are travelling along straight roads at right angles to one another, with uniform velocities of 21 m.p.h. and

28 m.p.h., respectively, towards C, the point at which the roads cross. If AC is half a mile when BC is three-quarters of a mile, find the shortest distance between the cars during the subsequent motion. (C.S.)

23. A steamer is going due west at 14 m.p.h., and the wind appears from the drift of the clouds to be blowing at 7 m.p.h. from the N.W. Find its actual velocity, and make a geometrical construction for its direction.

24. A ship A observes another B at a distance of 8 miles in a direction due north ; B is steaming south at 12 m.p.h. and A is steaming north-east at 15 m.p.h. Find (graphically or otherwise) the velocity of B relative to A ; and prove that the ships are nearest together about 17 minutes after B is first observed. (Q.E.)

25. A branch road running N.W. joins a main road running due north. At a particular instant two motor cars, A and B, each travelling at 12 m.p.h., are approaching the junction, A being on the branch road and distant 1½ miles from the junction, and B being on the main road, and 1 mile from the junction. If the speeds of the cars remain constant, find (i) how close to one another they get ; (ii) the distance of A from the junction when this occurs. (Q.E.)

§ 29. Angular Velocity.

If a point P be in motion in a plane, and if O be a fixed point in the plane and OA a fixed straight line through O, the angular velocity of P about O is defined as the rate at which the angle AOP increases.

Angular velocity is always measured in *radians per second*. When uniform, angular velocity is measured by the number of radians in the angle turned through by OP in 1 second. When variable, its value at any instant is measured by the angle through which OP would turn in 1 second, if it continued to turn at the same rate as at the instant considered.

If θ is the angle between OP and OA at any instant, the angular velocity is $\dfrac{d\theta}{dt}$ or $\dot{\theta}$.

§ **30.** *If the point P describe a circle with O as centre with uniform speed, its angular velocity about O is equal to its speed divided by the radius of the circle.*

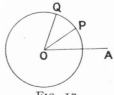

Fig. 17.

Let P (Fig. 17) be the position of the point at any time, Q its position 1 second later. The angular velocity is the number of radians in the angle POQ.

But the number of radians in POQ $= \dfrac{\text{arc PQ}}{\text{OP}}$.

Also, the arc PQ is described in 1 second, and is therefore equal to the speed v.

Hence, if ω be the angular velocity, and r the radius of the circle,

$$\omega = \frac{v}{r},$$

$$\therefore v = r\omega.$$

If n is the number of revolutions which P makes in 1 second, the angular velocity is $2\pi n$.

The rate at which a body is rotating is often given in revolutions per minute (abbreviated to R.P.M.).

It should be noticed that the angular velocity of a point P about another point O is independent of the distance of P from O ; it is the same for all points in the line OP. The linear speed of a point in OP does, however, depend on its distance from O. The speed of the point equals the angular velocity multiplied by the distance of the point from O.

§ **31.** *To find the velocity of any point on a circular disc which is rolling uniformly, without sliding, on a straight line.*

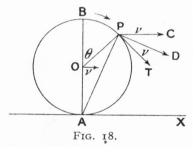

FIG. 18.

Let O (Fig. 18) be the centre and r the radius of the disc, A its point of contact with the line AX, and let v be the velocity with which O moves.

Now as the centre moves forward uniformly in a straight line the disc turns uniformly about the centre ; and, since each point of the rim in succession touches the ground, it is clear that each point of the rim describes the perimeter relative to the centre while the centre moves forward a distance equal to the perimeter. Hence the velocity of any point on the rim relative to the centre is equal in magnitude to the velocity v of the centre.

The angular velocity (ω) of the disc about its centre is therefore equal to $\dfrac{v}{r}$.

2 *

If B is the highest point of the disc, its velocity relative to O is v horizontally, and in the same direction as the velocity of O.

$$\therefore \text{ velocity of B} = v + v = 2v.$$

The velocity of A relative to O is also v, but in the opposite direction to the velocity of O.

$$\therefore \text{ velocity of A} = v - v = 0,$$

i.e. the point A is instantaneously at rest.

If P is a point on the rim, such that the angle $BOP = \theta$, the resultant velocity of P is obtained by compounding together its velocity relative to O, v along the tangent PT, and the velocity of O, i.e. v horizontally along PC.

Now the angle $CPT = \theta$, and if V is the resultant velocity of P,

$$V^2 = v^2 + v^2 + 2v^2 \cos \theta,$$

$$= 2v^2(1 + \cos \theta) = 4v^2 \cos^2 \frac{\theta}{2} ;$$

$$\therefore V = 2v \cos \frac{\theta}{2}.$$

The direction of this velocity is along PD bisecting the angle CPT, since the two components are equal.

If AP is joined we see that

$$\text{angle OPA} = \frac{\theta}{2},$$

$$\text{also angle TPD} = \frac{\theta}{2},$$

$$\therefore \text{ angle APD} = \text{angle OPT} = \text{a right angle.}$$

Hence each point of the rim is moving perpendicular to the line joining it to A, the lowest point ;

also $$\text{AP} = 2r \cos \frac{\theta}{2},$$

$\therefore$ the angular velocity of P about A is

$$\frac{2v \cos \frac{\theta}{2}}{2r \cos \frac{\theta}{2}} = \frac{v}{r}$$

$$= \text{the angular velocity of the disc.}$$

Since the disc is rigid, all points in AP must have the same angular velocity about A, and it follows that all points on the disc are at this instant turning about A with angular velocity ω equal to that of the disc about its centre.

The point A is called the *instantaneous centre of rotation.*

§ **32.** EXAMPLE (i).

An engine is travelling at 60 *m.p.h., and its driving wheel is* 6 *feet in diameter : find the velocity and direction of motion of each of the two points of the wheel which are at a height of* $4\frac{1}{2}$ *feet above the ground.*

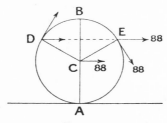

FIG. 19.

Let C (Fig. 19) be the centre of the wheel, A the point of contact with the rail, B the highest point, and D, E the points at a height of $4\frac{1}{2}$ feet.

$$60 \text{ m.p.h.} = 88 \text{ ft./sec.}$$
$$\text{angle BCE} = 60°.$$

The velocity of E is composed of its velocity relative to C, i.e. 88 ft./sec. perpendicular to CE downwards, and the velocity of C, i.e. 88 ft./sec. horizontal. These are inclined at an angle of 60°, and the resultant velocity V bisects the angle between them, i.e. it is inclined at 30° below the horizontal.

Also $\qquad V = \sqrt{88^2 + 88^2 + 2\cdot88^2 . \cos 60°} = 88 \sqrt{3}$ ft./sec.

$$= 60 \sqrt{3} \text{ m.p.h.}$$

The component velocities of D are 88 ft./sec. horizontal, and 88 ft./sec. perpendicular to CD and upwards.

The resultant is $88\sqrt{3}$ as for E, but it is inclined at an angle of 30° *above* the horizontal.

EXAMPLE (ii).

Explain how to find the angular velocity of the line joining two points whose velocities are given.

Let A and B (Fig. 20) represent the two points. Now it is evident that any component velocities of A and B parallel to AB will not affect the direction of AB, but the components perpendicular to AB will alter the direction of AB unless they happen to be equal and in the same direction.

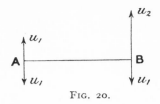

FIG. 20.

To find the angular velocity of AB we therefore proceed as follows :—

Resolve the velocities of A and B, along and perpendicular to AB. Let u_1, u_2 be the components for A and B respectively perpendicular to AB.

Compound with each of these a velocity equal and opposite to that of one of them, say u_1.

Then A is reduced to rest and B has a velocity of $u_2 - u_1$ perpendicular to AB,

$$\therefore \text{ the angular velocity of AB} = \frac{u_2 - u_1}{\text{AB}}.$$

This is only the *instantaneous* angular velocity, for as the direction of AB changes the components perpendicular to AB will change and so will the length AB.

EXAMPLE (iii).

Two small marbles A and B are moving in a clockwise direction in concentric circular grooves of 2 inches and 3 inches radii respectively. The velocity of A in its groove is 2 inches per second, and that of B is 9 inches per second. At a given instant the marbles are 1 inch apart ; what time will elapse before the distance between them is 5 inches ?

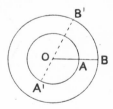

FIG. 21.

Let O (Fig. 21) be the common centre of the grooves. The marbles can only be 1 inch apart when they are on a common diameter and on the same side of the centre as at A and B. They will be 5 inches apart when they are on a common diameter, but on opposite sides of the centre as at A', B', and then B will have described 180° more than A.

It is easier to consider the *angular* velocities of the marbles than their linear speeds.

Since A's speed is 2 inches per second, it describes 360° or 2π radians in $\dfrac{2\pi \cdot 2}{2} = 2\pi$ seconds. Hence its angular velocity is 1.

B describes 360° in $\dfrac{2\pi \cdot 3}{9} = \dfrac{2}{3}\pi$ seconds, and its angular velocity is therefore 3.

∴. B's angular velocity *relative* to A is 2 radians per second ;

∴. the time B takes to gain 180° or π radians is $\dfrac{\pi}{2}$ seconds ;

∴. they will be 5 inches apart after $\dfrac{\pi}{2}$ or 1·5708 seconds.

EXAMPLES IV.

1. A wheel is making 300 R.P.M. about its centre; calculate the angular velocity of any point on the wheel about the centre. Also find the speed of a point at a distance of 2 ft. from the centre.

2. A point moves in a circle with uniform speed ; show that its angular velocity about any point on the circumference of the circle is constant.

3. A train is travelling at 40 m.p.h., and the diameter of one of the wheels of the engine is 5 ft. Find the velocities of the two points on this wheel which are at a height of 4 ft. above the ground.

4. A body travelling at right angles to the plane of a fly-wheel 30 inches in diameter, making 480 R.P.M. makes a mark across the rim of the wheel. The mark is found to make an angle of 60° with the edge of the rim. Calculate the speed of the body.

5. Compare the velocities of the extremities of the hour and minute hands of a clock, their lengths being 2 and 3 inches respectively.

6. A wheel of 8 feet diameter is rolling along the ground with a velocity of 20 ft./sec. ; find the angular velocity of the wheel and the magnitudes and directions of the velocities of the points at the extremities of the horizontal diameter.

7. The wheels of a bicycle are 30 inches in diameter, each crank is $7\frac{1}{2}$ inches long, and is geared so as to make 1 revolution while the wheels make two. Find the actual velocity of the end of the crank (i) when at the highest, (ii) when at the lowest point of its path, when the bicycle is travelling at 10 m.p.h. Work out the same problem supposing that two revolutions of the crank correspond to one of the wheels.

8. A circular ring moves uniformly in a straight line in its own plane, and a point on the ring moves uniformly round the ring. Find the actual velocity of the point when the line joining it to the centre of the ring makes angles of (i) 90°, (ii) 45°, (iii) 0° with the direction of motion of the ring. (N.B.—There is not necessarily any connection between the velocity of the ring and the velocity of the point.)

9. A bicycle wheel is 28 inches in diameter and the pedal crank is 7 inches long. If the pedals make one revolution to three revolutions of the wheels, and the speed of the bicycle is 14 m.p.h., find the velocity of each pedal when the top of the crank makes an angle θ with the vertical in a forward direction. (Q.E.)

ACCELERATION.

§ 33. Change of Velocity.

Since a velocity has both magnitude and direction, it will be changed if we alter either of these or both.

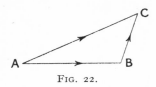

FIG. 22.

Thus, suppose AB (Fig. 22) represents the velocity of a point at any instant, and AC its velocity at a later instant. Then we know by the triangle of velocities that BC represents in magnitude and direction the change of velocity during the interval considered.

If AC = AB, then the *speed* has remained the same, but there has still been a change of *velocity* represented by BC. In dealing with motion in a straight line we have only to consider changes of speed, but when the path is a curve we must remember that the velocity is continually changing, although the speed may remain constant. This case will be dealt with in a later chapter.

§ 34. Acceleration.

This term is used to denote the rate at which the velocity is changing. It may be either uniform or variable. *If a point move so that the changes of velocity in any equal times, however small, are the same in direction and equal in magnitude, the acceleration is said to be uniform. The change of velocity in each unit of time measures the magnitude of the acceleration.*

§ 35. When the changes of velocity in equal times are unequal in magnitude or not in the same direction, the acceleration is said to be variable. When variable, the acceleration at any instant is measured by the change of velocity which would occur in the next unit of time if the acceleration remained constant in magnitude and direction during that interval.

§ 36. The magnitude of the unit of acceleration is the acceleration of a point which moves so that its velocity changes by the unit of velocity in each unit of time.

E.g. 1 foot per second every second, usually written 1 ft./sec.^{2}, or 1 f.s.s.

1 centimetre per second every second, written 1 cm./sec.^{2}

It is clear that acceleration, like velocity, is a vector quantity, and an acceleration expressed in these units only gives the change in *magnitude* of this vector.

§ 37. Parallelogram of Accelerations.

If a moving point have two accelerations represented in magnitude and direction by the straight lines OA, OB, they are equivalent to an acceleration represented by the diagonal OC of the parallelogram OACB.

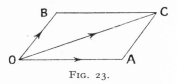

FIG. 23.

This theorem follows at once from the parallelogram of velocities.

For OA, OB (Fig. 23) represent the two velocities given to the point in unit time. By the parallelogram of velocities the diagonal OC represents the resultant change of velocity in unit time, and therefore represents the resultant acceleration.

§ **38.** It follows from the preceding paragraph that accelerations can be compounded and resolved in the same way as velocities, and propositions similar to the Triangle and Polygon of Velocities are true for accelerations.

§ 39. Expressions for Acceleration.

If s is the distance of a moving point from some fixed point of its path at time t, then its speed v is $\dfrac{ds}{dt}$. The speed-acceleration is the rate of change of v, i.e. $\dfrac{dv}{dt}$ or $\dfrac{d^2s}{dt^2}$.

Hence, if f is the speed-acceleration,

$$f = \frac{dv}{dt} = \frac{d^2s}{dt^2},$$

also

$$f = \frac{dv}{dt} = \frac{dv}{ds} \cdot \frac{ds}{dt} = v\frac{dv}{ds}.$$

It must be noted that, unless we use vector notation, expressions like $\dfrac{dv}{dt}$, $\dfrac{d^2s}{dt^2}$ only represent rates of change of *speed*, they do not take into account changes in *direction* of motion.

When the motion takes place in a straight line there is no difficulty, as speed and velocity are the same.

When the motion is not in a straight line, the difficulty is over come by considering *component* accelerations.

§ **40. Component Accelerations.**

If the co-ordinates of a moving point P (Fig. 24) be (x, y) at any

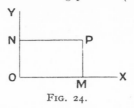

FIG. 24.

instant, the component velocities of P parallel to the axes OX, OY are $\dfrac{dx}{dt}$ and $\dfrac{dy}{dt}$, the velocities of M and N, the projections of P on the axes.

If the component accelerations of P are X, Y parallel to OX and OY,

$$X = \frac{d^2x}{dt^2}, \; Y = \frac{d^2y}{dt^2}.$$

$\dfrac{d^2x}{dt^2}$ and $\dfrac{d^2y}{dt^2}$ are often denoted by $\ddot{x}$ and $\ddot{y}$.

By working with these components we take into account changes in direction as well as changes in the magnitude of the velocity of P.

§ **41. Relative Acceleration.**

If $\overrightarrow{OA}$, $\overrightarrow{OB}$ (Fig. 25) represent the accelerations of two points P, Q at any instant, the relative acceleration of one point with respect to the other is the vector difference between $\overrightarrow{OA}$ and $\overrightarrow{OB}$.

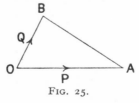

FIG. 25.

The acceleration of P relative to Q is

$$\overrightarrow{OA} - \overrightarrow{OB} = \overrightarrow{BA},$$

and the acceleration of Q relative to P is

$$\overrightarrow{OB} - \overrightarrow{OA} = \overrightarrow{AB}.$$

The relative acceleration can be obtained, as in the case of relative velocity, by compounding with the acceleration of one an acceleration equal and opposite to that of the other, and the latter will then have no acceleration.

If two points have accelerations which are equal in magnitude and in the same direction, their relative acceleration is zero, and their relative motion is the same as if neither of them had any acceleration.

This often enables us to simplify a problem on the motion of bodies subject to a common acceleration by ignoring this acceleration.

It should be noticed that a point at rest may have acceleration, and that two points whose velocities at any instant are equal and parallel (i.e. they have no relative velocity) may have relative acceleration with respect to each other.

§ 42. Velocity and Acceleration of the Centre of Mass of a System of Particles.

It is proved in statics that if the co-ordinates of a number of particles m_1, m_2, etc., are (x_1, y_1), (x_2, y_2), etc., then if X, Y are the co-ordinates of their centre of mass,

$$X = \frac{m_1 x_1 + m_2 x_2 + \cdots}{m_1 + m_2 + \cdots}.$$

Now, the component velocities of the centre of mass are

$$\frac{dX}{dt} \text{ and } \frac{dY}{dt},$$

and since m_1, m_2, etc., are constants, we have by differentation,

$$\frac{dX}{dt} = \frac{m_1 \dfrac{dx_1}{dt} + m_2 \dfrac{dx_2}{dt} + \cdots}{m_1 + m_2 + \cdots},$$

and similarly,

$$\frac{dY}{dt} = \frac{m_1 \dfrac{dy_1}{dt} + m_2 \dfrac{dy_2}{dt} + \cdots}{m_1 + m_2 + \cdots},$$

but $\dfrac{dx_1}{dt}$, $\dfrac{dx_2}{dt}$, etc., $\dfrac{dy_1}{dt}$, $\dfrac{dy_2}{dt}$, etc., are the component velocities of the particles, say, u_1, u_2, etc., v_1, v_2, etc.

∴ the component velocities of the centre of mass are

$$U = \frac{m_1 u_1 + m_2 u_2 + \cdots}{m_1 + m_2 + \cdots},$$

$$V = \frac{m_1 v_1 + m_2 v_2 + \cdots}{m_1 + m_2 + \cdots}.$$

The component accelerations of the centre of mass are $\dfrac{d^2X}{dt^2}$ and $\dfrac{d^2Y}{dt^2}$.

Hence, differentiating the values for $\dfrac{dX}{dt}$, $\dfrac{dY}{dt}$ again with respect to t, it is easy to see that if f_1, f_2, etc., f_1', f_2', etc., are the component accelerations of the particles and F, F', those of the centre of mass,

$$F = \frac{m_1 f_1 + m_2 f_2 + \ldots}{m_1 + m_2 + \ldots},$$

$$F' = \frac{m_1 f_1' + m_2 f_2' + \ldots}{m_1 + m_2 + \ldots}.$$

Motion in a Straight Line.

§ 43. We shall now consider the case of a point moving in a straight line with constant acceleration. Speed and velocity are then the same, and acceleration refers only to change of speed.

If the speed is increasing, the acceleration is said to be positive, if the speed is decreasing, the acceleration is negative.

A negative acceleration is, of course, the same as a retardation.

§ 44. Equations of Motion for Constant Acceleration.

If s denote the distance of a point at time t from the point at which it starts, so that $s = 0$ when $t = 0$; then, if the acceleration is constant and equal to f, we have

$$\frac{d^2s}{dt^2} = f.$$

$\therefore$ integrating,

$$\frac{ds}{dt} = ft + A.$$

Now A is obviously the value of $\dfrac{ds}{dt}$ when $t = 0$, i.e. A is the initial velocity, usually denoted by u.

$$\therefore \frac{ds}{dt} = u + ft,$$
$$\text{or } \mathbf{v} = \mathbf{u} + \mathbf{f}\,\mathbf{t} \qquad . \qquad . \qquad . \qquad . \qquad \text{(i)}$$

Integrating again, $\qquad s = ut + \tfrac{1}{2}ft^2 + B,$

and since $s = 0$ when $t = 0$, we have $B = 0$,

$$\therefore \mathbf{s} = \mathbf{u}\mathbf{t} + \tfrac{1}{2}\mathbf{f}\,\mathbf{t}^2 \qquad . \qquad . \qquad \text{(ii)}$$

From (i), $v^2 = u^2 + 2uft + f^2t^2 = u^2 + 2f(ut + \tfrac{1}{2}ft^2)$
$$= u^2 + 2fs, \text{ from (ii)},$$
$$\therefore \mathbf{v}^2 = \mathbf{u}^2 + \mathbf{2}\,\mathbf{f}\,\mathbf{s} \qquad . \qquad . \qquad . \qquad \text{(iii)}$$

These three equations are the equations of motion for a point or particle moving in a straight line with constant acceleration. They do *not* apply in cases where the acceleration is variable. It should be noticed that each equation contains f and three of the four quantities u, v, t, s, one of these being absent from each equation. These equations are of fundamental importance, and must be remembered. In working problems we select the equations which contain the quantities we are given and the one we want to find.

EXAMPLE (i).

A train which is moving with uniform acceleration is observed to take 20 and 30 seconds to travel successive quarter miles. How much farther will it travel before coming to rest if the acceleration remains uniform ?

We do not know what the initial velocity of the train is, but we are given two distances and two times.

The train goes $\frac{1}{4}$ mile, or 1320 feet, in 20 seconds,

$$\therefore 1320 = 20u + \tfrac{1}{2} f \cdot 400 \qquad . \qquad . \qquad . \qquad \text{(i)}$$

It also goes $\frac{1}{2}$ mile, or 2640 feet, in 50 seconds,

$$\therefore 2640 = 50u + \tfrac{1}{2} f \cdot 2500 \qquad . \qquad . \qquad . \qquad \text{(ii)}$$

$$\therefore 2u + 20f = 132,$$
$$5u + 125f = 264,$$

whence $\qquad\qquad f = -\tfrac{92}{25}$ ft./sec.²,

and $\qquad\qquad u = \dfrac{374}{5}$ ft./sec.

We can now find the whole distance (including the two $\frac{1}{4}$ miles) travelled before coming to rest,

$$0 = \frac{374^2}{25} - \frac{44}{25} s,$$

$$\therefore s = \frac{374 \times 374}{44} = \frac{374 \times 34}{4} = 3179 \text{ ft.,}$$

$\therefore$ the further distance travelled is

$$3179 - 2640 = 539 \text{ feet.}$$

Note.—In cases like this where the times taken to travel successive distances are given, write down one equation for the first distance, and the second equation for the *sum* of the two distances. If we consider the second $\frac{1}{4}$ mile separately we have a different value for u.

EXAMPLE (ii).

A train moves 2 miles from rest to rest in 4 minutes. The greatest speed is 45 m.p.h. and the acceleration and retardation are uniform. Find the distance travelled at full speed.

It must be noticed that we are not told that the acceleration and retardation are *equal*.

Let s_1, t_1 be the distance and time for which the acceleration is f_1.

Let s_2, t_2 be the distance and time for which the retardation is f_2.

Let s, t be the distance and time at uniform speed.

$$45 \text{ m.p.h.} = 66 \text{ ft./sec.}$$

$$\therefore 66 = f_1 t_1, \text{ and } s_1 = \tfrac{1}{2} f_1 t_1^2 = 33 t_1,$$
$$66 = f_2 t_2, \text{ and } s_2 = 66 t_2 - \tfrac{1}{2} f_2 t_2^2$$
$$= 66 t_2 - 33 t_2$$
$$= 33 t_2,$$
$$\text{also } s = 66 t,$$

$$\therefore s_1 + s + s_2 = 33 t_1 + 66 t + 33 t_2 = 10560,$$

$$\therefore t_1 + 2t + t_2 = 320,$$
$$\text{also } t_1 + t + t_2 = 240,$$

$$\therefore t = 80 \text{ seconds,}$$

$\therefore$ the distance travelled at full speed $= 66 \times 80$
$$= 5280 \text{ feet,}$$
$$= 1 \text{ mile.}$$

The data do not enable us to find t_1, t_2, etc., separately.

EXAMPLE (iii).

If an express train reduced speed from 60 m.p.h. to 15 m.p.h. in half a mile, for how long were the brakes applied, and how much longer would it take to come to rest?

We must, of course, assume that the retardation due to the brakes is uniform, let this be f.

$$60 \text{ m.p.h.} = 88 \text{ ft./sec., and } 15 \text{ m.p.h.} = 22 \text{ ft./sec.}$$

$$\text{Using } v^2 = u^2 + 2fs,$$
$$22^2 = 88^2 + 5280 f,$$

$$\therefore f = -\frac{88^2 - 22^2}{5280} = -\frac{110 \times 66}{5280}$$

$$= -\frac{11}{8} \text{ ft./sec.}^2$$

$$\text{Using } v = u + ft,$$
$$22 = 88 - \frac{11}{8} t,$$

$$\therefore t = \frac{66 \times 8}{11} = 48 \text{ sec.}$$

To find the time taken to come to rest, we have

$$0 = 22 - \frac{11}{8} t',$$

$$\therefore t' = \frac{22 \times 8}{11} = 16 \text{ sec.}$$

EXAMPLE (iv).

A cyclist riding at 12 m.p.h. passes a motor car just as it begins to move in the same direction. The car maintains an acceleration of $1\frac{1}{2}$ ft./sec.² for 20 seconds, and then moves uniformly. How far will it have run before overtaking the cyclist ?

The distance moved by the car during the 20 seconds is given by

$$s = \tfrac{1}{2} \cdot \tfrac{3}{2} \cdot 400 = 300 \text{ ft.}$$

The velocity at the end of this time is given by

$$v = \tfrac{3}{2} \cdot 20 = 30 \text{ ft./sec.,}$$

and the distance moved by the cyclist in this time is

$$\tfrac{88}{5} \times 20 = 352 \text{ ft.}$$

The velocity of the car relative to the cyclist is

$$30 - \tfrac{88}{5} = 6\tfrac{2}{5} \text{ ft./sec.}$$

∴ to gain 52 feet on the cyclist it takes $\dfrac{52 \times 5}{62}$ seconds, and in this time

it will have gone $\dfrac{52 \times 5 \times 30}{62} = 125\tfrac{25}{31}$ feet, or $425\tfrac{25}{31}$ feet altogether.

EXAMPLES V.

1. A cage goes down a mine shaft 750 yards deep in 45 seconds. For the first quarter of the distance only, the speed is being uniformly accelerated, and during the last quarter uniformly retarded, the acceleration and retardation being equal. Find the uniform speed of the cage while traversing the centre portion of the shaft.   (I.A.)

2. A train, starting from rest, is uniformly accelerated during the first $\frac{1}{4}$ mile of its run, then runs $\frac{3}{4}$ mile at the uniform speed acquired, and is afterwards brought to rest in $\frac{1}{8}$ mile under uniform retardation. If the time for the whole journey is 5 minutes, find the uniform acceleration and the uniform retardation in ft.-sec. units.   (I.A.)

3. A point starts from rest with a constant acceleration which ceases after an interval. It then moves uniformly at 15 ft./sec. for 10 seconds, after which it is uniformly retarded and is brought to rest. If the whole motion occupies 16 seconds, prove that the distance traversed is 195 feet. The initial acceleration being 5 ft./sec.², find the final retardation.   (I.E.)

4. A body, moving in a straight line with constant acceleration, passes over distances a, b, and c in equal consecutive intervals of time t. Find (i) the relation between a, b, and c ; (ii) the acceleration of the body ; (iii) its velocity at the start of the part a of its path.   (H.S.D.)

5. The cage of a pit performs the first part of its descent with uniform acceleration f and the remainder with uniform retardation $2f$. Prove that, if h is the depth of the shaft, and t the time of descent

$$h = \tfrac{1}{3} f t^2.$$ (I.E.)

6. A particle moving in a straight line with uniform acceleration f passes a certain point with velocity u. Three seconds afterwards

another particle, moving in the same straight line with constant acceleration $\frac{4}{5}f$, passes the same point with velocity $\frac{1}{3}u$. The first particle is overtaken by the second when their velocities are respectively 27 and 31 ft./sec. Find the values of u and f, and also the distance travelled from the point.   (I.S.)

7. The brakes of a train are able to produce a retardation of 3·5 ft./sec.^{2} If the train is travelling at 60 m.p.h., at what distance from a station should the brakes be applied, if it is desired to stop at the station ?   If the brakes are put on at half this distance, with what speed will the train pass the station ?   (H.S.D.)

8. A cyclist A riding at 10 m.p.h. is overtaken and passed by B riding at 12 m.p.h.   If A immediately increases his speed with uniform acceleration, show that he will catch B when his speed is 14 m.p.h. If, when he has increased his speed to 13 m.p.h., he continues to ride at this speed and catches B after he has gone 200 yards, find his acceleration.   (I.E.)

9. Two points P and Q move in the same straight line, being initially at rest and Q being 50 feet in front of P.   Q starts from rest with an acceleration of 10 ft./sec.^{2}, and P starts in pursuit with a velocity of 29 ft./sec. and an acceleration of 6 ft./sec.^{2} Prove that P will overtake and pass Q after an interval of 2 seconds, and that Q will in turn overtake P after a further interval of $10\frac{1}{2}$ seconds.   (H.S.D.)

10. A lift ascends with constant acceleration f, then with constant velocity, and finally stops under a constant retardation f.   If the total distance ascended is s, and the total time occupied is t, show that the time during which the lift is ascending with constant velocity is

$$\left(t^2 - \frac{4s}{f}\right)^{\frac{1}{2}}.$$ (H.S.D.)

11. A point moving in a straight line describes 16 feet in the 2nd second of its motion, 28 feet in the 5th second, 52 feet in the 11th second. Prove that these distances are consistent with the supposition that the motion of the point is uniformly accelerated ; also find the whole distance described in 10 seconds from the beginning of the motion.   (H.C.)

12. A point moving in a straight line covers 12 feet, 18 feet, and 42 feet in successive intervals of 3 seconds, 2 seconds, and 3 seconds.   Prove that these distances are consistent with the supposition that the point is moving with uniform acceleration.   (I.A.)

13. A body starts with velocity u and moves in a straight line with constant acceleration f.
     If when the velocity has increased to $5u$ the acceleration is reversed in direction, its magnitude being unaltered, prove that when the particle returns to its starting-point its velocity will be $-7u$.   (I.A.)

14. The two ends of a train moving with constant acceleration pass a certain point with velocities u and v.   Find in terms of u and v what proportion of the length of the train will have passed the point after a time equal to half that taken by the train to pass the point.   (I.E.)

15. A particle is moving in a straight line, and is observed to be at a distance a from a marked point initially, to be at a distance b after an interval of n seconds, to be at a distance c after $2n$ seconds,

and at a distance d after $3n$ seconds. Prove that if the acceleration is uniform

$$d - a = 3(c - b),$$

and that the acceleration is equal to

$$\frac{c + a - 2b}{n^2};$$

find also the initial velocity. (I.S.)

16. A train starts from A with uniform acceleration $\frac{1}{2}$ ft./sec.^{2}. After 2 minutes the train attains full speed, and moves uniformly for 11 minutes. It is then brought to rest at B by the brakes producing a constant retardation 5 ft./sec.^{2}. Find the distance AB. (H.C.)

17. A train approaching a station does two successive quarters of a mile in 16 and 20 seconds respectively. Assuming the retardation to be uniform, prove that the train runs a further distance of 1761 feet 10 inches before stopping. (H.C.)

18. A particle traverses a distance of 300 yards in a straight line at an average speed of 12 ft./sec., starting from rest and finishing at rest. It moves with a uniform acceleration for the first 10 seconds, and is brought to rest by a uniform retardation in the last 20 seconds of its motion, and moves at a uniform speed during the rest of its motion. Find the acceleration and retardation. (H.C.)

19. Prove that, if a particle move with uniform acceleration, the spaces described in consecutive equal intervals of time are in arithmetical progression.
    It is observed that a particle describes 396·9 metres in 3 seconds, 392·0 metres in the next 4 seconds, and 269·5 metres in the next 5 seconds. Show that this is consistent with the particle moving with uniform retardation and find the time before it comes to rest. (I.S.)

20. A train starting from rest travels the first part of its journey with constant acceleration f, the second part with constant speed v, and the third part with constant retardation f', being brought thereby again to rest. If the average speed for the whole journey is $\frac{4}{5}v$, show that the train is travelling at constant speed for three-quarters of the total time. Find also what fraction of the whole distance is described with constant speed. (I.S.)

21. A train is uniformly accelerated and passes successive milestones with velocities 10 m.p.h. and 20 m.p.h. respectively. Calculate the velocity when it passes the next milestone, and the times taken for each of these two intervals of 1 mile. (H.S.D.)

22. A train, moving with uniform acceleration, is observed to cover two consecutive half-miles in 60 seconds and 40 seconds respectively. Find the acceleration of the train, and show that it started from rest 70 seconds before the first observation, and that during that time it covered 1078 feet. (Q.E.)

23. A train passes another on a parallel track; the first is running at a uniform speed of 40 m.p.h., and the second is running at a speed of 10 m.p.h., with an acceleration of $\frac{1}{2}$ ft./sec.^{2}. How long will it be before the second train catches the first again, and how far will the trains run in the interval? (Q.E.)

24. An electric car travelling between two stopping places 500 yards apart is uniformly accelerated for the first 10 seconds, during which period it covers 100 feet. It then runs with constant speed until it is finally retarded uniformly in the last 50 feet. Calculate the maximum speed and the time taken over the journey.   (Q.E.)

25. A particle moving in a straight line with constant retardation starts from a point O with such velocity that in 3 seconds it is 75 feet east of O, and in 5 seconds it is 45 feet east of O ; prove that it will have reached its most easterly position in $3\frac{1}{16}$ seconds, and find its position 8 seconds after it leaves O.   (N.U.3.)

26. A train starts from rest and is uniformly accelerated for 2 minutes ; it then travels at constant speed for 56 minutes, and is subsequently uniformly retarded during a further 2 minutes, at the end of which time its velocity is one-third of the value of the constant speed with which it was travelling before retardation. If the total distance traversed during the hour is 42 miles, find the value of the constant maximum velocity, and draw a space-time diagram of the motion.   (C.W.B.)

§ **45.** When the acceleration is variable, but follows some known law, we can obtain the equation of motion in the same way as for the simple case of constant acceleration, i.e. by equating $\frac{d^2s}{dt^2}$ to the expression for the acceleration, but integration is required to obtain the solution.

These cases are harder, and will be postponed to a later chapter. In some cases of variable acceleration, especially those where, instead of a definite law, we are given a series of values of distances and times, or velocities and times, graphical methods may be used. We plot graphs connecting the quantities given, and obtain from them the other quantities connected with the motion.

There are several graphs which can be used in this way.

§ **46. Space-time Curve.**

If we plot successive intervals of time along OX (Fig. 26), and

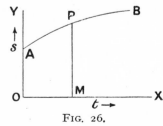

FIG. 26.

the corresponding distances from some fixed point parallel to OY, we obtain a curve APB.

If PM is the ordinate at P, then PM represents the distance of the point at the time represented by OM.

The slope of the curve at P is $\dfrac{ds}{dt}$, and therefore represents the velocity at P, i.e. at the time represented by OM.

Hence, by finding the slopes at different points on the curve we obtain the velocities (or speeds) at different times.

If we then plot the speed and time as in the next paragraph, we get the speed-time curve, and from this we can find the acceleration and the distance travelled.

§ 47. Speed-time Curve.

If we plot successive intervals of time along OX (Fig. 27) and the

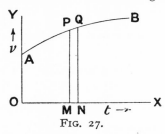

FIG. 27.

corresponding velocities parallel to OY we shall obtain a curve APB.

If PM is the ordinate at P, then PM represents the velocity at the time represented by OM.

Since acceleration $= \dfrac{dv}{dt}$, the slope of the curve APB at any point represents the acceleration at that point.

When the acceleration is uniform, the curve is a straight line.

If we take a point Q very close to P and draw the ordinate QN so that MN $= \delta t$, then the area of the strip PMNQ is very nearly PM $\times$ $\delta t = v\delta t$, where v is the value of the velocity at P, and this product represents the space described in the interval δt.

Hence, the space described between any two times t_1 and $t_2 = \displaystyle\int_{t_1}^{t_2} v\,dt$, the area under the curve APB between the ordinates at t_1 and t_2.

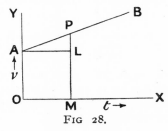

FIG 28.

3 *

When the acceleration is uniform and equal to f, the curve AB is a straight line (Fig. 28), and the space described in time t ($= OM$) is the area OMPA $=$ PAL $+$ rectangle OMLA. Now OA $= u$, the initial velocity, and PL $= ft$ the increment in time t.

$$\therefore \text{PAL} = \tfrac{1}{2}ft \times t,$$
$$\text{and OMLA} = ut,$$
$$\therefore \text{space} = ut + \tfrac{1}{2}ft^2.$$

§ 48. Acceleration-time Curve.

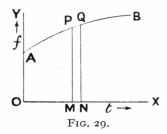

FIG. 29.

If we plot time along OX (Fig. 29) and the corresponding values of the acceleration parallel to OY we get the acceleration-time curve APB. The ordinate PM gives the value of the acceleration f at time OM $= t$. If we take a point Q on the curve close to P and draw the ordinate QN so that MN $= \delta t$, then the area PMNQ is very nearly equal to $f\delta t$, and this represents the change in velocity in the interval δt.

The change in velocity between any two times t_1 and t_2 is

$$\int_{t_1}^{t_2} f\,dt,$$

the area under the curve APB between the ordinates at t_1 and t_2.

§ 49. Acceleration-space Curve.

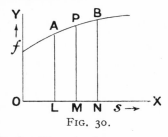

FIG. 30.

This curve is obtained by plotting acceleration against distance. The ordinate PM (Fig. 30) at any point P gives the acceleration f at distance OM from the starting-point.

Now we have seen that the acceleration at any instant is

$$\frac{dv}{dt} \text{ or } v\frac{dv}{ds},$$

and the area under the curve between any two ordinates AL and BN is

$$\int f ds,$$

taken between the limits OL and ON for s.

But this is the same as $\int v\frac{dv}{ds}ds$, or $\frac{1}{2}v^2$ taken between the values of v at A and B.

i.e. the area under the curve gives the change in $\frac{1}{2}v^2$.

§ 50. Other Curves for Motion with Variable Acceleration.

If we are given the velocities of a point at different distances from its starting-point, we can plot a velocity-space curve, but the area and slope of this curve do not represent anything in connection with the motion as they do in the previous cases. (The slope, of course, represents the rate of space change of the velocity, but this is not the acceleration.)

Now, the acceleration is $v\frac{dv}{ds}$, and this is the same as

$$\frac{d}{ds}(\tfrac{1}{2}v^2).$$

Hence, if we plot $\frac{1}{2}v^2$ against s, the slope of the resulting curve gives the acceleration at any distance.

Again, since

$$v = \frac{ds}{dt},$$

$$\frac{1}{v} = \frac{dt}{ds},$$

$$\therefore dt = \frac{1}{v}\,ds.$$

Hence, if we plot $\frac{1}{v}$ against s, the area under this curve gives the time required to describe a given distance.

Since

$$f = \frac{dv}{dt},$$

$$\frac{1}{f} = \frac{dt}{dv},$$

$$\therefore dt = \frac{1}{f}\,dv$$

Hence, if we plot $\dfrac{1}{f}$ against v, the area under this curve gives the time required to cause a given change in velocity.

§ 51. EXAMPLE (i).

Draw the velocity-time graph of a point describing a straight line with uniform acceleration, and deduce the formula $v^2 = u^2 + 2fs$.

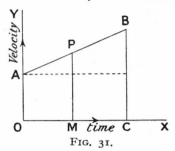

FIG. 31.

If A (Fig. 31) represent the initial velocity, then, since the increments in velocity during equal intervals of time are the same, the graph is a straight line AB.

The height of any point P above A is equal to the acceleration multiplied by the time represented by OM.

The area under the graph gives the distance travelled.

If B represents velocity v, then the area OABC represents the distance s.

Now area

$$\text{OABC} = \tfrac{1}{2}(\text{OA} + \text{CB}) . \text{OC},$$

and

$$\text{CB} - \text{OA} = f \times \text{OC},$$

$$\therefore \text{OC} = \frac{\text{CB} - \text{OA}}{f},$$

$$\therefore s = \frac{1}{2} . \frac{(\text{CB} + \text{OA})(\text{CB} - \text{OA})}{f}$$

$$= \frac{1}{2}\frac{(\text{CB}^2 - \text{OA}^2)}{f} = \frac{1}{2}\frac{v^2 - u^2}{f}.$$

$$\therefore v^2 = u^2 + 2fs.$$

EXAMPLE (ii).

A train starts from a station A to reach another station B, at a distance c from A ; the motion is at first uniformly accelerated for a given time t ; the velocity then remains constant for a given time t' ; and is then uniformly retarded for a time t". Represent the motion in a diagram, and by means of the diagram find the values of the acceleration and the retardation.

Let OABC (Fig. 32) represent the velocity-time graph, then AB is horizontal.

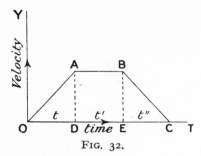

FIG. 32.

Draw AD, BE perpendicular to OT.

Then $\qquad c =$ area OABC,

$$= ADt' + \tfrac{1}{2}AD(t + t''),$$

$$= \frac{AD(t + t'' + 2t')}{2},$$

$$\therefore AD = \frac{2c}{t + t'' + 2t'}.$$

Now the acceleration = the slope of OA,

$$= \frac{AD}{OD},$$

$$= \frac{2c}{t(t + t'' + 2t')}.$$

The retardation = the slope of BC,

$$= \frac{BE}{EC},$$

$$= \frac{2c}{t''(t + t'' + 2t')}.$$

EXAMPLES VI.

1. Explain how the acceleration and the space covered may be obtained from the velocity-time diagram of a particle moving in a straight line.

    The velocity-time diagram consists of two straight lines AB, BC, where the co-ordinates of A, B, C are (o, 10), (10, 10), (20, 25), the first co-ordinate in each case being the time in seconds and the second co-ordinate the velocity in ft./sec.   Describe the motion of the particle and find the total distance covered. (H.C.)

2. If a sprinter can start with a velocity of 20 ft./sec., and run with uniform acceleration, find, graphically, the greatest speed attained in running the 100 yards in 10 seconds, and the necessary acceleration. (I.A.)

3. A train approaching a station does two successive quarters of a mile in 16 and 20 seconds respectively.   Assuming the retardation to be uniform, draw a graph to show the variation of the velocity with the time during this interval of 36 seconds. (H.C.)

4. The distance between two stations is 2000 yards. An electric train starts from rest at one station with a uniform acceleration of 1·5 f.s. units ; it comes to rest at the other station with a uniform retardation of 2·5 f.s. units, and the speed for the intermediate portion of the journey is constant. Sketch the general form of the velocity-time graph, and find what the constant velocity must amount to if the journey is to be completed in 3 minutes. (Q.E.)

5. A car is running steadily at 10 ft./sec. ; it then accelerates in such a way that for 200 feet the velocity increases by 1 ft./sec. for each 10 feet traversed. The acceleration then ceases. Draw curves showing the relation of v to s and f to s. What does the area of the latter curve denote ? (Q.E.)

6. A train starts from rest with an acceleration of 0·9 ft./sec.^{2} which decreases uniformly with the time until the train is travelling at full speed after 3 minutes. The train is then pulled up with a uniform retardation, and is stationary after a further 1·2 minutes. Plot the acceleration-time, velocity-time and distance-time graphs. Record the values of the retardation, velocity, and distance from the starting-point, at the instant when the brakes are applied. (Q.E.)

7. A train starts from a station, and for the first mile moves with a uniform acceleration, then for the next 2 miles with a uniform speed, and finally for another mile with uniform retardation, before coming to rest in the next station. The journey takes 8 minutes. Draw a graph showing how the speed varies with the time and from it find the maximum value of the speed.

8. The speed of a train for the first minute of its motion is given by the following table :—

Time in seconds	0	5	10	20	30	40	50	60
Speed in ft./sec.	0	8·5	14·6	23	29·2	33·6	37	39

Find the distance travelled in the first minute and also the time in which the train travels the first half of that distance. (Q.E.)

9. The relation between the velocity and the distance for a tramcar starting from rest is given in the following table :—

Velocity in ft./sec.	0	6	11	15	18	20·5	22·3	23·8	24·8	25·5	26
Distance in feet	0	15	30	45	60	75	90	105	120	135	150

Plot the velocity-distance curve, and show how to obtain the acceleration-distance curve from it. What is the acceleration in ft./sec. units at the mean distance ? (Q.E.)

10. The relation between distance and time for a car starting from rest is given in the table :—

Time in seconds	0	10	20	30	40	50	60	70
Distance in feet	0	36	160	395	660	880	1040	1160

Plot a distance-time curve, and deduce the velocity-time and acceleration-time curves for the first 60 seconds.

11. A car starts from rest and its velocity at the end of intervals of 10 seconds during the first minute is 13, 20·5, 25, 28, 29·5, and 30 ft./sec. respectively.

Plot the velocity-time graph and derive the velocity-distance graph. Thence obtain the mean values of the velocity during the first minute (i) with respect to time, (ii) with respect to distance. (Q.E.)

12. The speed of a train at intervals of 1 minute in a journey of 8 minutes are 0, 11, 21, 28, 30, 30, 26, 15, 0 miles per hour respectively. Draw the velocity-time graph, and estimate in miles the total distance travelled. Find the retardation in ft. per sec. per sec. at the end of the journey. (N.U.3)

13. The velocity, v ft./sec. of a car decreases with the time, t seconds, according to the formula

$$v = 40 - t^2.$$

Draw a velocity-time graph from $t = 0$ to $t = 7$. Find by graphical methods the distance travelled from $t = 3$ to $t = 6$ and the mean retardation in the same interval of time. (N.U.3)

14. A train travelling at 37·5 ft./sec. has steam shut off and brakes applied ; its speed in feet per second after t seconds is given by the formula

$$v = 37\cdot5 - t + 0\cdot005t^2.$$

Draw a time-speed graph from $t = 0$ to $t = 50$. Find the mean retardation during the 50 seconds and the instantaneous retardation at $t = 0$. (N.U.3)

15. The motion of a car on a track is found to be as given in the following table, in which the distance corresponding to a given time t is recorded :—

t (seconds)	3	4	5	6	7	8
s (feet)	58	73	92	115	142	173

Plot these values on a distance-time graph, and draw a smooth curve to represent this graph.

Determine from this curve the velocity of the car at the end of the 4th, 5th, 6th, and 7th seconds, and draw the velocity-time graph for this part of the motion. (N.U.3)

16. A graph is obtained by plotting the *reciprocal* of the velocity (v) of a moving point against the distance (s) measured from some fixed point. Prove that the time taken to travel between two given distances is represented by the area between the graph, the axis of s and the two ordinates of the $\frac{1}{v}$ curve corresponding to the two given distances.

If s and v are given by the following table :—

s	0·25	1	1·44	4	6·25	8·41	10·24
v	1	2	2·4	4	5	5·8	6·4

Find the time between the distances 1 foot and 8·41 feet. (N.U.3)

17. Two engines A, B, each having constant acceleration, are moving in the same direction along parallel sets of rails. When A passes B the speeds are respectively 20 and 10 m.p.h. Two minutes later B passes A, and B is then moving at 45 m.p.h. Draw the speed-time graphs and determine (i) the distance between the two places at which the engines overtake each other, (ii) the speed of A when B overtakes it, (iii) the instant at which the engines are moving with equal speeds, and the distance between them at this instant. (N.U.3)

18. A point moves on a line in such a way that its velocity v at time t is given by the following table :—

t (sec.) .	o	1	2	3	4	5	6	7	8	9	10
v (in./sec.)	o	29	55	62	68	63	55	52	40	32	30

Plot these values on a suitable graph, and deduce the space-time graph of the motion. (C.W.B.)

§ 52. EXAMPLE (i).

A tug leaves a port to intercept a liner, which is proceeding with uniform speed u m.p.h. on a straight course which, at the nearest point, is a miles from the port. The tug starts when the liner is b miles from the port, and has not yet reached the nearest point. Prove that the least uniform speed the tug must have in order to reach the liner is $\dfrac{au}{b}$.

Prove also that if the tug can go v m.p.h. $\left(u > v > \dfrac{au}{b} \right)$, *the liner is on a part of her course in which the tug can intercept her for*

$$\frac{2\sqrt{b^2 v^2 - a^2 u^2}}{u^2 - v^2} \text{ hours.}$$

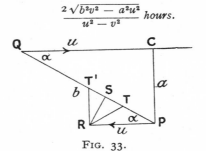

FIG. 33.

Let P (Fig. 33) be the position of the port, Q that of the liner, and QC the course, C being the nearest point to P.

Reduce Q to rest by applying velocities, equal and opposite to u, to Q and P.

Then if the tug is to reach Q the resultant of its velocity v and u reversed must lie along PQ, and if PR represents this reversed velocity it is obvious that the least value of v in order that the resultant of PR and v may lie along PQ is RS where RS is perpendicular to PQ.

Also RS $= u \sin \text{RPS} = \dfrac{ua}{b}$.

The resultant velocity of the tug is PS $= u \cos \alpha$,

$$= \frac{u}{b}\sqrt{b^2 - a^2}.$$

If v is greater than this value but less than u the tug can intercept the liner at any point within certain limits of its course, and we want to find the least and greatest times taken to meet it. These will be when the tug has its least and greatest velocities relative to the liner which are consistent with intercepting it. To find these we take R as centre and radius v and draw a circle to cut PQ. The circle will now cut PQ in two points, T and T', equidistant from S, and PT, PT' are the least and greatest relative velocities.

The difference in times required is given by

$$\frac{b}{PT} - \frac{b}{PT'} = \frac{2ST \cdot b}{PT \cdot PT'}.$$

Now
$$ST^2 = RT^2 - RS^2$$

$$= v^2 - \frac{a^2u^2}{b^2},$$

and
$$PT \cdot PT' = PS^2 - ST^2$$
$$= PR^2 - RT^2$$
$$= u^2 - v^2.$$

$$\therefore \text{ difference in times} = \frac{2\sqrt{b^2v^2 - a^2u^2}}{u^2 - v^2}.$$

EXAMPLE (ii).

To a person travelling due E. the wind appears to come from a direction N. $\alpha°$ W.; when he travels due N. at the same speed as before, the wind apparently makes $\beta°$ W. with the N. Show that the actual direction of the wind is N. $\theta°$ W. where

$$\tan \theta = \frac{\tan \alpha - 1}{1 - \cot \beta}. \qquad \text{(H.S.C.)}$$

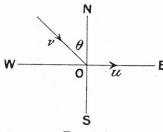

FIG. 34.

Let u be the velocity of the person and v that of the wind. The components of v are $v \sin \theta$ towards E. (Fig. 34) and $v \cos \theta$ towards S.

The apparent velocity of the wind in each case is the resultant of v and u reversed.

Now, when u is due E., the components of apparent velocity are $(v \sin \theta - u)$ due E., and $v \cos \theta$ due S.

$$\therefore \tan \alpha = \frac{v \sin \theta - u}{v \cos \theta} \qquad . \qquad . \qquad . \qquad . \qquad \text{(i)}$$

When u is due N. the components of apparent velocity are $v \sin \theta$ due E., and $(v \cos \theta + u)$ due S.

$$\therefore \tan \beta = \frac{v \sin \theta}{v \cos \theta + u} . \qquad . \qquad . \qquad . \qquad \text{(ii)}$$

These equations give

$$v \cos \theta \tan \alpha = v \sin \theta - u,$$

and $$v \cos \theta \tan \beta = v \sin \theta - u \tan \beta,$$

$$\therefore \cos \theta \tan \alpha = \sin \theta - \frac{u}{v},$$

$$\text{and } \cos \theta = \sin \theta \cot \beta - \frac{u}{v},$$

$$\therefore \cos \theta (\tan \alpha - \mathrm{I}) = \sin \theta (\mathrm{I} - \cot \beta),$$

$$\therefore \tan \theta = \frac{\tan \alpha - \mathrm{I}}{\mathrm{I} - \cot \beta}.$$

EXAMPLE (iii):

The relative velocity of the ends H and M of the hour and minute hands of a watch is calculated (i) *relatively to the face, and* (ii) *relatively to the seconds hand. Prove that the values obtained are different, their vector difference being $\frac{\pi x}{30}$ ft./sec. perpendicular to HM, if x feet is the length of HM.*

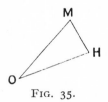

FIG. 35.

Let OM, OH (Fig. 35) represent the minute and hour hands. The angular velocities of the hands are

$$\text{for the seconds hand } \frac{2\pi}{60},$$

$$\text{for the minute hand } \frac{2\pi}{3600},$$

$$\text{for the hour hand } \frac{2\pi}{12 \times 3600}.$$

The velocities of M and H relative to the face are

$$\overrightarrow{OM} \frac{2\pi}{3600} \text{ perpendicular to OM,}$$

and $$\overrightarrow{OH} \frac{2\pi}{12 \times 3600} \text{ perpendicular to OH.}$$

Their relative velocity is

$$\overrightarrow{OM}\frac{2\pi}{3600} - \overrightarrow{OH}\frac{2\pi}{12 \times 3600} \qquad . \qquad . \qquad . \quad \text{(i)}$$

The angular velocities of OM and OH relative to the seconds hand are

$$-\frac{59 \times 2\pi}{3600} \text{ and } -\frac{719 \times 2\pi}{12 \times 3600},$$

hence the velocities of M and H relative to the seconds hand are

$$-\overrightarrow{OM}\frac{59 \times 2\pi}{3600} \text{ perpendicular to OM,}$$

$$-\overrightarrow{OH}\frac{719 \times 2\pi}{12 \times 3600} \text{ perpendicular to OH.}$$

Their relative velocity is

$$-\overrightarrow{OM}\frac{59 \times 2\pi}{3600} + \overrightarrow{OH}\frac{719 \times 2\pi}{12 \times 3600} \qquad . \qquad . \qquad . \quad \text{(ii)}$$

This value differs from (1) by

$$\overrightarrow{OM}\frac{60 \times 2\pi}{3600} - \overrightarrow{OH}\frac{720 \times 2\pi}{12 \times 3600},$$

or

$$\overrightarrow{OM}\frac{\pi}{30} - \overrightarrow{OH}\frac{\pi}{30},$$

or

$$\frac{\pi}{30}(\overrightarrow{OM} - \overrightarrow{OH}).$$

Now $\overrightarrow{OM} - \overrightarrow{OH} = \overrightarrow{HM}$, and since the velocities are perpendicular to OH and OM their difference will be perpendicular to HM, and its value is

$$\frac{\pi x}{30} \text{ ft./sec.}$$

EXAMPLES VII.

1. An express train, timed to run at a full speed of 60 m.p.h. over a certain section of its journey, is checked to 15 m.p.h. over a mile of road under repair. The train takes 1 mile from rest to get up full speed and $\frac{1}{4}$ mile in which to reduce speed from 60 to 15 m.p.h. Assuming uniform acceleration and retardation, find how much time is lost by the check. (H.S.C.)

2. The maximum possible acceleration of a certain body is 2 ft./sec.^{2}, and its maximum possible retardation is 8 ft./sec.^{2} What is the least time in which it can travel 1 mile from rest to rest ? (I.E.)

3. A circular disc rotates in its own plane about its centre O with uniform angular velocity. Show that the relative velocity of any two points on the disc is proportional to the distance between them, and find that point on a given radius OA whose velocity relative to another given point B of the disc is least, considering both the cases when the angle AOB is less than a right angle, and when it is greater. (H.S.C.)

4. A man can swim at a speed u relative to the water in a river flowing with speed v. Prove that it will take him

$$\frac{u}{\sqrt{u^2 - v^2}}$$

times as long to swim a certain distance up-stream and back as to swim the same distance and back perpendicular to the direction of the stream. What happens if v is greater than u? (H.S.C.)

5. A bullet is fired through three screens placed at equal intervals of a feet, and the times of passing the screens are t_1, t_2, t_3 seconds reckoned from the moment the bullet leaves the gun. Assuming that the retardation is uniform, prove that it is equal to

$$\frac{2a(t_3 - 2t_2 + t_1)}{(t_3 - t_1)(t_3 - t_2)(t_2 - t_1)}.$$ (H.S.C.)

6. Three steamers, A, B, C, are travelling at the rates of 12 knots, 9 knots, and 15 knots respectively. When they form a triangle in which AB = 4 miles, BC = 3 miles, CA = 5 miles, the velocity of C relative to A is along CB, and that of B relative to C is along BA. If it is known that A is actually moving in the direction AB, find the real directions of B and C, and the direction of A's motion relative to B. (Ex.)

7. Two bodies move in concentric circles, of centre O and radii a, b, with uniform speeds u, v, in the same sense. If P, Q be the positions of the bodies at a moment when their relative velocity is along the line joining them, obtain expressions for the ratios $b : a$ and $v : u$ in terms of the angles of the triangle OPQ ; and, if angle POQ = θ show that

$$\cos \theta = \frac{au + bv}{bu + av}.$$ (I.S.)

8. An aeroplane has a speed of v m.p.h. and a range of action (out and home) of R miles in calm weather. Prove that in a north wind of w miles per hour, its range of action in a direction θ east of north is

$$\frac{R(v^2 - w^2)}{v(v^2 - w^2 \sin^2 \theta)^{\frac{1}{2}}}.$$

Find also the direction in which its range is a maximum. (C.S.)

9. Two stopping points of an electric tramcar are 440 yards apart. The maximum speed of the car is 20 m.p.h., and it covers the distance between stops in 75 seconds. If both acceleration and retardation are uniform and the latter is twice as great as the former, find the value of each of them, and also how far the car runs at its maximum speed. (C.S.)

10. An aeroplane which travels at the rate of 80 m.p.h. in still air starts from A to go to B, which is 200 miles distant N.E. of A. If there is a wind blowing from the N. at 20 m.p.h., determine the direction in which the aeroplane must move, and the time required.

If at the end of an hour the wind drops to 5 m.p.h., determine the position relatively to B of the aeroplane at the time it should have arrived at B. Prove that, provided the velocity of the wind remains fixed in direction and magnitude, all points attainable by an aeroplane in a given time lie on a circle whose radius is independent of the wind. (C.S.)

11. A submarine sights a steamer proceeding on a due west to east course. The submarine is proceeding in a due S.W. to N.E. course at 10 m.p.h., and the steamer bears N.W. of the submarine all the while. The submarine stops when she is 7 miles from the ship, and after a short interval, fires a torpedo whose velocity is 30 m.p.h. in a direction due north. How long after stopping must she fire to make a hit ?   (Q.E.)

12. Two racing boats are moving at $9\frac{3}{4}$ and 10 m.p.h. respectively, the nose of the faster boat being 15 feet from the rudder of the slower one in a direction at right angles to the latter's course. If both boats are following straight courses, find the angle between them in order that a collision may occur in the shortest possible time. Find also what angle would cause the nose of the faster boat to cross the track of the slower one 3 feet astern of it.   (Q.E.)

13. A tug leaves port to intercept a liner, which is proceeding at 15 knots on a straight course which at the nearest point is 3 miles from the port, at the time when the liner is exactly 4 miles from the port and has not yet reached the nearest point. What is the minimum uniform speed which the tug must have in order to meet the liner ? If the tug can do 12 knots, for how long is the liner on a part of its course where the tug could intercept it ?   (1 knot = 1·152 m.p.h.)   (Q.E.)

14. A train, timed to run at a full speed of 54 m.p.h. has to reduce its speed to 18 m.p.h. over a mile of track under repair. The uniform retardation and acceleration of the train are the same as when stopping and starting. The train travels 1 mile in attaining full speed from rest, and a quarter of a mile in being brought to rest again. Calculate the time lost by the train owing to the track repair. Indicate (not to scale) the velocity-time and acceleration-time graphs.   (Q.E.)

15. The velocity of a body increases uniformly with the distance travelled, and is 15 m.p.h. at a distance of 60 feet from the start. Find, graphically, the time taken to travel the last 30 feet, and the acceleration at 60 feet.   (Q.E.)

16. A train passes a station A at 30 m.p.h., maintains this speed for $4\frac{1}{2}$ miles, and is then uniformly retarded, stopping at B, which is 5 miles from A. A second train starts from A at the instant the first train passes, and, being uniformly accelerated for part of the journey and uniformly retarded for the rest, reaches B at the same instant as the first train. What is the greatest speed on the journey ?

If the second train, after a certain uniform acceleration, runs at constant speed for 1 mile, and is then uniformly retarded, so that it reaches B with the first train, what is the value of the constant speed ?   (Q.E.)

VERTICAL MOTION UNDER GRAVITY.

§ 53. Acceleration of Falling Bodies.

When a heavy body is falling towards the earth, it is well known that its speed increases as it falls, or that it moves with an *acceleration*.

It has been shown by numerous experiments that, if the body is free from air resistance, this acceleration is always the same at the same place, but that it varies slightly for different places. The acceleration is also independent of the mass of the body.

The value of this acceleration, which is called the " acceleration due to gravity," is denoted by " g." Its numerical value in foot-second units in the latitude of London is about 32·19. At the equator it is about 32·091.

In centimetre-second units the value in London is about 981·17, and at the equator about 978.

(In numerical examples, unless otherwise stated, the value of g may be taken as 32 ft./sec.^{2}, or 981 cm./sec.^{2} ; the motion may be supposed to be *in vacuo*.)

§ 54. Vertical Motion under Gravity.

When a body is projected vertically upwards we regard the upward direction as the positive direction, and the body will experience a retardation or negative acceleration g. If u is the initial velocity of projection, the equations for motion with constant acceleration thus become

$$v = u - gt \quad . \quad . \quad . \quad . \quad \text{(i)}$$
$$s = ut - \tfrac{1}{2}gt^2 \quad . \quad . \quad . \quad \text{(ii)}$$
$$v^2 = u^2 - 2gs \quad . \quad . \quad . \quad \text{(iii)}$$

§ 55. At the highest point it is clear that the velocity v must be zero, so that by putting $v = 0$ in equation (i) we get the time taken to reach the highest point,

$$0 = u - gt, \text{ or } t = \frac{u}{g}.$$

Equation (iii) gives the greatest height,

$$0 = u^2 - 2gs, \text{ or } s = \frac{u^2}{2g}.$$

After reaching the highest point, the body begins to descend, and its speed increases.

§ 56. The velocity on returning to the point from which it was projected is given by putting $s = 0$ in equation (iii), and then

$$v^2 = u^2,$$
$$\text{i.e. } v = \pm u.$$

The $+$ sign gives the velocity on starting, and the $-$ sign the velocity on returning to the point of projection. The magnitude is the same as that of the velocity of projection, but the body is now moving downwards.

§ 57. The time of flight is obtained by putting $s = 0$ in equation (ii), and this gives

$$0 = ut - \tfrac{1}{2}gt^2,$$
$$\therefore t = 0, \text{ or } t = \frac{2u}{g}.$$

There are two values of t corresponding to the height $s = 0$, the value $t = 0$ obviously refers to the time of projection, while the value $\dfrac{2u}{g}$ gives the time required to return to the point of projection, i.e. the time of flight.

Notice that this is twice the time to the greatest height.

For any given height (less than the greatest) above the point of projection equation (ii) will give two values of t, one the time taken to reach that height on the way up, the other the time on the way down.

§ **58.** If we require the time taken to reach a point *below* the point of projection (when the body is projected upwards), we need not find the time up and down to the point of projection, and then the time taken to reach the point below. We simply substitute the distance below the point of projection for s in equation (ii), giving it a negative sign, as in the following example :—

A body is projected vertically upwards with velocity 24 *ft./sec. : how long will it take to reach a point* 280 *feet below the point of projection ?*

$$\text{Using } s = ut - \tfrac{1}{2}gt^2,$$
$$s = -280, \ u = 24, \ g = 32,$$
$$\therefore -280 = 24t - 16t^2,$$
$$\therefore 16^2 - 24t - 280 = 0,$$
$$\therefore 2t^2 - 3t - 35 = 0,$$
$$\therefore (2t + 7)(t - 5) = 0,$$
$$\therefore t = 5, \text{ or } t = -\tfrac{7}{2}.$$

The latter value is obviously impossible, and the required time is 5 seconds. (The value $\tfrac{7}{2}$ is, as a matter of fact, the time that would be taken if the body were projected *downwards*.)

§ **59.** *Velocity due to falling a given vertical height from rest.*

The positive direction is now downwards, and the equation of motion is

$$v^2 = u^2 + 2gs.$$

If the height is h, then $u = 0$, since the body starts from rest, and the velocity acquired is given by

$$v^2 = 2gh,$$
$$\therefore v = \sqrt{2gh}.$$

This is also the velocity required to take the body to a height h when projected vertically upwards.

VOL. I —4

EXAMPLES VIII.

1. A body is projected vertically upwards with a velocity of 60 ft./sec. ; find (i) how high it will go ; (ii) what times elapse before it is at a height of 36 feet.

2. A body is projected vertically upwards with a velocity of 80 ft./sec. ; find (i) when its velocity will be 16 ft./sec. ; (ii) how long it takes to return to the point of projection ; (iii) at what times it will be 64 feet above the point of projection.

3. A body falls from rest ; find (i) how far it will fall in 10 seconds ; (ii) how long it takes to fall 100 feet ; (iii) its velocity after falling 100 feet.

4. A body is projected vertically downwards from the top of a tower with a velocity of 40 ft./sec., and takes 3 seconds to reach the ground. What is the height of the tower ?

5. A body is projected vertically upwards with a velocity of 96 ft./sec. Find (i) how long it takes to reach its highest point ; (ii) the distance it ascends during the third second of its motion.

6. A body falls from rest from the top of a tower, and during the last second it falls $\frac{9}{25}$ of the whole distance. Find the height of the tower.

7. A body is projected vertically upwards with a certain velocity, and it is found that when it is 1344 feet from the ground it takes 8 seconds to return to the same point again. Find the velocity of projection and the whole time of flight.

8. A block falls from a mast-head, and is observed to take $\frac{2}{5}$ second in falling from the deck to the bottom of the hold, a distance of 25 feet. Calculate the height of the mast-head above the deck.
(I.S.)

9. A particle is projected vertically upwards, and t seconds afterwards another particle is projected vertically upwards with the same initial velocity. Prove that their velocities when meeting will be each $\frac{1}{2} gt$. (H.S.D.)

10. A particle is projected vertically upwards with a velocity of u ft./sec., and after t seconds another particle is projected upwards from the same point and with the same initial velocity. Prove that the particles will meet after a lapse of

$$\left(\frac{t}{2} + \frac{u}{g}\right) \text{ seconds}$$

from the instant of projection of the first particle. (H.S.D.)

11. A particle is projected vertically upwards with a velocity of u ft./sec., and after an interval of t seconds another particle is projected upwards from the same point and with the same initial velocity. Prove that they will meet at a height of

$$\frac{4u^2 - g^2t^2}{8g} \text{ feet.}$$ (I.E.)

12. If a stone falls past a window 8 feet high in half a second, find the height from which the stone fell. (H.C.)

13. A ball is thrown vertically upwards with a velocity of 56 ft./sec. ; find its height when it is moving at the rate of 40 ft./sec., and find the time between the instants at which it is at this height. (H.C.)

14. A particle projected vertically downwards descends 300 feet in 4 seconds. Show that it describes the last 100 feet in a little less than $\frac{4}{5}$ second.

15. A particle is projected vertically upwards and at the same instant another is let fall to meet it. Show that, if the particles have equal velocities when they impinge, one of them has travelled three times as far as the other.   (H.C.)

16. A ball is thrown vertically upwards with a speed of 128 ft./sec. Find where it is after 5 seconds, and the total distance it has actually travelled. If it falls past the point of projection into a well of depth 120 feet, find when it strikes the bottom.   (N.U.3)

§ 60. Motion down a smooth Inclined Plane.

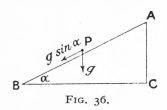

FIG. 36.

Let ABC (Fig. 36) represent the vertical section of a smooth plane inclined at an angle α to the horizontal, and P a particle on the plane. The line AB represents a line of greatest slope on the plane. The vertical acceleration g of P can be resolved into two components :—

   (i) An acceleration $g \sin \alpha$ down the plane ;
   (ii) An acceleration $g \cos \alpha$ perpendicular to the plane.

It is obvious that the plane prevents' motion perpendicular to itself, so that the particle moves down the plane with acceleration $g \sin \alpha$.

If l is the length of the plane AB, the velocity acquired in sliding from rest from A to B is obtained from the equation

$$v^2 = u^2 + 2fs,$$

by putting $u = 0, f = g \sin \alpha$, and $s = l$;

$$\therefore v^2 = 2g \sin \alpha \, . \, l = 2gh, \text{ where } h = \text{AC},$$
$$\therefore v = \sqrt{2gh}.$$

It is therefore the same as the velocity acquired in falling freely through a vertical height equal to that of the plane. The time taken to slide down AB is *not* the same, however, as that taken to fall freely through AC.

4 *

The time taken to slide down AB is obtained from the equation

$$s = ut + \tfrac{1}{2}ft^2,$$

by putting $s = l, u = 0, f = g \sin \alpha,$

$$\therefore l = \tfrac{1}{2}g \sin \alpha \cdot t^2,$$

$$\therefore t = \sqrt{\frac{2l}{g \sin \alpha}}.$$

The time taken to fall from A to C is given by

$$h = \tfrac{1}{2}gt^2, \text{ or } t = \sqrt{\frac{2h}{g}} = \sqrt{\frac{2l \sin \alpha}{g}}.$$

If the particle is projected up the plane, we simply use the ordinary equations of motion (§ 44) and put $f = -g \sin \alpha$.

If the particle is made to slide down the plane in a direction inclined to a line of greatest slope (e.g. in a smooth groove), the acceleration is no longer $g \sin \alpha$, but $g \sin \alpha \cos \beta$ where β is the inclination of the direction of motion to the line of greatest slope.

EXAMPLE.

A particle is projected (a) *upwards,* (b) *downwards, on a plane inclined to the horizontal at* 30° ; *if the initial velocity be* 16 *ft./sec., in each case, find the distances described and the velocities acquired in* 4 *seconds.*

(a) For motion *up* the plane we have

$$v = u - g \sin 30°t,$$

$$s = ut = \tfrac{1}{2}g \sin 30°t^2,$$

$$\therefore v = 16 - \frac{32}{2} \cdot 4 = -48 \text{ ft./sec.,}$$

$$s = 16 \times 4 - \frac{32}{2 \times 2} \cdot 16 = -64 \text{ feet,}$$

i.e. the body is moving *down* the plane with a velocity of 48 ft./sec., and is 64 feet below the point from which it started.

(b) For motion *down* the plane

$$v = u + g \sin 30°t,$$

$$s = ut + \tfrac{1}{2}g \sin 30°t^2,$$

$$\therefore v = 16 + \frac{32}{2} \cdot 4 = 80 \text{ ft./sec.,}$$

$$s = 16.4 + \frac{32}{2 \times 2} \cdot 16 = 192 \text{ feet.}$$

EXAMPLES IX.

1. A particle is projected with a velocity of 60 ft./sec. up a smooth inclined plane of inclination 30° ; find the distance described up the plane, and the time that elapses before it comes to rest.

2. A particle sliding down a smooth plane, 12½ feet long, acquired a velocity of 20 ft./sec. ; find the inclination of the plane.

3. A particle slides from rest down a smooth inclined plane which is 40 feet long and 9 feet high. What is its velocity on reaching the bottom of the plane, and how long does it take to get there ?

4. Two particles start together from a point O and slide down smooth straight wires inclined at angles 30°, 60° to the vertical, and in the same vertical plane and on the same side of the vertical through O. Show that the relative acceleration of the second particle with respect to the first is vertical and equal to $g/2$.   (I.S.)

5. A smooth inclined plane of length l and height h is fixed on a horizontal plane. Find the velocity with which a particle must be projected down the plane from the top in order that it may reach the horizontal plane in the same time as a particle let fall vertically from the top. Show that if the particles are of equal mass their kinetic energies will increase by the same amount.   (H.S.D.)

6. A long hollow straight tube AB, smooth inside, lies fixed on an inclined plane at an angle β with the lines of greatest slope, these being at an angle α to the horizontal. A smooth particle is put in at the upper end A and allowed to slide down. Find the distance it travels in t seconds, and the locus of all such points for different values of β, the end A always remaining at the same place.   (H.S.C.)

§ **61.** *The time taken by a body to slide down any smooth chord of a vertical circle, starting from the highest point, or ending at the lowest point of the circle, is constant.*

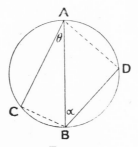

FIG. 37.

Let AB (Fig. 37) be a diameter of a vertical circle, of which A is the highest point, and AC any chord.

Let $\widehat{BAC} = \theta$, and $AB = d$, then $AC = AB \cos \theta = d \cos \theta$.

The acceleration down AC is $g \cos \theta$, and the time t taken to slide down AC from rest is obtained from

$$s = ut + \tfrac{1}{2}ft^2,$$

by putting $\qquad s = d \cos \theta, \ u = 0, f = g \cos \theta,$

$$\therefore d \cos \theta = \tfrac{1}{2}g \cos \theta \cdot t^2,$$

$$\therefore t^2 = \frac{2d}{g},$$

$$\therefore t = \sqrt{\frac{2d}{g}}.$$

Now, this is independent of θ, and it is easy to show that it is the same as the time taken to fall vertically from A to B.

The time taken to slide down all chords of the circle from A is therefore the same.

Let DB be any chord ending at B, and $\widehat{ABD} = \alpha$.

The length of DB is $d \cos \alpha$, and the acceleration down DB is $g \cos \alpha$.

The time taken to slide down DB is therefore given by

$$d \cos \alpha = \tfrac{1}{2}g \cos \alpha \cdot t^2,$$

$$\therefore t^2 = \frac{2d}{g},$$

$$\therefore t = \sqrt{\frac{2d}{g}},$$

the same value as before.

§ 62. Lines of Quickest Descent.

The line of quickest descent from a given point to a given curve in the same vertical plane is the straight line down which a body would slide from the point to the curve in the least time. It is not usually the shortest line geometrically.

From the result in the last paragraph we can show that the line of quickest descent is obtained as follows :—

The line of quickest descent from a given point P to a curve in the same vertical plane is PQ, where Q is a point on the curve where a circle, having P for its highest point, touches the curve.

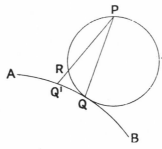

FIG. 38.

Let a circle be drawn having its highest point at P (Fig. 38), and touching the given curve AB at Q.

Take any point Q' on the curve and let PQ' meet the circle again at R.

Then, since PQ' > PR, time down PQ' > time down PR.

But time down PR = time down PQ,

∴ time down PQ′ > time down PQ.

Hence the time down PQ is less than that down any other line from P to the curve.

EXAMPLE (i).

To find the straight line of quickest descent from a given point to a given straight line in the same vertical plane as the given point.

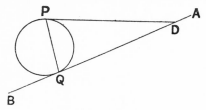

FIG. 39.

Let P (Fig. 39) be the given point, AB the given straight line.

We have to describe a circle having P as its highest point and also touching AB.

Draw PD horizontal to meet AB in D, then since P is the highest point of the circle PD is the tangent at P ; and since DB is also a tangent the point of contact will be at Q where DQ = DP.

Then PQ is the required line of quickest descent.

EXAMPLE (ii).

To find the line of quickest descent from a given vertical circle to a given point in the same plane as the circle.

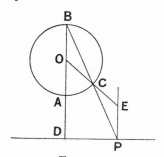

FIG. 40.

Let ABC (Fig. 40) be the circle, O its centre, and P the given point. We have to describe a second circle having P as its *lowest* point and touching ABC. Through P draw PD horizontal to meet the vertical through O in D and produce DO to meet the circle again in B. Then PD is a tangent to the required circle whose centre must lie on PE the perpendicular to DP at P.

Join PB, cutting ABC at C, join OC and produce it to cut PE at E.

Then $\widehat{EPC} = \widehat{OBC}$, alternate angles,

$= OCB$, since $OC = OB$,

$= ECP$, vertically opposite.

∴ $EP = EC$, and EC passes through O,

∴ a circle with centre E and radius EP will touch ABC at C,

∴ CP is the required line of quickest descent.

EXAMPLES X.

1. A right-angled triangle is placed with the side BC horizontal, and the side BA pointing vertically down, give a geometrical construction for finding the line of quickest descent from B to the hypotenuse AC.
(H.S.C.)

2. A particle slides down a smooth chord of a vertical circle ending in the lowest point. Show that the velocity acquired varies as the length of the chord.

3. A particle slides down a smooth chord of a vertical circle, starting from one end of the horizontal diameter. Show that the time taken varies as the square root of the tangent of the inclination of the chord to the vertical.

CHAPTER II.

FORCE, MOMENTUM, WORK AND ENERGY.

§ **63.** In the last chapter we dealt with motion without considering the cause of it. We have now to consider the cause of motion and changes of motion, and this introduces the idea of force. We recognise forces by the effects they produce, and among these is the tendency to alter the state of rest or uniform motion of bodies. It is this effect with which we are concerned in Dynamics, and we can give the following definition :—

§ **64.** *Force is any cause which produces or tends to produce a change in the existing state of rest of a body, or of its uniform motion in a straight line.*

If one body A is acting on another B, the mutual action between them is a force. If we are considering only one of the bodies we say that this force is an *external* one, or an *impressed* force ; if we are considering both bodies we say that the action is an *internal* force. When the bodies are in contact, their mutual action is called a *pressure* or a *tension*, when they are at a distance, the action is called a *repulsion* or *attraction* (e.g. the action between two electrified bodies).

§ **65.** For the present we shall consider the bodies to be *particles*, i.e. of such small dimensions that the distances between different portions of the bodies may be neglected, and that there can be no question of rotation of the body. The rotation of bodies of finite size will be dealt with later.

We have now to consider (i) how a body A will move when left to itself ; (ii) how the motion is affected by the action of an external force ; (iii) if this external force is due to another body B, how the action of B on A is related to the reaction of A on B.

The answer to these questions is given in Newton's Laws of Motion, but before enunciating these we require one or two definitions.

§ **66.** *The* **Mass** *of a body is the quantity of matter in the body.*

The **Momentum** *of a body, all the points of which are moving in parallel straight lines with equal velocities, is the product of the mass of the body and its velocity.*

In the case of a particle, if m is its mass and v its velocity, the momentum is mv. There is no special name for the unit of momentum ; if m is in lb. and v in ft./sec., we say that the momentum is mv lb.-ft. units of momentum.

It should be noticed that momentum is a vector quantity, it possesses both magnitude and direction.

In dealing with bodies of finite size we shall see later that we have to distinguish between *linear momentum*, due to the motion of translation of the centre of gravity of the body, and *angular momentum*, due to any rotation of the body about its centre of gravity.

For the present, if the body is not a particle, we shall treat it as if all the mass were concentrated at the centre of gravity and the momentum will be the product of the mass and the velocity of the centre of gravity.

§ 67. Newton's Laws of Motion may be stated as follows :—

1. *Every body continues in its state of rest or of uniform motion in a straight line, except in so far as it be compelled to change that state by external impressed forces.*
2. *Change of momentum per unit time is proportional to the impressed force, and takes place in the direction of the straight line in which the force acts.*
3. *To every action there is always an equal and contrary reaction ; or, the mutual actions of any two bodies are always equal and oppositely directed.*

These laws were known in various forms before Newton's time, but he was the first to put them into formal shape in his *Principia*, published in 1686.

No strict proof of these laws, experimental or otherwise, can be given, but the arguments for their truth may be classified as follows :—

(i) Common experience suggests their truth in a general way. We can never obtain the conditions to test Law I., but we can approximate to them, and we find that the smaller the external forces acting against a moving body the longer it will continue to move in a straight line. We also know that bodies do not move from rest of their own accord.

(ii) Assuming the laws to be true, the motions of various bodies, such as the moon and planets, can be worked out and then compared with observation. The positions of planets, the time of eclipses, etc., are worked out and published in the Nautical Almanac several years beforehand. The predicted places and times are found to agree with observations.

§ **68.** In many of these calculations the truth of another law enunciated by Newton is assumed. This is called *Newton's Law of Gravitation*, and can be stated as follows :—

Every particle of matter attracts every other particle of matter with a force which varies directly as the product of the masses of the particles and inversely as the square of the distance between them.

Numerous experiments have been made to verify this law by direct experiment, but the chief argument for its truth is the accuracy of the various calculations based on it.

§ **69.** The first law of motion implies what is sometimes called the *Principle of Inertia*, i.e. that a body has no power of itself to change its state of rest or motion, but goes on moving in the same direction with the same velocity, or continues in its state of rest when not acted upon by any external force.

§ **70.** The first part of the second law enables us to define units of force and establish the fundamental equation of dynamics. Let a force whose measure is P acting on a mass m produce an acceleration f in the mass.

Then, by the second law,

$P \propto$ rate of change of momentum,

$\propto$ rate of change of mv,

$\propto m \times$ rate of change of v (if m is constant),

$\propto mf$,

$\therefore P = kmf$, where k is some constant.

It is convenient to choose our unit of force so that k is equal to unity, i.e. $P = 1$ when $m = 1$ and $f = 1$, and if we do this our unit of force will be as follows :—

The unit of force is that force which, acting on unit mass, generates in it unit acceleration.

The fundamental equation then becomes

$$P = mf.$$

§ **71.** When the unit of mass is the pound, and the units of space and time are the foot and second, the unit force is called a *Poundal* (abbreviated to pdl.).

When the unit of mass is the gram, and the units of space and time are the centimetre and second, the unit force is called a *Dyne*.

These units are called *Absolute Units* because their values are the same everywhere, and do not depend on the earth's attraction as the unit discussed in the next paragraph does.

In using the equation $P = mf$, it is most important to remember that P must be in the absolute unit corresponding to the units used for m and f.

§ 72. The unit of force used by engineers is the *Pound-weight* (lb.-wt.), i.e. the force with which the earth attracts a pound of matter. This unit is not constant, but has different values at different parts of the earth's surface.

It is known that bodies fall to the earth with an acceleration denoted by g. This has different values in different places, but in this country the value of g is about 32 in ft.-sec. units, or 981 in centimetre-second units.

The weight of 1 lb. produces in it an acceleration of g ft./sec.^{2}, and is therefore equal to g poundals.

In foot-pound-second units,

1 lb.-wt. = 32 poundals (approximately).

In centimetre-gram-second units,

1 gm.-wt. = 981 dynes (approximately).

The poundal is therefore equal to the weight of about half an ounce. The dyne is equal to the weight of 1/981 gram, a little more than a milligram.

§ 73. It is found by experiment that, at the same place, bodies of different masses fall in a vacuum with the same acceleration g.

Hence, if W_1 and W_2 be the weight of masses m_1 and m_2 at the same place

$$W_1 = m_1 g,$$
$$W_2 = m_2 g,$$
$$\frac{W_1}{W_2} = \frac{m_1}{m_2},$$

i.e. the weight of bodies at the same place are proportional to their masses.

This enables us to compare masses by comparing their weights with an ordinary balance, and if we take the same set of standard masses or weights to different places any given mass will be found to have the same value at all these places.

A spring balance measures the force of the earth's attraction on a body, i.e. its weight, and such a balance will give different readings in different places with the same mass attached to it.

Note that mg gives the weight of m in *absolute* units.

§ 74. The second part of the second law implies the principle of the *Physical Independence of Forces*. The change of momentum produced by any force takes place in the direction of the straight line in which the force acts. If several forces act on a particle each will produce its own change of momentum quite independently of the others ; the *resultant* change of momentum will be the resultant of the separate changes produced by the individual forces.

§ 75. The Parallelogram of Forces.

If two forces represented in magnitude and direction by two straight lines OA, OB act on a particle placed at O, their resultant is represented in magnitude and direction by the diagonal OC of the parallelogram OACB.

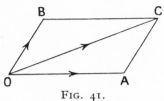

FIG. 41.

Since each force acts independently of the other, it will generate the same velocity in the particle in a given time whether the other acts or does not act. Also the velocity generated will be proportional to the force. Hence we may consider OA and OB (Fig. 41) to represent (to some scale) the velocities generated by the two forces, and at the end of the given time its resultant velocity will, by the parallelogram of velocities, be represented by OC. But this is also a measure of the force which would generate this velocity.

Hence the two forces represented by OA, OB are together equivalent to the single force represented by OC.

§ 76. *The Third Law of Motion.*

This law tells us that any action between the component parts of a system of bodies, such as a number of particles, whether due to attraction or repulsion at a distance or to actual contact, cannot affect the momentum of the system as a whole. For if two of the bodies A and B act on each other, the reaction of A on B is equal and opposite to the action of B on A, the action and reaction therefore generate equal and opposite amounts of momentum in the two bodies. Hence the total momentum reckoned in any fixed direction is unaltered.

This constitutes a very important principle known as the

Conservation of Linear Momentum.

In any system of mutually attracting or impinging particles the linear momentum in any fixed direction remains unaltered unless there is an external force acting in that direction.

This principle will be used in dealing with impulsive forces in the next chapter.

§ 77. In the equation $P = mf$, the acceleration f, and the force P may be either constant or variable.

For the present we shall consider cases where they are constant, and where the motion takes place in a straight line.

A more general form of this equation is

$$P = m\frac{d^2x}{dt^2}.$$

The product of the mass and the acceleration of a particle is called the effective force.

$$m\frac{d^2x}{dt^2} \text{ and } m\frac{d^2y}{dt^2}$$

are the Cartesian components of the effective force on the particle m.

§ 78. Friction.

In many problems it is assumed that a particle is resting on a *smooth* surface, so that there is no force between the surface and the particle tending to prevent motion along the surface.   This is, of course, an ideal case, in all actual cases when a particle is moved over a surface a force called friction is called into play which tends to prevent the particle moving.   It is found by experiment that, when one body is moved over another in contact with it, the force of friction tending to prevent motion bears a constant ratio to the normal reaction between the two surfaces, the value of this ratio depending only on the nature of the surfaces in contact.   This constant ratio is called the *coefficient of dynamical friction* for the given surfaces.   If R is the normal reaction between the surfaces, F the force of friction,

$$\frac{F}{R} = \mu, \text{ or } F = \mu R,$$

where μ is the coefficient of dynamical friction.

If a particle is moving on a horizontal surface, and not acted on by any other force inclined to the horizontal, the normal reaction

$$R = mg,$$
and then
$$F = \mu mg.$$

If a particle is moving on an inclined plane of slope α, and not acted on by other forces except in directions parallel to the plane, the reaction between the plane and the particle is

$$mg \cos \alpha,$$
and then
$$F = \mu mg \cos \alpha.$$

If there is any force, such as the tension of a string, tending to pull the particle away from the surface, this reduces the normal pressure and consequently the friction.

§ 79. EXAMPLE (i).

What force in pounds weight will give a mass of 9 tons a velocity of 25 m.p.h. in 1 minute ?

As one of the chief sources of error in dynamical problems is the use of wrong units, it is safer always to reduce all measurements to foot-pound-second or C.G.S. units.

In this case we use F.P.S. units :—

$$25 \text{ m.p.h.} = \frac{25 \times 88}{60} \text{ ft./sec.}$$

1 minute = 60 seconds.

We must first find the acceleration necessary to produce this velocity in 60 seconds.

Using $v = u + ft$,

$$\frac{25 \times 88}{60} = 60f,$$

$$\therefore f = \frac{25 \times 88}{60 \times 60} \text{ ft./sec.}^2$$

The mass acted on is 9×2240 lb., and the force required to produce the acceleration f, using $P = mf$, is

$$P = \frac{9 \times 2240 \times 25 \times 88}{60 \times 60} \text{ poundals,}$$

$$= \frac{224 \times 25 \times 88}{20 \times 2 \times 32} \text{ lb. wt.}$$

$$= 385 \text{ lb. wt.}$$

EXAMPLE (ii).

An engine and train weigh 203 tons, and the engine can exert a pull of 4 tons. The resistance to the motion of the train is 20 lb. wt. per ton, and the brake power is an additional 400 lb. wt. per ton. The train starts from rest and moves uniformly till it acquires a velocity of 40 m.p.h. ; steam is then shut off and the brakes are put hard on. Find the whole distance the train will have run before it comes to rest, and the whole time taken. (I.E.)

While the engine is pulling the tractive force is $4 \times 2240g$ poundals, and the resistance is $203 \times 20g$ poundals,

∴ the resultant accelerating force is

$$4 \times 2240g - 203 \times 20g,$$
$$= (8960 - 4060)g,$$
$$= 4900g \text{ poundals ;}$$

∴ the acceleration

$$= \frac{P}{m} = \frac{4900g}{203 \times 2240} \text{ ft./sec.}^2$$

$$= \frac{10}{29} \text{ ft./sec.}^2$$

40 m.p.h. $= \dfrac{176}{3}$ ft./sec., and we have to find how far the train goes in acquiring this velocity with acceleration $\dfrac{10}{29}$ ft./sec.^{2}.

Using $v^2 = u^2 + 2fs$,

$$\frac{176^2}{9} = \frac{20}{29}s,$$

$$\therefore s = \frac{176 \times 176 \times 29}{9 \times 20} \text{ ft.}$$

To find the time taken we use

$$v = u + ft,$$

$$\therefore \frac{176}{3} = \frac{10}{29}\, t,$$

$$\therefore t = \frac{176 \times 29}{3 \times 10} \text{ sec.}$$

The retarding force is $(203 \times 20g + 203 \times 400g)$ poundals.

$$= 203 \times 420g \text{ poundals.}$$

$\therefore$ the retardation

$$= \frac{203 \times 420 \times 32}{203 \times 2240} = 6 \text{ ft./sec.}^2$$

To find the distance travelled in losing the velocity of $\dfrac{176}{3}$ ft./sec., we have

$$0 = \frac{176^2}{9} - 12s,$$

$$\therefore s = \frac{176 \times 176}{9 \times 12} \text{ ft.}$$

To find the time to rest, we have

$$0 = \frac{176}{3} - 6t,$$

$$\therefore t = \frac{176}{3 \times 6}.$$

The whole distance run

$$= \frac{176^2 \times 29}{9 \times 20} + \frac{176^2}{9 \times 12} = \frac{176^2}{9} \cdot \frac{87 + 5}{60}$$

$$= \frac{176^2 \times 92}{9 \times 60} \text{ ft.}$$

$$= \frac{2024}{2025} \text{ mile.}$$

The whole time

$$= \frac{176 \times 29}{30} + \frac{176}{18} = \frac{176 \times 92}{90} \text{ seconds,}$$

$$= 3 \text{ minutes, nearly.}$$

Note.—When a train is running at uniform speed, the resultant force acting on it is zero, i.e. the pull of the engine must be just equal to the resistances.   If the pull is greater than the resistances the train will accelerate.

If a body slides down an incline with uniform speed, the component of its weight down the incline must be equal to the resistance.

EXAMPLE (iii).

A train travelling uniformly on the level at the rate of 48 m.p.h. begins an ascent of 1 in 75.   The tractive force that the engine exerts during the ascent is the same as that exerted on the level.   How far up the incline will the train go before coming to rest ?   Assume that the resistance due to friction, etc., is the same on the incline as on the level.

Since the train is moving uniformly on the level the pull of the engine is equal to the resistances.

On coming to the incline these forces still balance, but we now have the component of the weight of the train down the slope retarding it.

If *m* lb. is the mass of the train, the component of weight down the slope is $\dfrac{mg}{75}$ poundals, and as this is the resultant force acting parallel to the slope the retardation will be $\dfrac{g}{75}$ ft./sec.² The initial velocity is

$$\frac{48 \times 88}{60} \text{ ft./sec.}$$

The distance travelled before losing this velocity is given by

$$0 = \left(\frac{48 \times 88}{60}\right)^2 - \frac{64}{75} s,$$

$$\therefore s = \frac{88 \times 88 \times 16}{25} \cdot \frac{75}{64} \text{ ft.,}$$

$$= \frac{88 \times 88 \times 3}{4 \times 5280} \text{ mile,}$$

$$= 1 \cdot 1 \text{ mile.}$$

EXAMPLE (iv).

An engine of mass 105 tons is coupled to and pulls a carriage of mass 30 tons ; the resistance to the motion of the engine is $\frac{1}{100}$ of its weight ; the resistance to the motion of the carriage is $\frac{1}{150}$ of its weight.   Find the tension in the coupling if the whole tractive force exerted by the engine is equal to the weight of 6000 lb.

We must first find the acceleration produced in the engine and carriage.

The total resistance

$$= \left(\frac{105}{100} + \frac{30}{150}\right) \text{tons wt.}$$

$$= \tfrac{5}{4} \text{ tons wt.}$$

$$= 2800 \text{ lb. wt.}$$

The accelerating force

$$= (6000 - 2800) \text{ lb. wt.}$$
$$= 3200 \text{ lb. wt.}$$

The total mass

$$= 135 \times 2240 \text{ lb.,}$$

∴ the acceleration

$$= \frac{3200 \times 32}{135 \times 2240} \text{ ft./sec.}^2$$
$$= \frac{64}{189} \text{ ft./sec.}^2$$

The accelerating force on the carriage is

$$\frac{30 \times 2240 \times 64}{189} \text{ poundals,}$$
$$= \frac{22400 \times 2}{63} \text{ lb. wt.}$$
$$= 711\frac{1}{9} \text{ lb. wt.}$$

The accelerating force = tension in coupling — resistance, and the resistance to the carriage

$$= \frac{30 \times 2240}{150} = 448 \text{ lb. wt.,}$$

∴ the tension in the coupling

$$= (711\frac{1}{9} + 448) \text{ lb. wt.}$$
$$= 1159\frac{1}{9} \text{ lb. wt.}$$

EXAMPLE (v).

A body, of mass m lb., is placed on a horizontal plane which is moving with an upward vertical acceleration f. Find the pressure between the body and the plane.

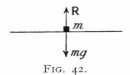

FIG. 42.

Let R be the reaction between the body and the plane. Since the body is moving upwards with an acceleration, it is evident that R is greater than the weight mg.

The resultant upward force acting on the body is $R - mg$,

$$\therefore R - mg = mf,$$
$$\therefore R = m(g + f).$$

If the plane be moving downwards with acceleration f, the weight mg is now greater than R. The resultant downward force acting on m is $mg - R$, and

$$mg - R = mf,$$
$$\therefore R = m(g - f).$$

If in the latter case $f = g$, then $R = 0$, i.e. there is no pressure between the body and the plane.

EXAMPLE (vi).

A rifle bullet passes through two planks in succession, and the average resistance of the second plank is 50 per cent. more than that of the first. The initial velocity is 2000 ft./sec., and the bullet loses 400 ft./sec. in passing through each plank. Show that the thicknesses of the planks are as 27 : 14. (I.E.)

Since the resistance of the second plank is 50 per cent. more than that of the first, it will produce $1\frac{1}{2}$ times the retardation produced by the first.

Let f ft./sec.^{2} be the retardation produced by the first, then $\frac{3}{2}f$ is the retardation produced by the second.

Let s_1, s_2 ft. be their thicknesses, then we have

$$1600^2 = 2000^2 - 2fs_1,$$
$$1200^2 = 1600^2 - 3fs_2,$$
$$2fs_1 = 3600 \times 400,$$
$$\therefore 3fs_2 = 2800 \times 400,$$
$$\therefore \frac{2s_1}{3s_2} = \frac{36}{28} = \frac{9}{7},$$
$$\therefore \frac{s_1}{s_2} = \frac{27}{14}.$$

Note.—In problems similar to that in Example (vi), great care must be taken to distinguish the cases (i) when the body is moving horizontally, and (ii) vertically.

In (i) if u is the initial velocity, m the mass, s the distance penetrated, R the average resistance, and f the retardation

$$0 = u^2 - 2fs, \text{ or } f = \frac{u^2}{2s}.$$

In (ii) the first equation is the same,

$$0 = u^2 - 2fs,$$

but now the weight of the body mg is acting vertically downwards, so that the *resultant retarding force* is not R but $R - mg$, so that

$$R - mg = mf.$$

The resistance is greater by the weight of the body than in the case where the motion is horizontal.

EXAMPLES XI.

1. Find the acceleration produced when (i) a force of 6 poundals acts on a mass of 12 lb. ; (ii) a force of 6 lb. wt. acts on a mass of 12 lb.
2. What force (in lb. wt.) acting on a mass of 12 cwt., will generate in it a velocity of 15 m.p.h. in 5 minutes ?
3. A body of mass 100 tons is acted on by a force of 70 lb. wt. How long will it take to acquire a velocity of 15 m.p.h. ?

4. A ship of 10,000 tons slows, with engines stopped, from 6 knots to 5 knots in a distance of 90 feet ; assuming the resistance to be uniform, calculate its value in tons weight. (A knot may be assumed to be a speed of $\frac{5}{3}$ ft./sec.) (I.A.)

5. A truck is found to travel with uniform speed down a slope which falls 1 foot vertically for every 112 feet length of the slope. If the truck starts from the bottom of the slope with a speed of 10 m.p.h., how far up will it travel before coming to rest ? (I.A.)

6. Find in lb. wt. per ton the force exerted by the brakes of a train travelling at 60 m.p.h. which will bring it to rest in half a mile, and find the time during which the brakes act. (H.C.)

7. A force equal to the weight of 10 gm. acts on a mass of 218 gm. for 5 seconds. Find the velocity generated and the distance moved in this time.

8. Find the magnitude of the force which, acting on a mass of 1 kilogram for 5 seconds, causes the mass to move through 10 metres from rest in that time.

9. The resistance to the motion of a train due to friction, etc., is equal to the weight of 14 lb. per ton. If the train is travelling on a level road at 50 m.p.h. and comes to the foot of an incline of 1 in 150 and steam is then turned off, how far will the train go up the incline before it comes to rest ? (H.S.D.)

10. A train travelling uniformly on the level at the rate of 48 m.p.h. begins an ascent of 1 in 75. The tractive force that the engine exerts during the ascent is constant and equal to $2\frac{1}{2}$ tons wt., the resistance (due to friction, etc.) is constant, and equal to 30 cwt., and the weight of the whole train is 225 tons. Show that the train will come to a standstill after climbing for 1·65 miles. (H.C.)

11. A body of mass 25 gm. is observed to travel in a straight line through 369, 615, and 861 cm. in successive seconds. Prove that this is consistent with a constant force acting on the body. What is the value of this force ?

12. Some trucks, starting from rest on an incline of 1 in 160, acquired a speed of 15 m.p.h. in 10 minutes. Calculate the resistance to the motion of the trucks in lb. wt. per ton mass of the trucks. (I.E.)

13. A force equal to the weight of 1 ton acts for 3 seconds on a mass of 5 tons. Find the velocity produced and the space passed over, stating the units in which the results are measured. (I.S.)

14. A mass of 10 lb. rests on a horizontal plane which is made to ascend (i) with a constant velocity of 5 ft./sec. ; (ii) with a constant acceleration of 5 ft./sec.² ; find in each case the reaction of the plane.

15. A man, of mass 10 stone, stands on a lift, which moves with a uniform acceleration of 12 ft./sec.² ; find the reaction of the floor when the lift is (i) ascending, (ii) descending.

16. A scale pan, on which rests a mass of 50 gm., is drawn upwards with a constant acceleration, and the reaction between the mass and the pan is found to be 50,000 dynes ; find the acceleration of the scale pan.

17. A body whose true weight was 13 oz. appeared to weigh 12 oz. when weighed by means of a spring balance in a moving lift. What was the acceleration of the lift at the instant of weighing ? (I.A.)

18. A train of mass 160 tons starts from a station, the engine exerting a tractive force of $2\frac{1}{2}$ tons in excess of the resistances until a speed of $37\frac{1}{2}$ m.p.h. is attained. This speed continues constant until the brakes, causing a retardation of $2\frac{1}{2}$ ft./sec.^{2}, bring the train to rest 5 miles away. Find the time taken (i) during acceleration ; (ii) during retardation ; (iii) altogether. (I.S.)

19. The pull exerted by an engine is $\frac{1}{80}$ of the weight of the whole train, and the maximum brake force, which can be exerted is $\frac{1}{30}$ of the weight of the train. Find the time in which the train travels from rest to rest up a slope of 1 in 240 and 3 miles long, the brakes being applied when steam is shut off. (H.S.C.)

20. In a lift, accelerated upwards at a certain rate, a spring balance indicates a mass to have a weight of 10 lb. When the lift is accelerated downwards at twice the rate, the mass appears to be 7 lb. in weight. Find the actual weight of the mass, and the upward acceleration of the lift. (I.C.)

21. A vertical shield is made of two plates of wood and iron respectively, the iron being 2 inches, and the wood 4 inches thick. A bullet fired horizontally goes through the iron first and then penetrates 2 inches into the wood. A similar bullet fired with the same velocity from the opposite direction goes through the wood first and then penetrates 1 inch into the iron. Compare the average resistance exerted by the iron and the wood. (I.E.)

22. A 4-oz. bullet, travelling at 500 ft./sec., will penetrate 5 inches into a fixed block of wood. Find the velocity with which it would emerge, if fired through a fixed board $2\frac{1}{2}$ inches thick, the resistance being supposed uniform and to have the same value in each case. (H.S.D.)

23. A bullet weighing 30 gm. is fired into a fixed block of wood with a velocity of 294 metres per second, and is brought to rest in $\frac{1}{150}$ second. Find in dynes, and in grams weight, the resistance exerted by the wood, supposing it to be uniform. (H.C.)

§ **80.** In the last paragraph we considered the motion of a single mass. We shall now consider some simple cases of the motion of two masses connected by a light inextensible string. In such cases we can apply the equation $P = mf$ to each of the masses, as in the following examples :—

EXAMPLE (i).

Two particles of masses m_1 and m_2 are connected by a light inextensible string passing over a small smooth fixed pulley. To find the resulting motion of the system and the tension in the string.

Since the pulley is smooth the tension is the same throughout the string, let this be T poundals, the masses m_1 and m_2 being in pounds. Suppose m_1 greater than m_2, then m_1 will move downwards and m_2 upwards, and, since the string is inextensible, the upward acceleration of m_2 is equal to the downward acceleration of m_1. Let this acceleration be f.

Now, the forces acting on m_1 are m_1g downwards and T upwards, ∴ the resultant force on m_1 is $m_1g - T$ poundals downwards.

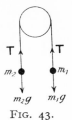

Fig. 43.

Hence, using
$$P = mf,$$
$$m_1 g - T = m_1 f \quad . \qquad . \qquad . \qquad . \qquad . \qquad \text{(i)}$$

The resultant force on m_2 is $T - m_2 g$ upwards,
$$\therefore T - m_2 g = m_2 f \quad . \qquad . \qquad . \qquad . \qquad \text{(ii)}$$

We now solve equations (i) and (ii) to find f and T.
Adding,
$$(m_1 - m_2)g = (m_1 + m_2)f,$$
$$\therefore f = \frac{m_1 - m_2}{m_1 + m_2} g.$$

The value of f can also be found as follows.   The resultant force producing motion is $(m_1 - m_2)g$, and the total mass moved is $(m_1 + m_2)$,
$$\therefore f = \frac{m_1 - m_2}{m_1 + m_2} g.$$

From (i)
$$T = m_1(g - f),$$
$$= m_1 \left(1 - \frac{m_1 - m_2}{m_1 + m_2} \right) g,$$
$$= \frac{2 m_1 m_2}{m_1 + m_2} g \text{ poundals.}$$

If the parts of the string not in contact with the pulley hang vertically, the pressure on the pulley
$$= 2T = \frac{4 m_1 m_2}{m_1 + m_2} g \text{ poundals.}$$

EXAMPLE (ii).

A mass m_2 is placed on a smooth horizontal table, and connected by a light inextensible string passing over a small smooth pulley at the edge to a mass m_1, hanging freely. Find the resulting motion and the tension in the string.

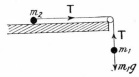

Fig. 44.

m_1 will move downwards and m_2 along the table. Since the string is inextensible the accelerations of m_1 and m_2 are equal ; let this acceleration be f. Let T poundals be the tension in the string. The forces acting on m_1 are m_1g downwards and T upwards,

∴ the resultant force on m_1 is $m_1g - T$ poundals,

∴ using $P = mf$,

$$m_1g - T = m_1f \quad . \qquad . \qquad . \qquad . \quad \text{(i)}$$

Since m_2 is resting on a smooth horizontal surface its weight has no effect as far as motion along the surface is concerned. The weight is balanced by the reaction of the plane $(= mg)$. The resultant force tending to produce motion horizontally is therefore the tension T poundals. Hence, for m_2, we have

$$T = m_2f \quad . \qquad . \qquad . \qquad . \quad \text{(ii)}$$

Adding (i) and (ii), $m_1g = (m_1 + m_2)f$,

$$\therefore f = \frac{m_1}{m_1 + m_2}g.$$

The value of f may also be found directly by dividing the resultant force, tending to produce motion (m_1g) by the total mass moved $(m_1 + m_2)$. Substituting in (ii)

$$T = \frac{m_1 m_2}{m_1 + m_2}g \text{ poundals.}$$

In this case R, the pressure on the pulley, is the resultant of two equal forces T at right angles,

$$\therefore R = \sqrt{T^2 + T^2} = \sqrt{2} \, . \, T,$$

$$= \frac{\sqrt{2}m_1 m_2}{m_1 + m_2}g \text{ poundals.}$$

EXAMPLE (iii).

A particle of mass m_2 rests on the surface of a smooth plane inclined at an angle α to the horizontal, and is connected by a light inextensible string, passing over a small smooth pulley at the top of the plane, to a mass m_1 hanging freely. Find the resulting motion and the tension in the string.

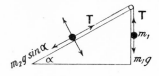

FIG. 45.

The tension of the string is the same throughout, let this be T poundals. The accelerations of the masses are the same, let this be f. The forces acting on m_1 are its weight m_1g vertically downwards and T vertically upwards. If m_1 moves downwards

$$m_1g - T = m_1f \qquad . \qquad . \qquad . \qquad . \quad \text{(i)}$$

The forces acting on m_2 *parallel to the surface of the plane* are $m_2g \sin \alpha$ down the plane and T up the plane; the resultant force tending to produce motion is therefore $T - m_2g \sin \alpha$,

$$\therefore T - m_2g \sin \alpha = m_2f \qquad . \qquad . \qquad . \qquad . \text{(ii)}$$

Adding (i) and (ii) $g(m_1 - m_2 \sin \alpha) = (m_1 + m_2)f$,

$$\therefore f = \frac{m_1 - m_2 \sin \alpha}{m_1 + m_2}g.$$

T is obtained by substituting for f in (i).

Note.—In working numerical examples similar to those above, the results there given must not be used as formulæ for substituting the numerical values. Each question should be worked as shown in Examples (i) to (iii), using the numbers given in the question instead of letters.

EXAMPLE (iv).

A particle slides down a rough inclined plane of inclination α. *If* μ *be the coefficient of friction, find the motion.*

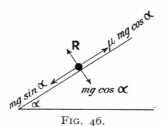

FIG. 46.

Let m be the mass of the particle, and R the normal reaction of the plane, then the friction is μR.

Now as there is no motion perpendicular to the surface of the plane the reaction of the plane must equal the component of the weight of the particle perpendicular to the plane,

$$\therefore R = mg \cos \alpha.$$

The resultant force acting down the plane is

$$mg \sin \alpha - \mu R,$$
$$= mg \sin \alpha - \mu mg \cos \alpha.$$

The acceleration down the plane is

$$\frac{mg \sin \alpha - \mu mg \cos \alpha}{m} = g(\sin \alpha - \mu \cos \alpha).$$

If $\sin \alpha < \mu \cos \alpha$, or $\tan \alpha < \mu$,

there will be no acceleration down the plane, and as the particle obviously cannot move up the plane, this means that it will remain at rest.

If the particle is projected up the plane, the resultant retarding force down the plane is

$$mg \sin \alpha + \mu mg \cos \alpha.$$

EXAMPLE (v).

Two particles of masses m_1 and m_2 rest on the rough faces of a double inclined plane and are connected by a light inextensible string passing over a small smooth pulley at the vertex of the plane. If the faces of the plane are equally rough, find the resulting motion.

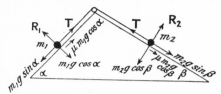

FIG. 47.

Let the inclinations of the faces on which m_1 and m_2 rest be α and β respectively, and suppose that m_1 moves downwards.

Let T be the tension in the string.

Since the particles do not move perpendicular to the faces, the reactions of the faces are equal to the components of the weights perpendicular to the faces, i.e. $m_1 g \cos \alpha$ for m_1, and $m_2 g \cos \beta$ for m_2.

Since m_1 moves *down*, the friction on it acts *up* the plane. Hence the total downward force on m_1 is

$$m_1 g \sin \alpha - T - \mu m_1 g \cos \alpha,$$

and the total upward force on m_2 is

$$T - m_2 g \sin \beta - \mu m_2 g \cos \beta,$$

hence, if f is the common acceleration

$$m_1 g \sin \alpha - T - \mu m_1 g \cos \alpha = m_1 f \qquad . \qquad . \quad \text{(i)}$$
$$T - m_2 g \sin \beta - \mu m_2 g \cos \beta = m_2 f \qquad . \qquad . \quad \text{(ii)}$$

Adding (i) and (ii),

$$f(m_1 + m_2) = g(m_1 \sin \alpha - m_2 \sin \beta - \mu m_1 \cos \alpha - \mu m_2 \cos \beta),$$

giving f.

T is obtained by substituting for f in either (i) or (ii).

EXAMPLE (vi).

Two masses 10 lb. and 3 lb. respectively are connected by a fine string which passes over a smooth pulley fixed at the head of a smooth inclined plane 5 feet long and 1 foot high. The heavier particle is on the plane and the lighter particle just hangs over the pulley, the string being 5 feet long. Find the acceleration of the masses and the tension of the string. How long will it be after the 3-lb. mass reaches the ground before the string is again taut?
(I.A.)

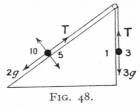

FIG. 48.

Let T poundals be the tension of the string, f the common acceleration.

The resultant force downwards acting on the 3 lb. mass is

$$3g - T \text{ poundals,}$$

the resultant force on the 10 lb. mass acting up the plane is

$$T - 10 \cdot \tfrac{1}{5}g = T - 2g \text{ poundals,}$$
$$\therefore 3g - T = 3f,$$
$$T - 2g = 10f ;$$
$$\therefore 13f = g, \text{ or } f = \tfrac{1}{13}g, \text{ ft./sec.}^2$$
$$T = 2g + 10f = 2g + \tfrac{10}{13}g = \tfrac{36}{13}g \text{ poundals.}$$

When the 3 lb. mass reaches the ground the masses will have moved 1 foot from rest with acceleration $\dfrac{g}{13}$,

$\therefore$ their common velocity v is given by

$$v^2 = 2\,\frac{g}{13}\cdot 1 = \frac{64}{13},$$

$$\therefore v = \frac{8}{\sqrt{13}} \text{ ft./sec.}$$

Now the 3 lb. mass is stopped by the ground, the string becomes slack and the 10 lb. mass moves on with velocity v, and subject to a retardation $\dfrac{g}{5}$.

The time taken to go up the plane and return to the point from which it began to move freely is given by

$$0 = \frac{8}{\sqrt{13}}t - \frac{1}{2}\cdot\frac{g}{5}\,t^2,$$

$$\therefore t = \frac{5 \times 8}{16\sqrt{13}},$$

$$= \frac{5\sqrt{13}}{26} \text{ seconds.}$$

After this interval the string again becomes taut.

EXAMPLE (vii).

A mass of M lb. rests on a smooth horizontal table and is attached by two inelastic strings to masses m, m' lb. (m' > m), which hang over smooth pulleys at opposite edges of the table. Find the acceleration of the system and the tensions in the strings.

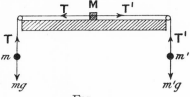

FIG. 49.

If T be the tension in the string connecting m and M, T' that in the other string, we have, if f is the acceleration,

$$\text{For } m', \qquad m'g - T' = m'f \qquad . \qquad . \qquad . \quad \text{(i)}$$
$$\text{,, } m, \qquad T - mg = mf \qquad . \qquad . \qquad . \quad \text{(ii)}$$
$$\text{,, } M, \qquad T' - T = Mf \qquad . \qquad . \qquad . \quad \text{(iii)}$$

Adding the three equations

$$(m' - m)g = (m' + m + M)f,$$

$$\therefore f = \frac{m' - m}{m' + m + M}g.$$

The values of T' and T are obtained by substituting in (i) and (ii).

EXAMPLES XII.

1. Two particles, of masses 6 and 10 lb., are connected by a light string passing over a smooth pulley. Find (i) their common acceleration, (ii) the tension in the string, (iii) the pressure on the pulley.

2. Two particles, of masses 5 and 7 lb., are connected by a light string passing over a smooth pulley. Find their common acceleration and the tension in the string.

3. Two particles, of masses 7 and 9 oz., are connected by a light string passing over a smooth pulley. Find their common acceleration and the tension in the string.

4. Two particles, of masses 20 and 30 gm., are connected by a fine string passing over a smooth pulley. Find their common acceleration and the tension in the string.

5. A mass of 9 lb. resting on a smooth horizontal table is connected by a light string, passing over a smooth pulley at the edge of the table, to a mass of 7 lb. hanging freely. Find the common acceleration, the tension in the string, and the pressure on the pulley.

6. In the last question, if the 7 lb. mass starts from the level of the edge, which is 7 feet above the ground, and the string, which is 14 feet long, is taut and perpendicular to the edge; find (i) how long the 7 lb. mass takes to reach the ground; (ii) how long after that the 9 lb. mass takes to reach the edge of the table.

7. A mass of 5 lb. is placed on a smooth horizontal table 6 feet high at a distance of 18 feet from the edge and connected by a light string 18 feet long to a mass of 3 lb. on the edge of the table. If

the 3 lb. mass is pushed gently over the edge, find (i) how long it takes to reach the ground ; (ii) how much longer the 5 lb. mass takes to reach the edge.

8. A particle, of mass 5 lb., is placed on a smooth plane whose height is 4 feet and length 20 feet. The particle is connected by a light string passing over a smooth pulley at the top of the plane to a mass of 3 lb. hanging freely. Find the common acceleration and the tension of the string.

9. If, in question 8, the 5 lb. mass is initially at the bottom of the slope and the 3 lb. mass hanging just over the pulley, find (i) how long the 3 lb. mass takes to reach the ground, (ii) the time that elapses after this happens before the string again becomes taut.

10. Two masses of $\frac{1}{4}$ oz. and $7\frac{3}{4}$ oz. connected by an inextensible string 5 feet long, lie on a smooth table $2\frac{1}{2}$ feet high. The string being straight and perpendicular to the edge of the table, the lighter mass is drawn gently just over the edge and released. Find (i) the time that elapses before the first mass strikes the floor, and (ii) the time that elapses before the second mass reaches the edge of the table.   (I.S.)

11. A mass of 2 lb. lies at the bottom of an inclined plane 30 feet long and 10 feet high. It is attached by a light cord 30 feet long, which lies along the line of greatest slope of the plane, to a mass of 1 lb., which hangs just over the top of the plane. The system is allowed to move. Assuming that the hanging mass comes to rest when it reaches the ground, find the distance that the mass of 2 lb. will travel before it first comes to rest.   (H.S.D.)

12. A particle of weight 5 lb. resting on a smooth plane of inclination 30°, is attached to a light string which passes over a smooth pulley at the highest point of the plane and carries a hanging weight of 2 lb. Calculate the acceleration of each weight, assuming that the whole motion takes place in the vertical plane through the pulley and the line of greatest slope. Find also the tension in the string.   (H.S.D.)

13. A mass of 5 lb. rests on a rough horizontal table, and is connected by a light string with a mass of 3 lb. hanging freely. If the co-efficient of friction between the 5 lb. mass and the table is $\frac{1}{5}$, find the resultant acceleration and the tension in the string.

14. A mass of 4 lb. rests on a rough horizontal table (coefficient of friction $\frac{1}{2}$), and is connected by a light string with a mass of 3 lb. hanging freely. Find the velocity acquired and the distance described by the masses in 7 seconds.

15. A particle slides down a rough inclined plane, whose inclination to the horizontal is 45°, and whose coefficient of friction is $\frac{3}{4}$; show that the time of descending any distance is twice what it would be if the plane were smooth.

16. Two rough planes, inclined at 30° and 60° to the horizontal and of the same height, are placed back to back ; masses of 4 and 12 lb. are placed on the faces and connected by a light string passing over a smooth pulley at the top of the planes ; if the coefficient of friction is $\frac{1}{2}$, find the resulting acceleration.

17. A rough plane is 50 feet long and 30 feet high, the coefficient of friction is $\frac{1}{2}$, and a particle slides down the plane from rest at the

highest point ; find the velocity of the particle on reaching the bottom and the time taken.

18. A light inextensible string, passing over a small smooth fixed pulley, carries at one end a weight of 4 oz., and at the other two weights each of 3 oz. If the system is allowed to move, find the acceleration with which the weight of 4 oz. ascends.

If one of the 3 oz. weights falls off after the 4 oz. weight has ascended a distance of $2\frac{1}{2}$ inches, how much farther will the 4 oz. weight ascend ?
(H.C.)

19. A particle held at rest on a smooth table is attached by a light inextensible string to a second particle, of the same mass as the first, which hangs over the edge of the table, the string being taut and at right angles to the edge of the table. If the particle on the table is released, find the acceleration with which it begins to move. If the string connecting the particles is 5 feet long and both particles are initially on the table, one 5 feet from the edge and the other at the nearest point of the edge from the first, and the particle at the edge is pushed gently over the edge, find the time that elapses before the other particle reaches the edge.
(H.C.)

20. A mass of 20 lb. slides from rest through a distance of 100 feet down a rough rail whose angle of inclination with the horizontal is $\tan^{-1}\frac{7}{24}$, the coefficient of friction being 0·25. Find in foot-poundals the work done on the mass by the forces acting on it. Also find the velocity acquired by the mass.

21. An engine driver of a train at rest observes a truck moving towards him down an incline of 1 in 60 at a distance of half a mile. He immediately starts his train away from the truck at a constant acceleration of 0·5 ft./sec.^{2} If the truck just catches the train, find its velocity when first observed. Assume that friction opposing the truck's motion is 14 lb. wt. per ton.
(C.S.)

22. A mass M is moving with velocity V. It encounters a constant resistance F ; write down equations to determine the time before it is brought to rest and the distance it has travelled, stating the principles on which these equations depend. Two moving masses are brought to rest by equal constant resistances. If the one mass moves for twice as long as the other but goes only half the distance, find the ratio of the masses and also that of their velocities. (C.S.)

23. A body of weight W_1 hangs vertically from a string which is tied to a body of weight W_2 on a horizontal table. The coefficient of friction between the second body and the table is μ, while owing to the friction at the edge of the table the tension of the vertical part of the string must be n times that of the horizontal part. Find the acceleration and the tensions. Find the relation between W_1, W_2, so that the tension of the horizontal part of the string may be equal to W_2
(N.U.3)

24. State the relation between force and acceleration in C.G.S. units. Two bodies of mass 1 and 1·1 kilos. hang from the ends of a light inextensible string, which passes over a smooth light pulley. Find the acceleration of the bodies and the tension in the string.

The whole system is placed in a lift which has a downward acceleration of 98 cm./sec.^{2} Find the acceleration of each body relative to the lift.
(N.U.3)

§ 81. Attwood's Machine.

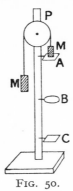

FIG. 50.

In the simplest form of this machine two equal masses (M), are connected by a light cord passing over a light pulley P, as in Fig. 50.

The axis of the pulley is supported horizontally so that it can turn with very little friction.

If the masses are set in motion they will move with a velocity which is very nearly constant for a short time, and by measuring the time taken by one of the masses to describe a given distance the value of this velocity can be obtained.

The machine is used to verify the laws of motion and to obtain a rough value for g.   [The best method of determining g is by means of the pendulum which will be described in a later chapter.]   The masses are set in motion by placing a small rider of known mass (m) on one of the large masses which can be released from a platform A, attached to the stand which supports the pulley.

A ring B is fixed to the stand vertically below A, and is of such size that M can pass through it, but the rider m remains on the ring. The masses will then move with uniform velocity and the time taken for the descending mass to go from B to a platform C at a known distance below B is measured by a stop-watch.

The distance from A to B is also known.

Now until the rider is removed the acceleration of the system is

$$\frac{mg}{2M + m}.$$

If AB $= h_1$, the velocity v on reaching the ring is given by

$$v^2 = 2\,\frac{mg}{2M + m}\,h_1.$$

If h_2 is the distance BC, and t the time taken for the mass to go from B to C

$$v = \frac{h_2}{t},$$

$$\therefore \frac{h_2^2}{t^2} = \frac{2mgh_1}{2M + m},$$

$$\therefore g = \frac{h_2^2}{2mh_1t^2}(2M + m).$$

§ 82. The chief causes of inaccuracy in the experiment are as follows :—

(1) The string may slip on the pulley, and, as this is not perfectly smooth, friction is introduced.

This cannot be avoided entirely, but can be partly allowed for as in (3) by means of an additional rider.

(2) The pulley, although light, requires some force to make it rotate.

Allowance can be made for this as explained in Chapter IX.

(3) There is some friction at the axle of the pulley. This can be reduced by supporting the axle of the pulley on the edges of four light wheels called friction wheels, or by attaching a small rider to the mass which carries the rider m. The mass of this extra rider is adjusted until the masses (without m) run uniformly when set in motion.

(4) It is difficult to measure accurately the time taken for the mass M to go from B to C.

The error in measuring the time can be reduced by the device used in what is called the " ribbon " Attwood's machine.

In this type of machine the string supporting the masses is replaced by a tape. A fine brush is attached to the end of a spring, or vibrator, which is adjusted to make a given number of vibrations per second.

The brush, which is inked, is placed so that it touches the tape where the latter passes over the top of the pulley.

A lever is arranged so that, as it releases the mass with the rider from its platform, the vibrator is set in motion. The brush then traces a wavy line on the tape as it passes over the pulley. The distances between successive portions of the curve so traced are the actual distances moved by the masses, while the time taken to move any distance is known from the period of the vibrator.

§ 83. The following examples are of a more difficult nature. If the accelerations of the various parts of the system are not the same it is essential to find what connections there are between them. The principle of the method, i.e. applying the equation $P = mf$ to each part of the system, is the same as before.

EXAMPLE (i).

A string passing over a smooth fixed pulley supports at its two ends smooth movable pulleys of masses 5 lb. and 7 lb. respectively. Over the first of the movable pulleys passes a string having masses of 3 lb. and 4 lb. at its ends, and over the second a string having masses of 2 lb. and 3 lb. at its ends. Find the acceleration of the movable pulleys and of each of the masses. (H.S.D.)

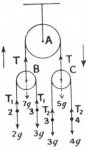

FIG. 51.

Let A (Fig. 51) represent the fixed pulley and B and C the movable pulleys.

It is clear that the acceleration of B is the same as that of C, let this be F.

The actual accelerations of the 2 lb. and 3 lb. masses hanging over B are *not* the same, but their accelerations *relative* to B are the same, i.e. the 2 lb. mass approaches B with the same acceleration as the 3 lb. mass goes away from it (this follows since the length of the string is unaltered).

In problems of this kind it is essential to consider only the *actual* accelerations of the particles, otherwise we cannot apply the equation $P = mf$ to them.

Let T be the tension in the string passing over A, T_1 and T_2 the tensions in those passing over B and C.

Let f_1, f_2 be the *actual* accelerations of the 2 lb. and 3 lb. masses over B, f_3 and f_4 those of the 3 and 4 lb. masses over C. Assume that C moves downwards and B upwards (it will not matter if this is incorrect, we shall merely get a negative value for F).

The resultant forces acting on B, C, and the particles are as follows :—

On B,	$T - 2T_1 - 7g$,	upwards.
,, C,	$5g + 2T_2 - T$,	downwards.
,, the 2 lb. mass of B,	$T_1 - 2g$,	upwards.
,, ,, 3 lb. ,, B,	$3g - T_1$,	downwards.
,, ,, 3 lb. ,, C,	$T_2 - 3g$,	upwards.
,, ,, 4 lb. ,, C,	$4g - T_2$,	downwards.

Hence, applying $P = mf$ to each of these masses,

$$T - 2T_1 - 7g = 7f \qquad . \qquad . \qquad . \qquad \text{(i)}$$
$$5g + 2T_2 - T = 5F \qquad . \qquad . \qquad . \qquad \text{(ii)}$$
$$T_1 - 2g = 2f_1 \qquad . \qquad . \qquad . \qquad \text{(iii)}$$
$$3g - T_1 = 3f_2 \qquad . \qquad . \qquad . \qquad \text{(iv)}$$
$$T_2 - 3g = 3f_3 \qquad . \qquad . \qquad . \qquad \text{(v)}$$
$$4g - T_2 = 4f_4 \qquad . \qquad . \qquad . \qquad \text{(vi)}$$

Also, since the accelerations of the masses relative to their pulleys are equal,

$$f_1 - F = f_2 + F \qquad . \qquad . \qquad . \qquad \text{(vii)}$$
$$f_3 + F = f_4 - F \qquad . \qquad . \qquad . \qquad \text{(viii)}$$

We have thus eight equations to determine the three unknown tensions and the five accelerations.

These equations give

$$F = \frac{1}{414}g \; ; \; f_1 = \frac{42}{207}g \; ; \; f_2 = \frac{41}{207}g \; ;$$

$$f_3 = \frac{29}{207}g \; ; \; f_4 = \frac{30}{207}g.$$

EXAMPLE (ii).

A_1 and A_2 are two fixed pulleys in the same horizontal line. A light string is placed over A_1 and A_2, and carries weights W_1 and W_2 at its free ends. Another pulley B carrying a weight W_3 is placed on the part of the string between A_1 and A_2. If A_1 and A_2 are so close together that all the portions of the string not in contact with the pulleys are vertical, prove that when all the weights are in motion the tension in the string is

$$\frac{4}{W_1^{-1} + W_2^{-1} + 4W_3^{-1}}.$$

Prove also that the condition that W_3 shall remain at rest while W_1 and W_2 are in motion is $4W_1W_2 = W_3(W_1 + W_2)$.   (H.S.D.)

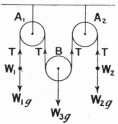

FIG. 52.

It is evident that the distance moved by B is equal to half the algebraic sum of the distances moved by W_1 and W_2. For if W_1 and W_2 both move downwards through distances x_1 and x_2, B will move up a distance $\frac{x_1 + x_2}{2}$; if W_1 moves down and W_2 up through the same distance, B will move *up* a distance $\frac{x_1 - x_2}{2}$.

Hence, if f_1, f_2, f_3 be the accelerations of W_1, W_2, W_3, then

$$f_3 = \frac{f_1 + f_2}{2}.$$

Suppose that W_1 moves down, W_2 and W_3 move up, and let T be the tension in the string.

$$\text{Then } f_3 = \frac{f_1 - f_2}{2}.$$

For W_1, $\quad W_1 g - T = W_1 f_1$, $\quad$ or $\quad g - \dfrac{T}{W_1} = f_1$. $\qquad$. $\qquad$ (i)

,, $\quad W_2$, $\quad T - W_2 g = W_2 f_2$, $\quad$ or $\quad \dfrac{T}{W_2} - g = f_2$. $\qquad$. $\qquad$ (ii)

,, $\quad W_3$, $\quad 2T - W_3 g = W_3 f_3 = \frac{1}{2}W_3 f_1 - \frac{1}{2}W_3 f_2$ $\qquad$. $\qquad$ (iii)

$$\therefore \frac{4T}{W_3} - 2g = f_1 - f_2,$$

$$\therefore \frac{4T}{W_3} - 2g = 2g - \frac{T}{W_1} - \frac{T}{W_2}, \text{ from (i) and (ii)},$$

$$\therefore T\left(\frac{1}{W_1} + \frac{1}{W_2} + \frac{4}{W_3}\right) = 4g,$$

$$\therefore T = \frac{4g}{W_1{}^{-1} + W_2{}^{-1} + 4W_3{}^{-1}} \text{ in absolute units},$$

$$= \frac{4}{W_1{}^{-1} + W_2{}^{-1} + 4W_3{}^{-1}} \text{ in gravitation units}.$$

If W_3 is to remain at rest, f_3 must be zero.
Now, from (iii)

$$f_3 = \frac{2T}{W_3} - g,$$

$$= \frac{8g}{\dfrac{W_3}{W_1} + \dfrac{W_3}{W_2} + 4} - g,$$

$$= \frac{4g - \dfrac{W_3}{W_1}g - \dfrac{W_3}{W_2}g}{\dfrac{W_3}{W_1} + \dfrac{W_3}{W_2} + 4},$$

and this is zero if

$$\frac{W_3}{W_1} + \frac{W_3}{W_2} = 4,$$

or $$4W_1 W_2 = W_3(W_1 + W_2).$$

EXAMPLE (iii).

Particles of mass m and 2m are connected by a light string which passes over a pulley at the vertex of a wedge-shaped block, one particle resting on each of the faces which are smooth. The mass of the wedge being M, and the inclination of the faces to the horizontal being α, find the acceleration of the wedge and the particles when the wedge is placed on a smooth horizontal table. (H.S.C.)

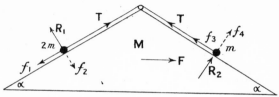

FIG. 53.

Let F be the acceleration of the wedge, f_1 and f_2 the components of
the *actual* acceleration of $2m$ parallel and perpendicular to the face of
the wedge, f_3 and f_4 those of m. Let R_1, R_2 be the reactions of the
wedge on $2m$ and m (these will be perpendicular to the faces), and T
the tension in the string.

Consider the motions of the particles in directions perpendicular to
the faces of the wedge. The resultant force on $2m$ in this direction is
$2mg \cos \alpha - R_1$, and that on m is $R_2 - mg \cos \alpha$,

$$\therefore 2mg \cos \alpha - R_1 = 2mf_2 \qquad . \qquad . \qquad . \qquad \text{(i)}$$
$$R_2 - mg \cos \alpha = mf_4, \qquad . \qquad . \qquad . \qquad \text{(ii)}$$

The horizontal force acting on the wedge is
$$R_1 \sin \alpha - R_2 \sin \alpha,$$
$$\therefore R_1 \sin \alpha - R_2 \sin \alpha = MF \qquad . \qquad . \qquad . \qquad \text{(iii)}$$

Since the particles remain in contact with the faces, their accelerations perpendicular to the faces must equal the component accelerations of the wedge in these directions,

$$\therefore f_2 = F \sin \alpha = f_4 \qquad . \qquad . \qquad . \qquad . \qquad \text{(iv)}$$

Multiplying (i) and (ii) by $\sin \alpha$ and adding to (iii),

$$mg \sin \alpha \cos \alpha = 2mf_2 \sin \alpha + mf_4 \sin \alpha + MF,$$
$$= 3mF \sin^2 \alpha + MF, \qquad \text{from (iv)}$$
$$= (3m \sin^2 \alpha + M)F,$$
$$\therefore F = \frac{mg \sin \alpha \cos \alpha}{M + 3m \sin^2 \alpha},$$

also $f_2 = f_4 = F \sin \alpha = \dfrac{mg \sin^2 \alpha \cos \alpha}{M + 3m \sin^2 \alpha}.$

To find the components of acceleration parallel to the faces, we
consider the motion in this direction, this is unaffected by the motion
of the wedge.

For $2m$, $2mg \sin \alpha - T = 2mf_1,$.   .   .   .   (v)

,, m, $T - mg \sin \alpha = mf_3,$.   .   .   .   (vi)

$$\therefore mg \sin \alpha = 2mf_1 + mf_3.$$

Now the accelerations along the faces *relative to the faces* must be
equal,

$$\therefore f_1 + F \cos \alpha = f_3 + F \cos \alpha \qquad . \qquad . \qquad . \qquad \text{(vii)}$$
$$\therefore f_1 = f_3,$$
$$\therefore f_1 = f_3 = \frac{mg \sin \alpha}{3m} = \frac{g \sin \alpha}{3}.$$

6 *

The resultant accelerations of the particles can be obtained by compounding f_1 and f_2, f_3 and f_4.

EXAMPLE (iv).

A man weighing 12 stone, and a weight of 10 stone, are suspended by a light rope over a smooth pulley. Find the acceleration of the man. If the man pull himself up the rope so that his downward acceleration is only half this value, find the upward acceleration of the weight, and show that

the upward acceleration of the man relative to the rope is $\dfrac{g}{10}$.

If f is the acceleration when the man is not pulling

$$12g - T = 12f,$$
$$T - 10g = 10f,$$
$$\therefore 22f = 2g, \text{ or } f = \tfrac{1}{11}g.$$

When the man is pulling on the rope we must consider the force P he exerts on the rope ; his acceleration is now $\tfrac{1}{22}g$.

$$\therefore 12g - P = 12 \cdot \frac{g}{22},$$
$$\therefore P = 12g - \tfrac{6}{11}g.$$

If F is the acceleration of the weight

$$P - 10g = 10F,$$
$$\therefore 12g - \tfrac{6}{11}g - 10g = 10F,$$
$$\therefore F = \tfrac{8}{55}g.$$

The upward acceleration of the man relative to the rope is

$$\frac{8}{55}g - \frac{1}{22}g = \frac{g}{10}.$$

EXAMPLES XIII.

1. A fine string passes over a smooth fixed pulley and carries at its ends masses of m and $5m$ lb. respectively. Find the acceleration of the masses and the tension of the string, stating clearly the units you employ.

   A string with one end fixed passes under a movable pulley A of mass m lb., over a fixed pulley and under a movable pulley B of mass $5m$ lb., its other end being attached to the axle of the pulley A, and all the hanging parts of the string being vertical. Show that the tension of the string is the same as that of the string in the first part of the question, that the acceleration of the pulley A is equal to that of the mass m, but that the acceleration of the pulley B is half that of the mass $5m$. (I.S.)

2. Two pulleys, of weights 12 lb. and 8 lb., are connected by a fine string hanging over a smooth fixed pulley. Over the former is hung a fine string with weights 3 lb. and 6 lb. at its ends, and over the latter a fine string with weights 4 lb. and x lb. Determine x so that the string over the fixed pulley remains stationary, and find the tension in it. (I.E.)

3. Masses of 5 lb. and 2 lb. are suspended from the ends of a string which passes over two fixed pulleys and under a movable pulley whose mass is m lb., the portions of the string not in contact with the movable pulley being vertical. Find the value of m in order that when the system is released, the movable pulley may remain at rest, and find in this case the accelerations of the other masses and the tension of the string.   (H.S.C.)

4. To one end of a light string passing over a smooth fixed pulley is attached a particle of mass M, and the other end carries a light pulley over which passes a light string to whose ends are attached particles of mass m_1 and m_2. Find the accelerations of the particles, and show that if $M = \dfrac{4m_1 m_2}{m_1 + m_2}$ the mass M will remain at rest or move with uniform velocity.   (Ex.)

5. A particle of mass M on a smooth horizontal table is tied to one end of a string which passes over a fixed pulley at the edge and then under a movable pulley of mass m, its other end being fixed so that the parts of the string beyond the table are vertical. Show that m descends with acceleration $\dfrac{m}{4M + m}g$, and find the horizontal and vertical components of the acceleration of the centre of mass of M and m.   (I.S.)

6. A string with one end fixed passes under a movable pulley A, of mass m lb., and then over a fixed pulley, and carries at its free end a mass B of $3m$ lb. Find the tension of the string and the accelerations of A and B, stating clearly the units that you employ (All portions of the strings are to be regarded as vertical.)   (I.S.)

7. A string is attached to a fixed point A. It passes round the lower part of a movable pulley B, to which a weight $2W$ is attached, then over a fixed pulley C, and a weight $W + w$ hangs from its extremity. The parts of the string not in contact with the pulleys are vertical. Neglecting friction and the mass of the pulleys, find the acceleration with which the system moves when left to itself.   (I.S.)

8. Masses of 100 gm. and 60 gm. are attached to the ends of a fine string, which passes over a smooth fixed pulley. Find the acceleration of the masses and prove that the tension of the string is equal to the weight of 75 gm. The pulley, whose mass is 50 gm., is now detached from its fastening, and attached by means of another fine string to a mass of 100 gm., which lies on a smooth table over whose edge the string passes. Prove that the pulley moves as if the original weights were removed and its own mass were increased by 150 gm.   (H.C.)

9. A, B are masses of 6 oz. and 3 oz. respectively resting on two smooth tables, placed with their edges parallel. They are connected by a fine string, which hangs between the tables with its hanging parts vertical and carries in its loop a smooth pulley C of mass 4 oz. The string lies in a vertical plane and crosses the edges of the tables at right angles to the edges. Find the tension in the string (i) when A and B are held fast, (ii) when B is held but A moves, (iii) when A and B both move ; and show that in the three cases the tensions are in the ratio 21 : 18 : 14.   (H.C.)

10. A light string ABCD has one end fixed at A, and passing under a movable pulley of mass M at B and over a fixed pulley at C, carries a mass M' at D. The parts of the string are supposed vertical. Show that M descends with acceleration

$$\frac{M - 2M'}{M + 4M'}g \qquad \text{(H.C.)}$$

11. A string with one end fixed passes under a pulley A of mass M, then over a fixed pulley, then under a pulley B of mass M', and its other end is attached to the axle of A. The string is taut and its hanging parts are vertical. Find the ratio of the velocities of A and B when the system is in motion, and show that the acceleration of A is

$$\frac{4M - 2M'}{4M + M'}g$$

downwards. (I.S.)

12. A particle of mass m is placed on the sloping face (angle of slope α to the horizontal) of a smooth wedge of mass M, whose base rests on a smooth table. Find the acceleration of the wedge and the horizontal and vertical components of the acceleration of the particle. (H.S.C.)

13. A wedge of mass M and angle α is placed on a rough horizontal plane, the coefficient of friction being μ. A smooth particle of mass m is placed gently on the inclined face of the wedge. Show that, if the wedge moves, its acceleration will be

$$\frac{m \cos \alpha(\sin \alpha - \mu \cos \alpha) - \mu M}{m \sin \alpha(\sin \alpha - \mu \cos \alpha) + M}g \qquad \text{(H.S.C.)}$$

14. A string passing over a smooth pulley carries a mass $4m$ at one end and a pulley of mass m at the other. A string carrying masses m and $2m$ at its ends passes over the latter pulley. Find the acceleration of the mass $4m$ when the system is moving freely under gravity. (C.S.)

15. A string, of which one end is attached to a mass m lying on a smooth table, passes over the edge of the table, and after passing over a smooth fixed pulley close to the table and on a level with it has its other end attached to a mass m'; between the table and the pulley the string hangs in a loop and supports a smooth ring of mass M. The string lies in a vertical plane perpendicular to the edge of the table. Find the motion and the tension of the string, and show that the mass m' will remain at rest if

$$M = \frac{4mm'}{2m - m'}. \qquad \text{(C.S.)}$$

16. A mass m lying on a smooth horizontal table is attached to a string which, after passing over the edge of the table, hangs in a loop on which a heavy smooth ring of mass M is threaded and then passes over a smooth fixed pulley and supports a mass m'. If the free portions of the string are vertical and the whole system lies in a vertical plane, determine the tension of the string, and show that the mass M will remain at rest provided that

$$\frac{2}{M} = \frac{1}{m} + \frac{1}{m'}. \qquad \text{(C.S.)}$$

17. On a smooth fixed inclined plane of angle α there is placed a smooth wedge of mass M and angle α, in such a way that the upper face of the wedge is horizontal; on this horizontal face is placed a particle of mass m. Prove that the resultant acceleration of the particle in the subsequent motion is

$$\frac{(M + m)g \sin^2 \alpha}{M + m \sin^2 \alpha},$$

and evaluate the pressure between the wedge and the plane. (I.A.)

18. A truck weighing 16 cwt. is pulled up a railway on an inclined plane by a rope which passes round a pulley fixed at the top of the incline, and is attached to a truck which weighs with contents 40 cwt. and runs down a parallel railway. The speed of the trucks is controlled by a brake on the pulley which is operated when the speed reaches 30 ft./sec., and keeps the speed constant. The incline is 400 feet long, and the height of the upper end above the lower 100 feet. Neglecting friction, find the time during which the trucks run freely and the whole time of the journey. Find also the greatest tension of the rope. (I.E.)

19. In a mountain railway, of uniform inclination 30°, the ascending and descending cars are connected by a rope which passes round a pulley at the top of the incline, and their masses are $\frac{3}{4}$ M and M tons respectively; the ordinary resistances due to friction, etc., are 20 lb. wt. per ton mass for each car, and the brake resistance is Q lb. wt. per ton mass. Show that if motion can be prevented by applying the brakes to the descending car alone, Q must be at least 245. If Q has this value, calculate the retardation when the cars are in motion and the brakes are applied to both cars. (I.E.)

20. On a cable railway a car, of weight $2\frac{1}{2}$ tons, is drawn up a slope of 1 in 10 from rest with an acceleration of 2 ft./sec.² against a constant frictional resistance of $\frac{1}{2}$ cwt. Find the tension in the cable. (H.S.C.)

21. The angle of a smooth wedge of mass M is α. The wedge is placed with one face on a smooth horizontal table and a particle of mass m is allowed to slide down its face. Prove that a horizontal force $mg \sin \alpha \cos \alpha$ must be applied to the wedge to keep it from moving, and that the reaction between the wedge and the table is

$$(M + m \cos^2 \alpha)g \qquad \text{(H.S.D.)}$$

22. A wedge of mass M, whose section ABC is a triangle right angled at A, is placed with the face BC on a smooth, horizontal table. The faces AB, AC are rough, the coefficient of friction being μ. Two masses m_1, m_2, connected by a light inextensible string passing over a light frictionless pulley at A, rest on the faces AB, AC, respectively, and m_1 moves down AB with acceleration f relative to the wedge. Write down the equations necessary to find f, and the acceleration F of the wedge. (Ex.)

23. A cord passing over a fixed pulley A carries pulleys B, C at its ends. A second cord with one end fixed to the ground passes over B and carries 20 lb. at the other end; and a third cord with an end fixed to the ground passes over C and has 30 lb. at the other end. All parts of the cords are vertical except where they go round the pulleys. Neglecting friction and the weights of the cords and pulleys find the accelerations of the weights and the tensions in the cords. (H.S.C.)

24. A bucket can be raised from a well by a counterpoise of mass m_1 in t seconds, and by a counterpoise of mass m_2 in nt seconds. Show that the mass of the bucket is the positive root of the equation

$$x^2 + (m_1 - m_2)\frac{n^2 + 1}{n^2 - 1}x - m_1 m_2 = 0,$$

and that the depth of the well is

$$\tfrac{1}{2}gt^2 y,$$

where y is the positive root of the equation

$$y^2 + y\frac{m_1 + m_2}{m_1 - m_2}(n^2 - 1) - n^2 = 0. \qquad \text{(H.S.C.)}$$

25. Draw a velocity-time graph for the case of a body moving in a straight line, at first with uniform acceleration, secondly with uniform velocity, and finally with uniform retardation.

A train of 180 tons starts from rest with an engine pull of 3 tons and makes a run of 1 mile from one station to rest at the next. At the instant of maximum speed, the steam is shut off and the brakes are applied, producing an effective coefficient of friction $\frac{1}{30}$. Prove that the time occupied is about 172 seconds, and that the maximum speed is about 42 m.p.h. (Frictional resistances, other than those due to the brakes, are neglected.) (H.C.)

26. A body of mass M is lifted vertically from rest by means of a constant lifting force, which acts from the beginning of the ascent till a certain time before the end, when it is relaxed, and the body is brought to rest by gravity at height b. The time taken is n seconds. Find the force required. (H.S.D.)

27. A particle P of mass m rests on a rough horizontal table whose coefficient of friction is μ, and is attached to one end of a fine inextensible string which passes over a smooth fixed pulley A at the edge of the table. The string then passes under a smooth movable pulley B of mass m and over a smooth fixed pulley C, the other end of the string being attached to a particle D of mass m which hangs vertically. All the portions of the string not in contact with a pulley are horizontal and vertical. Prove that if $\mu > \frac{3}{5}$, P will not move, and that if $\mu < \frac{3}{5}$, D will move with acceleration

$$\frac{(3 - \mu)g}{6}. \qquad \text{(C.S.)}$$

28. A particle of mass 2 lb. is placed on the smooth face of an inclined plane of mass 7 lb. and slope 30°, which is free to slide on a smooth horizontal plane in a direction perpendicular to its edge. Show that if the system start from rest the particle will slide down a distance of 15 feet along the face of the plane in 1·25 seconds.

(C.S.)

29. A man of 10 stone and a weight of 8 stone are suspended by means of a light rope over a smooth pulley. If the man pull himself up the rope so that his downward acceleration is $\frac{g}{18}$, find the acceleration of the weight, and the acceleration of the man relative to the rope.

30. A man of 12 stone lets himself down one portion of a light rope hanging over a smooth pulley with an acceleration of 2 ft./sec.² Find with what uniform acceleration a man of 8 stone must pull himself up by the other portion so that the rope may remain at rest.

31. A smooth wedge, weighing 5 lb., can slide on a smooth horizontal plane. A weight of 1 lb. is placed on the sloping face of the wedge, 1 foot from the bottom edge, and allowed to slide down. If the angle of the wedge is 30°, and if the weight and wedge start from rest, prove that the weight reaches the bottom of the slope in about $\frac{1}{3}$ second. (Q.E.)

32. A weightless string passes over a smooth, fixed pulley of mass 1 lb., and has attached to it at one end a mass of 12 lb., and at the other end a mass of 8 lb. ; the moment of inertia of the pulley about its axis can be neglected. Find the acceleration of the weights.

    If the pulley, instead of being fixed, is pulled vertically upwards by a force of 21 lb. wt., find the accelerations of the pulley and of the string relative to the pulley. (N.U.3)

33. Particles of masses m and m' lie at rest one on each of two rough tables, whose edges are parallel ; μ, μ' are the respective coefficients between the particles and the tables. The particles are connected by a fine string which hangs between the tables and carries a smooth pulley, of mass M, in the loop formed by the hanging parts, which are parallel and lie in a plane perpendicular to the edges of the tables between which they lie. The system being let go, all the parts begin to move. Prove that the tension (T) of the string is given by the equation

$$T\left(\frac{1}{m} + \frac{1}{m'} + \frac{4}{M}\right) = g(2 + \mu + \mu').$$

Prove that if $\mu m > \mu' m'$, the motion as described cannot take place unless

$$\frac{4}{M} + \frac{1}{m'} < \frac{2 + \mu'}{\mu m}.$$ (N.U.3)

34. A smooth hemispherical bowl, of mass M, with centre C, lies rim downwards on a smooth table, and a particle, of mass m, is placed on it at a point A, whose angular distance from the vertex V of the bowl is α. Show that if a horizontal force of suitable magnitude is applied to the bowl in the plane VCA, the particle will remain at rest relatively to the bowl as it moves. (N.U.3)

35. A wheel of radius $4a$ is fastened to an axle of radius a. A weight of mass m_1 is suspended by a rope fastened to the axle and coiled round it, and another weight of mass m_2 is suspended by a rope fastened to the wheel and coiled round its rim in such a way that m_2 descends when m_1 rises, and vice versa. If the system is left to itself, prove that the upward acceleration of m_1 is

$$\frac{4m_2 - m_1}{16m_2 + m_1}g,$$

and find the tensions in the ropes. The inertia of the wheel and axle may be neglected. (C.W.B.)

36. A long string fixed at one end to the ceiling passes down under a pulley of mass m which it supports, then up over a fixed pulley also attached to the ceiling, and finally down to a weight of mass m' which is hanging freely. Assuming that the hanging portions of the string are all vertical, prove that the upward acceleration of the mass m' is

$$\frac{2(m - 2m')}{m + 4m'}g.$$ (C.W.B.)

37. A wedge of mass M is at rest on a smooth horizontal plane, and a particle of mass m is placed gently on its smooth inclined face and allowed to fall down this face. Prove that when the particle has descended a vertical distance h the wedge has moved through a horizontal distance

$$\frac{mh \cot \alpha}{m + M},$$

where α is the inclination of the face of the wedge to the horizontal.
(C.W.B.)

§ 84. Work.

When a force moves its point of application it is said to do work, and the measure of the work is the product of the force and the distance through which the point of application moves *in the direction of the force.*

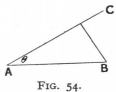

Fig. 54.

Let a force F move its point of application from A to B (Fig. 54), where the distance AB = s.

Then, if the force is in the direction AB the work done is Fs. If the direction of the force is along AC, inclined at an angle θ to AB, the work done is $F \times$ the projection of AB on AC,

$$= Fs \cos \theta.$$

If the force is variable, the work done for an infinitely small displacement ds, in which the force may be considered constant, is $F ds$ (or $F \cos \theta\, ds$). The total work done is the integral of $F ds$ (or $F \cos \theta\, ds$) taken between the initial and final values of s, i.e.

$$\int_{s_1}^{s_2} F ds.$$

§ 85.

The absolute unit of work in the F.P.S. system is the work done by a poundal in moving its point of application through 1 foot in the direction of the force.

This unit of work is called a *Foot-Poundal.*

The absolute unit of work in the C.G.S. system is the work done by a force of 1 dyne in moving its point of application through 1 centimetre in the direction of the force.

This unit is called an *Erg.*

§ 86.

The unit of work used by engineers is called a *Foot-Pound,* it is the work done by a force of 1 lb. weight in moving its point of application through 1 foot in the direction of the force, or the work done in raising a weight of 1 lb. vertically through 1 foot.

Since

$$1 \text{ lb. wt.} = g \text{ poundals,}$$
$$1 \text{ ft. lb.} = g \text{ ft. poundals.}$$

§ 87. **Power** is the rate of doing work, i.e. the work done in unit time.

The British unit of power is the *Horse-Power*, which is 550 ft. lb. per second, or 33,000 ft. lb. per minute.

The C.G.S. unit of power is the *Watt*, which is 10^7 ergs ($= 1$ Joule) per second.

One horse-power is equivalent to about 746 watts.

If a force of F lb. wt. keeps its point of application moving in the direction of the force with uniform speed v feet per second, the work done per second is Fv ft. lb. and the H.P. is $\dfrac{Fv}{550}$.

In the case of a train running at a speed of v feet per second, the work done by the engine per second is equal to the pull multiplied by v, and the H.P. of the engine is obtained by dividing this product by 550. If the speed v is uniform, then the pull of the engine is equal to the resistance R due to friction, etc., and the H.P. is equal to $\dfrac{Rv}{550}$.

If the train is accelerating the work per second is not Rv, as work is also being done in accelerating the train.

§ 88. EXAMPLE (i).

The total mass of an engine and train is 200 tons, what is the H.P. of the engine if it can just keep the train moving at a uniform speed of 60 m.p.h. on the level, the resistances due to friction, etc., amounting to 10 lb. wt. per ton ?

Since the speed is uniform, the pull of the engine is equal to the total resistance, i.e. 200 × 10 or 2000 lb. wt.

$$60 \text{ m.p.h.} = 88 \text{ ft./sec.}$$
$$\therefore \text{ the work per second} = 2000 \times 88 \text{ ft. lb.}$$

and the

$$\text{H.P.} = \frac{2000 \times 88}{550} = 320.$$

EXAMPLE (ii).

What H.P. is required to take a train weighing 200 tons at a uniform speed of 30 m.p.h. up an incline of 1 in 100, the resistance due to friction, etc., being 10 lb. wt. per ton ?

The resistance = 2000 lb. wt., the component of weight down the slope = 2 tons = 4480 lb. wt. Since the speed is constant, the pull of the engine must be equal to the resistance + the component of the weight,

$$\therefore \text{ the pull} = 2000 + 4480 = 6480 \text{ lb. wt.,}$$
$$\text{the work per second} = 6480 \times 44 \text{ ft. lb.,}$$
$$\therefore \text{ the H.P.} = \frac{6480 \times 44}{550} = 518\tfrac{2}{5}.$$

EXAMPLE (iii).

An engine of 200 *H.P. is taking a train of mass* 150 *tons up an incline of* 1 *in* 250, *and the resistance is* 5 *lb. wt. per ton mass. What is the maximum uniform speed of the train in m.p.h. ?*

The maximum work per second which can be done by the engine is 200 × 550 ft. lb.

The resistance is 150 × 5 = 750 lb. wt.

The component of weight down the slope

$$= \frac{150 \times 2240}{250} \text{ lb. wt.,}$$
$$= 1344 \text{ lb. wt.}$$

At uniform speed v ft./sec. the pull of the engine must equal the resistance + component of weight,

$$\therefore \text{ the pull} = 1344 + 750 = 2094 \text{ lb. wt.,}$$
$$\text{and the work per second} = 2094v \text{ ft. lb.,}$$
$$\therefore 2094v = 200 \times 550,$$
$$\therefore v = \frac{200 \times 550}{2094} \text{ ft./sec.}$$
$$= \frac{200 \times 550 \times 60}{2094 \times 88} \text{ m.p.h.}$$
$$= 35\frac{285}{349} \text{ m.p.h.}$$

§ 89. Work done by a Couple.

Let the forces of the couple be each P and let the arm AB be of length p. Suppose AB to move to the position A'B', where the angle between AB and A'B' is the small angle $\delta\theta$.

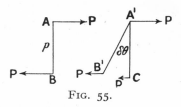

FIG. 55.

We may suppose the motion of AB (Fig. 55) to take place in two stages. First, suppose the forces to move parallel to themselves so that AB comes to the position A'C. The work done by the equal and opposite forces P during this displacement is zero.

Now suppose the forces to turn through the angle $\delta\theta$ about A'.

The force P at A′ does no work as its point of application does not move. The displacement of the point of application of the other force P at C is $p\delta\theta$, and the total work done is thus $Pp\delta\theta$, i.e. *the moment of the couple multiplied by the elementary angle turned through.*

If the moment of the couple M remains constant, the work in turning through an angle θ is

$$\int_0^\theta M d\theta = M\theta.$$

If the moment is variable the work is still

$$\int_0^\theta M d\theta.$$

§ 90. Transmission of Power by Belts.

Suppose a belt passes round a pulley which it turns without any slipping,

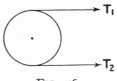

FIG. 56.

Let T_1, T_2 lb. wt. be the tensions in the portions of the belt which are receding from and approaching the pulley $(T_1 > T_2)$.

These tensions both act away from the pulley, and the total work done by them when the belt moves through any distance will be the product of the difference of the tensions and the distance.

If r feet is the radius of the pulley, n the number of revolutions per second, then the distance moved by the belt in 1 second is $2\pi r n$ feet.

The work done per second by the belt is therefore

$$2\pi r n (T_1 - T_2) \text{ ft. lb.,}$$

and this is the amount of work transmitted per second. The H.P. transmitted is

$$\frac{2\pi r n}{550}(T_1 - T_2).$$

EXAMPLE.

Power is transmitted from one shaft to another by means of a single belt running at 60 ft./sec. If the tensions in the two straight parts of the belt are in the ratio of 5 : 2, and if the greatest power that can be transmitted without breaking the belt is 20 H.P., what is the tension which will just break the belt? (I.S.)

The actual tension on the tighter side is the limiting tension. If T_1, T_2 are the tensions on the two sides in lb. wt., the work per second is

$$(T_1 - T_2)60 \text{ ft. lb.,}$$
$$\therefore (T_1 - T_2)60 = 20 \times 550,$$
$$\therefore \frac{3}{5} T_1 = \frac{550}{3},$$
$$\therefore T_1 = \frac{2750}{9} = 305\tfrac{5}{9} \text{ lb. wt.}$$

A tension slightly over this will break the belt.

§ 91. Tension in an Elastic String.

It is found by experiment that the tension of an elastic string varies as the extension of the string beyond its natural length. This fact was discovered by Hooke, and is embodied in what is usually known as Hooke's Law. This may be stated as follows :—

If l is the natural length of an elastic string, and l' the stretched length, then the tension T is given by

$$T = \frac{E}{l}(l' - l),$$

where E is a constant depending on the thickness and material of the string. E is usually called the *Modulus of Elasticity of the String*, and is often denoted by λ.

It is obvious that E is the tension required to stretch the string to double its natural length.

Young's Modulus is the value of E for a string of unit area cross-section.

§ 92. Work done in Stretching an Elastic String.

Let E be the modulus and l the natural length, then for an extension x,

$$T = \frac{E}{l}x,$$

the work done in stretching the string through a further distance dx, so small that T may be supposed constant throughout dx, is

Tdx or $\frac{E}{l}xdx$.

Hence the work done in increasing the extension from x_1 to x_2 is

$$\int_{x_1}^{x_2} \frac{E}{l}xdx = \frac{E}{l}\left[\frac{x^2}{2}\right]_{x_1}^{x_2}$$
$$= \frac{E}{l}\frac{x_2{}^2 - x_1{}^2}{2}$$
$$= \frac{E}{l}\frac{x_2 + x_1}{2}(x_2 - x_1).$$

Now $\dfrac{E}{l}x_2$ is the final tension, and $\dfrac{E}{l}x_1$ is the initial tension,

$$\therefore \frac{E}{l}\,\frac{x_2 + x_1}{2}$$

is the mean of the initial and final tensions.

Also $(x_2 - x_1)$ is the extension produced.

Hence the work done is the product of the mean of the initial and final tensions and the extension.

EXAMPLE.

An elastic string, of natural length 2 feet, is stretched 1 inch by a weight of 1 lb. hanging on it. Find the work done in stretching it from a length of 2½ feet to 3 feet.

The fact that 1 lb. wt. stretches the string 1 inch enables us to find E,

$$\text{for } 1 = \frac{E}{2}\cdot\frac{1}{12}, \quad \therefore E = 24 \text{ lb. wt.}$$

The tension for an extension of 6 inches is,

$$T_1 = \frac{E}{2}\cdot\frac{1}{2} = 6 \text{ lb. wt.}$$

The tension for an extension of 12 inches is,

$$T_2 = \frac{E}{2}\cdot 1 = 12 \text{ lb. wt.}$$

$\therefore$ the mean of the initial and final tensions is

$$\frac{T_1 + T_2}{2} = 9 \text{ lb. wt.,}$$

and the extension is 6 inches or ½ foot,

$$\therefore \text{ the work done} = 9 \times \tfrac{1}{2} = 4\tfrac{1}{2} \text{ ft. lb.}$$

Note.—Care must be taken in using Hooke's Law to keep all length measurements in the same units, e.g. in the above example 1 inch must be brought to feet.

§ 93. Energy.

The energy of a body is its capacity for doing work. Since the energy of a body is measured by the work it can do, the units of energy will be the same as those of work.

A body may possess energy owing to a variety of causes, e.g. heat and electricity are forms of energy, which can be converted into mechanical work. In dynamics, however, we are only concerned with purely mechanical energy which may be of two kinds, *Kinetic* or *Potential*.

§ 94. *The Kinetic Energy of a body is the energy it possesses in virtue of its motion, and is measured by the amount of work which it does in coming to rest.*

Consider a particle of mass m moving with velocity v, and suppose it is brought to rest by a constant force P which produces in it a retardation f, then $P = mf$.

Let x be the space described by the particle before it comes to rest, then

$$0 = v^2 - 2fx,$$
$$\therefore fx = \tfrac{1}{2}v^2.$$

Now the work done by the particle is Px, $= mfx$,

$$\therefore \text{ the work done } = \tfrac{1}{2}mv^2,$$
$$\therefore \text{ the kinetic energy of the body } = \tfrac{1}{2}mv^2.$$

It should be noticed that $\tfrac{1}{2}mv^2$ gives the kinetic energy in *absolute* units, e.g. ft./pdls. or ergs.

§ **95.** *The Potential Energy of a body is the work it can do in moving from its actual position to some standard position.*

Examples of potential energy are : the energy of a weight above the ground (the standard position being the surface of the earth), compressed air (the standard position being the volume it would occupy at atmospheric pressure), a bent or compressed spring (the standard position being its natural shape).

§ **96.** *A particle of mass m falls from rest at a height h above the ground. Show that the sum of its potential and kinetic energy is constant throughout the motion.*

The potential energy at height h is the work the particle can do in falling to the ground, and this is equal to the work done in raising it to height h, viz. mgh absolute units.

Let v be the velocity of the particle when it has fallen through a distance x to a point P,
then $$v^2 = 2gx.$$

Its kinetic energy at P $= \tfrac{1}{2}mv^2 = mgx$.
Its potential energy at P $= mg(h - x)$,
$\therefore$ the sum of its kinetic and potential energies at P is

$$mgx + mgh - mgx = mgh.$$

On reaching the ground the velocity V is given by
$$V^2 = 2gh,$$

the kinetic energy $= \tfrac{1}{2}mV^2 = mgh,$
$$= \text{ potential energy at height } h.$$

Hence, on reaching the ground, all the potential energy has been transformed into kinetic energy.

§ **97.** The example in the last paragraph is a simple illustration of the principle of the *Conservation of Energy*. In its most general form this principle states that—

The total amount of energy in the universe is constant, energy cannot be created or destroyed, although it may be converted into various forms, e.g. heat, light, sound.

In the example of the last paragraph, when the particle hits the ground it apparently loses all its energy. Actually the kinetic energy has been converted into other forms of energy, mainly heat.

Similarly, when a body is projected along a rough horizontal surface which reduces it to rest, its kinetic energy is gradually transformed into heat. In dynamics we are not concerned with the energy once it has been transformed, but it must be remembered very carefully that in all cases where there are sudden jerks or impacts in a system, or where there is motion against friction of any kind, some mechanical energy is always apparently lost ; it is actually converted to other forms.

If we exclude forces of this nature which cause conversion of energy to other forms, and consider a system of bodies acted on only by forces (such as gravity) which depend only on the positions of the various parts of the system and not on their motion, we can use a restricted form of the general principle applicable to mechanical energy alone (i.e. apart from other forms), and often called the *Principle of Energy.*

In the case of forces such as gravity the work done in bringing a system from one position to another depends only on the initial and final positions and not on the manner in which the transition is made. Such forces are called *Conservative,* and the principle of energy so often used in dynamical problems may be stated as follows :

If a system of bodies in motion be under the action of a conservative system of forces, the sum of the kinetic and potential energies of the bodies is constant.

In most cases dealt with in dynamics the conservative system of force is that due to gravity. Other examples of conservative forces are (i) the attraction between two particles which is a function of their distance apart, (ii) any force which acts towards a fixed point, and is a definite function of the distance from that point.

§ **98.** The principle of energy is most commonly used when considering motion under gravity; it tells us that, in the absence of friction and impacts, for any loss in kinetic energy there must be an equal gain in potential energy and *vice versa.*

Thus, for a body sliding down a smooth inclined plane the kinetic energy acquired is equal to the loss of potential energy, and depends only on the vertical distance descended.

The kinetic energy, and therefore the velocity, acquired in sliding down the plane is the same as that acquired by falling vertically through the height of the plane.

If a ring threaded on a smooth vertical circle is projected up from the lowest point, the velocity at any point depends only on the vertical height of that point above the bottom of the circle. Similarly, for a particle sliding down any smooth curve ; the velocity at the bottom depends only on the vertical height descended.

Great care must be taken never to use this principle in problems where there is any friction, or any sudden jerk or impact. In such cases energy is nearly always converted.

§ 99. EXAMPLE (i).

A tramcar weighing 5 tons runs freely down an incline of 1 in 40, with a constant speed of 12 m.p.h. What horse-power is required to drive it at the same speed up the same incline, the frictional resistance being the same in each case ? (I.E.)

Since the car runs down the incline with constant speed, the frictional resistance must equal the weight component, i.e.

$$\frac{1}{8} \text{ ton wt., or } \frac{2240}{8} = 280 \text{ lb. wt.}$$

In going up the incline, the total force to be overcome is therefore $280 + 280 = 560$ lb. wt., and this must be the tractive force.

$$12 \text{ m.p.h.} = \tfrac{88}{5} \text{ ft./sec.,}$$

$$\therefore \text{ the work per second} = \frac{560 \times 88}{5} = 112 \times 88 \text{ ft. lb.,}$$

$$\therefore \text{ the H.P. required} = \frac{112 \times 88}{550} = 17 \cdot 92.$$

EXAMPLE (ii).

A man is cycling at 10 m.p.h. up a slope of 1 in 30. If the man and machine weigh 180 lb., and frictional resistances are equivalent to 2 lb. wt., find the rate, in horse-power, at which the man is working. Assuming that the man exerts a constant vertical pressure on each pedal in its downward path, find this pressure when the cranks are 6½ inches long and the gear is 72 inches. (I.E.)

The component of weight down the slope is 6 lb. wt.,

$$\therefore \text{ the total force overcome} = 6 + 2 = 8 \text{ lb. wt.,}$$

$$\therefore \text{ the work per second} = \frac{8 \times 88}{6} \text{ ft. lb.,}$$

$$\therefore \text{ the H.P.} = \frac{8 \times 88}{6 \times 550} = \frac{16}{75}.$$

The gear being 72 inches means that for each revolution of the crank the bicycle moves forward a distance 72π inches.

The external work done in one revolution $= 8 \times 6\pi = 48\pi$ ft. lb.

In one revolution the man exerts a pressure P through a distance of $4 \times 6\frac{1}{2}$ inches $= \frac{13}{6}$ ft.,

$$\therefore \text{ the work he does} = \tfrac{13}{6} P \text{ ft. lb.,}$$

$$\therefore \tfrac{13}{6} P = 48\pi,$$

$$\therefore P = \frac{6 \times 48 \times 22}{13 \times 7} = 69 \cdot 6 \text{ lb. wt.}$$

EXAMPLE (iii).

A mass of 12 lb. is attached to one end of an elastic string of natural length 4 feet, whose other end is fixed at a point A. The modulus of the string is such that the 12 lb. mass hanging vertically would stretch the string 6 inches. The mass is held at A and allowed to fall vertically. How far below A will it come to rest?

Since 12 lb. wt. stretches the string 6 inches or $\frac{1}{2}$ foot,

$$12g = \frac{E}{4} \cdot \frac{1}{2}, \text{ or } E = 96g \text{ poundals.}$$

When the mass has fallen 4 feet its velocity is $\sqrt{2g \times 4} = 16$ ft./sec., and its kinetic energy is $\frac{1}{2} \cdot 12 \times 16^2$ ft. poundals.

The mass now begins to stretch the string, and the extension will go on until the work done in stretching is equal to the loss of kinetic and potential energy of the 12 lb. mass.

If the extension produced when the mass comes to rest is x feet, the final tension is $\frac{E}{4} \cdot x$ poundals, and the initial tension is zero. Hence the work done in stretching

$$= \frac{E}{8}x^2 \text{ ft. poundals}$$

$$= \frac{96g}{8}x^2 = 12gx^2 \text{ ft. poundals.}$$

The loss of kinetic energy of the mass is 6×16^2 poundals, and the loss of potential energy of the mass is $12\,gx$ ft. poundals.

$$\therefore 12gx^2 = 6 \times 16^2 + 12gx,$$
$$\therefore 12x^2 = 48 + 12x,$$
$$\therefore x^2 - x - 4 = 0,$$
$$\therefore x = \frac{1 + \sqrt{1 + 16}}{2} = 2{\cdot}56 \text{ ft.}$$

Hence the distance below A at which the mass comes to rest is 6·56 feet.

Note (i).—It is important to remember that as the mass descends and stretches the string it loses *both kinetic and potential energy.* In solving the quadratic for x, the root with the negative sign in front of the radical can be ignored as it would be negative.

Note (ii).—After the mass comes to rest the string will contract and pull it up again, and, assuming that no energy is dissipated in the stretching, when it reaches the point 4 feet below A it will have the same velocity as it had when going down, and this will be just sufficient to take it up to A again.

§ **100.** In problems where a mass loses velocity owing to the action of a retarding force, e.g. a bullet passing through a plank, or a train being pulled up by its brakes, we can obtain a measure of the retarding force in two ways :—

INTERMEDIATE MECHANICS

(1) If we know the time during which the force acts, and the initial and final velocities u and v of the mass m, then if F is the *average* force,

$$Ft = m(u - v).$$

(2) If we know the distance s travelled during the retardation we can obtain the average force by equating the work done to the loss of kinetic energy,

$$Fs = \tfrac{1}{2}m(u^2 - v^2).$$

It must be clearly understood that the measure of the force thus obtained is an *average* value. In the first case it is a time average, and in the second a space average.

If the force is constant the two methods will give the same value, but if the force is not constant the values will be different. For if

$$\frac{m(u^2 - v^2)}{2s} = \frac{m(u - v)}{t},$$

$$\frac{u + v}{2} = \frac{s}{t},$$

i.e. the average velocity $\left(\dfrac{s}{t}\right)$ is equal to the means of the initial and final velocities. Now, this is not necessarily the case unless the acceleration is constant, i.e. unless the force is constant.

EXAMPLES XIV.

1. A vessel of 30,000 tons, whose engines are of 30,000 H.P., is steaming at the rate of 15 m.p.h. Find the resistance per ton of the vessel's mass. (I.S.)

2. A motor car, of total weight 30 cwt., is running on a level road at a uniform speed of 30 m.p.h. On reaching a hill, which descends at a uniform gradient of 1 in 20, it is allowed to free-wheel, and the speed is observed to remain the same as before. Calculate the resistance of the road, and the horse-power exerted on the level. (I.S.)

3. A train whose mass is 250 tons runs up an incline of 1 in 200 at a uniform rate of 20 m.p.h., the resistance due to friction, etc., is equal to the weight of 3 tons. At what horse-power is the engine working? (I.S.)

4. A train of mass 100 tons acquires uniformly a speed of 30 m.p.h. from rest in 400 yards. Assuming a resistance of 7 lb. wt. per ton mass of the train, find the tension in the coupling between the engine and the train, and the maximum horse-power at which the engine is working during the 400 yards run. The mass of the engine may be neglected. (I.S.)

5. A locomotive of 896 H.P. and weight 90 tons is dragging a train of weight 120 tons up a slope of 1 in 84. The frictional resistances amount to 80 lb. wt. per ton. Find the maximum uniform speed at which the train can travel up the incline. (I.S.)

6. A train of total mass 250 tons is drawn by an engine working at 560 H.P. If at a certain instant the total resistance is 16 lb. wt. per ton, and the speed is 30 m.p.h., what is the train's acceleration measured in m.p.h. per second ?   (I.S.)

7. A load of 3 tons is being hauled by a rope up a railway line which rises 1 in 140. There is a retarding force, due to friction, etc., of 50 lb. wt. per ton of load. At a certain instant the speed is 10 m.p.h. and the acceleration is 2 ft./sec.^{2} Find the pull in the rope, and the horse-power exerted at that instant.   (I.A.)

8. A motor car of mass 2 tons arrives at the bottom of a hill half a mile long, which rises 1 in 112, with a speed of 20 m.p.h., and reaches the top of the hill with a speed of 10 m.p.h. If there is a retarding force, due to friction, of 10 lb. wt., calculate the number of foot-pounds of work done by the engine in getting the car up the hill.   (I.A.)

9. Find the ratio of (1) the momenta, (ii) the kinetic energies, of a mass of 8 oz. moving at $1\frac{1}{2}$ miles a minute, and a mass of 10 kilograms moving at 2 metres per second. (1 lb. = 454 gm., 1 ft. = 30·5 cm.)   (I.A.)

10. A car weighing $2\frac{1}{2}$ tons is accelerating at 2 ft./sec.^{2} up an incline of 1 in 50, the resistance being 30 lb. wt. per ton. Find the horse-power exerted when the speed is 20 m.p.h.   (I.S.)

11. A man with his bicycle weighs 200 lb. He begins to ascend an incline of 1 in 10, with a speed of 25 m.p.h., and with uniform retardation. He has to dismount when his speed is not greater than 5 m.p.h. If he works at an average of $\frac{1}{10}$ H.P., how far will he ascend ? How far would he have ascended if he had not worked at all ?   (I.E.)

12. A particle is set moving with kinetic energy E straight up a rough inclined plane, of inclination α and coefficient of friction μ. Prove that the work done against friction before the particle comes to rest is

$$\frac{E\mu \cos \alpha}{\sin \alpha + \mu \cos \alpha}.$$

What is the condition that the particle, once reduced to rest, shall remain at rest ?   (I.S.)

13. Express in ft. lb. the kinetic energy of 5 cwt. moving at 6 m.p.h. A mass of 10 tons is drawn up a slope of 1 in 96 against a resistance of 125 lb. wt. If 43 H.P. is used, find the greatest speed that the mass can have.   (I.A.)

14. Find the uniform force that will move a 1 lb. mass from rest through 1 foot in 1 second. If this force is exerted while the mass moves through 100 yards from rest, find the number of ft. lb. of work done by the force and the maximum horse-power attained.   (I.A.)

15. A train is running at 30 m.p.h. when it is at a distance of $\frac{1}{4}$ mile from a station. Steam is then shut off and the train runs against a uniform resistance equal to $\frac{1}{100}$ of the weight of the train. If the uniform brake force that can be exerted on the train provides a resistance equal to $\frac{1}{10}$ of the weight of the train in addition to the above resistance, find how far from the station the brake must be applied so that the train may be brought to rest at the station.   (I.A.)

16. Calculate the number of ft. lb. of energy which are required to raise a 16 lb. shot to a height of 7 feet, and then project it with an initial velocity of 36 feet per second. What is the horse-power required for a motor car, which weighs 3000 lb. and can travel at 30 m.p.h., against an air resistance equal to $\frac{1}{30}$ of its own weight ? (I.A.)

17. A man lifts a stone weighing 12 oz. from the ground to a height of 5 feet 8 inches, and then throws it away horizontally with a velocity of 20 ft./sec. How many ft. lb. of work has to be done on the stone ? If the man does this twenty times a minute, find the average rate in horse-power at which he is working, neglecting the work he does in moving himself. (I.A.)

18. Express 1 H.P. in (a) gravitational, (b) absolute units, when the units of mass, length, and time are 1 ton, 1 mile, and 1 hour respectively. A motor car engine, working at a uniform rate of 7·5 H.P., can drive a car at a uniform speed of 18 m.p.h. against a uniform resistance. The car weighs 30 cwt. At what speed will the engine drive the car up a slope of 1 in 10, if it works at the same power and meets the same resistance ? (I.S.)

19. A man and his cycle are of total mass m ; he can work at a uniform horse-power of H ; his least speed consistent with remaining on his machine is V. What is the inclination of the steepest hill he can ascend at a constant speed, assuming that there is a constant frictional resistance R to be overcome ? What is the average pressure on his pedal at right angles to the crank if the gear multiplication is n ? Find numerical results if $m = 150$ lb., $V = 4$ m.p.h., $H = \frac{1}{10}$, $R = 5$ lb. wt., $n = 10$. (I.S.)

20. A bicycle is geared up to 70 inches, and the length of the pedal cranks is 6 inches. Calculate the velocity of the pedal (a) at its highest point, (b) at its lowest point, when the bicycle is going at 10 m.p.h. If the bicycle and rider weigh 160 lb., find the pressure on the pedals in climbing a hill of 1 in 50. (I.E.)

21. An engine draws a train of weight 250 tons along a level track at a speed of 35 m.p.h. against resistances which may be taken at 12 lb. wt. per ton. Find the horse-power necessary to draw the train at the same speed up an incline of 1 in 160. (I.S.)

22. Find the horse-power required to enable a 200-ton train to travel up a slope of 1 in 80 at 30 m.p.h., frictional resistances being 20 lb. per ton. What is the maximum speed (in m.p.h.) which it could maintain on the level ? (Ex.)

23. An engine draws a load weighing half a ton out of a pit 300 feet deep by means of a rope which cannot bear safely a load greater than three-quarters of a ton. Find the least time required to raise the load to rest at the surface, and the greatest horse-power exerted by the engine. (Ex.)

24. The weight of an engine and train is 250 tons ; what is the least horse-power of the engine if it is capable of increasing the speed of the train from 20 m.p.h. to 50 m.p.h. in a distance of half a mile on the level ? The total resisting force is 14 lb. wt. per ton, and the pull of the engine is assumed to be constant. (H.S.C.)

25. Find the horse-power of an engine which pulls a train of 150 tons at a speed of 40 m.p.h. on the level, the resistance due to friction being 16 lb. per ton. Also find the maximum speed at which the engine could draw the train up a slope of 1 in 200. (H.S.D.)

26. A train, of weight 250 tons, meets with a constant frictional and air resistance of 16 lb. per ton of its weight. When the engine is doing 600 H.P. on the level and the train is running at 25 m.p.h., what is the acceleration of the train ? What would be the greatest possible speed for the train at this rate of working, if the resistances did not alter ?
(H.S.D.)

27. A train travelling uniformly on the level at 60 m.p.h. begins an ascent of 1 in 50. The tractive force due to adhesion has a maximum value of 3 tons, the resistances due to friction, etc., are 30 cwt., and the weight of the whole train is 200 tons. Show that it cannot surmount the incline if this exceeds $\frac{11}{6}$ miles in length, and find the horse-power exerted by the engine, (i) just before beginning the ascent, (ii) just after.
(I.S.)

28. Assuming that the frictional and other resistances to the motion of a train on the level are 10 lb. wt. per ton in a route which ascends 660 feet in 10 miles, and then descends through the same height in the same distance ; show that if a detour on the level, avoiding the incline, would not exceed in total distance 38 miles there would be economy in running, supposing that in descent steam is shut off.
(I.E.)

29. A force equal to the weight of 5 lb. acts on a mass of 30 lb., originally at rest, for 10 seconds. Find, in feet, the distance travelled by the mass, and in ft. lb. the kinetic energy generated in it. (H.C.)

30. Find the horse-power required to pump 500 gallons of water per minute from a depth of 100 feet, the water being delivered through a circular pipe 3 inches in diameter. (Assume that 1 cubic foot of water is $6\frac{1}{4}$ gallons, and that 1 gallon of water weighs 10 lb., and neglect friction.)
(H.C.)

31. Find the horse-power of an engine which can fill a cistern 200 feet above the level of a river, with 30,000 gallons of water in 24 hours ; assuming that a gallon of water weighs 10 lb., and that only two-thirds of the work actually done by the engine is available for raising the water.
(H.C.)

32. An engine is raising water from a depth of 55 feet and discharging 16 gallons a second with a velocity of 44 feet per second. Taking the weight of a gallon of water to be 10 lb., find separately in ft. lb. the potential energy and the kinetic energy of the water discharged per second, and find the horse-power at which the engine is working.
(H.C.)

33. Calculate the horse-power of an engine which can pull a train of 400 tons up an incline of 1 in 100 at a uniform speed of 40 m.p.h. against a track resistance of 9 lb. wt. per ton.
(H.S.D.)

34. The horse-power developed by a locomotive going at 25 m.p.h. is 20, the weight is 40 tons, and the resistance 7 lb. per ton ; if the acceleration be constant, find the tractive force, the time taken, and the distance gone from rest. The maximum horse-power that can be developed being 35, find the greatest distance that can be gone in 3 hours from rest.
(I.E.)

35. A train of mass 300 tons is ascending a slope of 1 in 120 with an acceleration of 0·5 ft./sec.² At a speed of 15 m.p.h. the horse-power developed is 1225. Find the magnitude of the resistances, apart from gravity, acting on the train.
(H.S.C.)

36. If a body move in a straight line under the action of a constant force, prove that the increase in the kinetic energy of the body

during any interval is equal to the work done by the force. A lift weighing 5 cwt. rises from rest through a height of 50 feet in 5 seconds, with a uniform acceleration. Find the average horse-power exerted during this time. (H.S.D.)

37. A motor car weighing a ton is travelling on the level at 20 m.p.h. Coming to a slope of 1 in 20 the car is allowed to free-wheel, and runs down the slope at this same uniform speed. At what horse-power was its engine working on the level ? (H.S.D.)

38. A motor lorry weighing 2 tons runs down an incline of 1 in 200 with a uniform velocity of 15 m.p.h., the engine being cut off. What is the resistance of the road in lb. wt. per ton ? What horse-power would the engine require to maintain the same speed on the level ? (H.S.C.)

39. Express an acceleration of 15 m.p.h. per minute, in feet per second per second. Find the force which would produce this acceleration in a 160-ton train on the level, neglecting frictional resistance, and find the final horse-power needed to continue this acceleration for 4 minutes from rest. (H.S.C.)

40. Find the horse-power required to draw a train of 200 tons on the level at 50 m.p.h. if the resistance is 10 lb. wt. per ton. A train is drawn on the level at a certain constant speed by using horse-power H ; if H' is the horse-power required to draw the train at the same speed up an incline of 1 in 100, the resistance being 10 lb. wt. per ton in each case, show that $H' = 3 \cdot 24\ H$. (H.S.D.)

41. An engine of 748 h.p. is taking a train of 200 tons total weight up a slope of 1 in 100, road resistances being 15 lb. per ton. Find the greatest steady speed in m.p.h. which can be maintained. (H.S.C.)

42. Find the horse-power required to pump 1000 gallons of water per minute from a depth of 50 feet and deliver it through a pipe of 6 square inches cross-section. (Assume that 1 cubic foot of water is $6\frac{1}{4}$ gallons, and that a gallon of water weighs 10 lb., and neglect the effects of friction.) (H.S.C.)

43. A particle is projected with velocity V up a line of greatest slope of a rough inclined plane of $\alpha°$ slope, the angle of friction being $\lambda°$ (λ less than α). Show that it reaches the point of projection again with a velocity

$$V\sqrt{\sin(\alpha - \lambda)\ \mathrm{cosec}\ (\alpha + \lambda)},$$

after a time,

$$\frac{V}{g}\cos\lambda\left[\mathrm{cosec}\ (\alpha + \lambda) + \sqrt{\mathrm{cosec}(\alpha + \lambda)\ \mathrm{cosec}(\alpha - \lambda)}\right].$$

44. What must be the horse-power of an engine which is to fill a reservoir 500 yards long and 300 yards wide to a depth of 11 feet by pumping water from a river a mile away and 500 feet lower in level, in fifteen days working day and night. (1 cubic foot of water weighs 62·5 lb.) (I.S.)

45. Express the weight of a pound in dynes, supposing that 1 lb. = 453·6 gm., 1 metre = 39·37 inches, and $g = 32 \cdot 2$ ft. sec. units.
   Find the horse-power of an engine that can pull a train of 300 tons up an incline of 1 in 200 at a steady rate of 45 m.p.h., the resistance to motion being 12 lb. wt. per ton. (I.S.)

46. An engine of horse-power 550 and weight 40 tons pulls a train of 280 tons against a resistance of 14 lb. wt. per ton. Find the maximum speed on the level. Find also the maximum speed up an incline of 1 in 156 ; and calculate what is the slope of the incline down which the train can run at constant speed without the use of steam or brakes. (H.S.D.)

47. Two engines of weights 50 tons and 40 tons and of horse-powers 600 and 500, respectively, pull a train of weight 460 tons against a resistance of 12 lb. wt. per ton, the heavier engine being in front. Find the maximum speed on the level, and the tension in the coupling between the two engines when this speed is attained.

(H.S.D.)

48. A car weighing 3 tons will just run down a slope of 1 in 20 under its own weight. Assuming that the forces resisting its motion remain constant, and that the engine exerts a constant tractive force, find to the nearest unit the horse-power of its engine if it can attain a velocity of 30 m.p.h. in 4 minutes on the level. (C.S.)

49. A 20 H.P. motor lorry, weighing 5 tons, including load, moves up a hill with a slope of 1 in 20. The frictional resistance is equivalent to 13 lb. wt. per ton, and may be supposed independent of the velocity. Find the maximum steady rate at which the lorry can move up the slope, and the acceleration capable of being developed when it is moving at 6 m.p.h. (C.S.)

50. A particle is projected with velocity V directly up a rough plane of inclination α. Show that when it again has velocity V it will be at a distance

$$\frac{V^2}{g} \cdot \frac{\cos \alpha \sin 2\lambda}{\cos 2\lambda - \cos 2\alpha}$$

from the point of projection, λ being the angle of friction which is less than α. (H.S.D.)

51. An engine in 7 seconds has raised a load of 1 ton through a height of 3 feet, and has communicated to it a speed of 10 ft./sec. At what average horse-power has it been working ? (H.C.)

52. A dock 600 feet long and 120 feet wide, with a depth of water 36 feet, has to be pumped dry in 6 hours, all the water being lifted to a level of 2 feet above the original water level in the dock. If the useful horse-power exerted by the pumping engines is constant, calculate what it must amount to, and show that it takes $1\frac{3}{4}$ hours to empty the last 6 foot of water in the dock. (Q.E.)

53. A car weighing 1 ton has climbed a height of 100 feet in going 1 mile ; it started from rest and is proceeding at 40 m.p.h. at the end. The frictional resistance of the road is 50 lb. wt. What is the ratio of the gains of kinetic and potential energy, what fraction of the total work done is stored, and what is the average horse-power exerted if the climb took 3 minutes ? (Q.E.)

54. A car weighing 7 tons moves from rest along a horizontal track under a uniform tractive force on the wheels, the horse-power after 1 minute being 20. How long will the car take to acquire a velocity of 15 m.p.h., and what will be the horse-power at that moment ? (Q.E.)

55. A car weighing 2 tons is accelerating at $1\frac{1}{2}$ ft./sec.^{2} up a 10 per cent. gradient, the resistance being 35 lb. per ton. When the car is running at 25 m.p.h. what is the horse-power ? (Q.E.)

56. A jet of water issues from a pipe, of cross-section equal to 5 square inches, at the rate of 400 gallons per minute. If the whole of its energy could be used, show that it would be doing work at the rate of 1·8 H.P. nearly, given that a gallon of water weighs 10 lb., and that its volume is $277\frac{1}{2}$ cubic inches. (I.S.)

57. A belt is 6 inches wide and $\frac{1}{4}$ inch thick, and the diameter of the pulley is 3 feet, the safe stress for the belt is 1000 lb. per square inch, and it runs at 12 ft./sec. ; find the maximum horse-power that can be transmitted to the pulley when the approaching part of the belt is quite slack. Determine the angular speed of the pulley, and the torque or moment transmitted to it. (I.E.)

58. A pulley $1\frac{1}{2}$ feet in diameter receives 10 H.P. when revolving 180 times per minute, and the tension of the belt on the tight side is $2\frac{1}{2}$ times that on the slack side. Find the tension on the tight side, and the width of the belt required if its thickness is $\frac{1}{2}$ inch, and the greatest tension it can support is 330 lb. per square inch of cross-section. (H.S.C.)

59. An engine of M tons, working at horse-power H, draws n carriages, each of mass M' tons, at a uniform rate of v m.p.h. Assuming the resistance on the engine and on each carriage to be proportional to the weight, prove that the tension of the coupling between the engine and the nearest carriage is equal to

$$\frac{75}{448} \frac{HnM'}{(M+nM')v} \text{ tons.} \qquad \text{(I.C.)}$$

60. A weight of 4 kilos will compress a spring through 2·5 cm. A model truck, weighing 250 gm., runs into the spring, used as a buffer, with a velocity of 90 cm./sec. How far will the spring be compressed before the truck is brought to rest ? (H.C.)

61. A mass of 160 lb. is attached to one end of a light rope, the other end of which is made fast at a point A. The rope is elastic, obeying Hooke's law, and its breaking tension is 2000 lb. wt. If the rope does not break when the mass is dropped freely from A, prove that the elongation of the rope under its breaking tension must exceed 19 per cent. (C.S.)

62. A truck weighing 1000 lb. is hauled up a slope of 1 in 20 measured along the slope. The truck starts from rest. The acceleration is uniform and the velocity after 10 seconds is 15 ft./sec. Prove that the pull on the truck is about 97 lb. wt., and draw the graph showing the rate of working in horse-power in terms of the time. (Q.E.)

63. Two men exerting together a force of 90 lb. wt. put a railway wagon into motion. The wagon weighs 6 tons, and the resistance to motion is 10 lb. per ton. How far does the wagon advance in 1 minute ; and at what rate, in horse-power, are the men working at the end of the minute ? If the men can at most do work at the rate of 0·8 H.P., at what constant speed can they keep the wagon moving ? (Q.E.)

64. Three equal weights are attached to the middle and ends of a light cord which is placed over two smooth pulleys at the same level, so that the central weight hangs symmetrically between the pulleys and the others hang vertically. If the central weight is pulled down until its connecting cord makes angles of 50° with the hori-

zontal, and is then let go, find what the angles will be when next
the weights come to momentary rest.   (H.S.C.)

65. A car of weight 10 tons is ascending an incline of 1 in 25, the frictional and other resistances being 17 lb. wt. per ton. If the
maximum speed is 15 m.p.h., find the horse-power of the engine.
Calculate the maximum speed on the level with the same resistances.   (N.U.3)

66. Determine the relation between the power exerted on a body and
its velocity and acceleration, using lb. wt., ft., sec., units.
A body which weighs W lb. is subject to a constant resistance
0·1 W lb. wt., and is moving down a slope of 1 in 20 under a constant tractive *power* kW. ft. lb. per second. By considering the
power used, prove that when the speed is 10 k ft./sec., the
acceleration is about 1·6 ft./sec.^{2} (N.U.3)

67. Define work and average power. State the relation between the
work done by the forces acting on a body for any interval and the
kinetic energy of the body at the beginning and at the end of the
interval.
A car weighing 20,000 lb. is moving with constant acceleration,
and its speed increases from 15 to 20 ft./sec. in 50 seconds. Find
the average horse-power used to produce this acceleration.
                                                               (N.U.3)

68. Find the rate at which work is being done by a couple of moment G
acting on and in the plane of a lamina rotating with angular
velocity ω about a fixed point in it.
A 10 H.P. electric motor is getting up speed from rest against
a resisting couple whose moment is 320 poundal-feet. Find the
maximum angular velocity of the rotating part and the time taken
to attain it, if the acceleration is constant and equal to 40 radians
per second per second.   (N.U.3)

69. An aeroplane propeller is performing 1800 R.P.M. when the engine
of 200 H.P. is exerting its full power. What is the magnitude of
the couple exerted by the engine on the shaft of the propeller ?
                                                               (N.U.3)

70. A train of 375 tons is being drawn up an incline of 1 in 168 with a
uniform acceleration of $\frac{1}{4}$ ft./sec.^{2} by two engines, each weighing
75 tons.   If the frictional resistance is 16 lb. wt. per ton, and both
engines are working at the same rate, show that when the speed
of the train is 30 m.p.h., each engine is working at 983$\frac{1}{2}$ H.P.
Also find the pulls in the couplings (i) between the second engine
and the train, (ii) between the engines.
[*Note.*—The slope of the track is $\sin^{-1} \frac{1}{168}$. Take $g = 32$.]
                                                               (N.U.3)

71. The engine of a goods train weighs 80 tons, and it is working at
500 H.P. while drawing at 20 m.p.h. a train of forty trucks, each
weighing 13 tons. If the resistance to the motion of the engine
and each truck is proportional to its weight, find the tension in
the coupling between the engine and the first truck.
If the coupling between the thirtieth and thirty-first trucks
breaks, show that if the engine continues to work at the same
rate the front portion of the train will have an acceleration which
continually decreases, and find the greatest speed which it can
attain.   (N.U.4)

72. An engine working at 600 H.P. pulls a train of 250 tons along a level track, the resistances to the motion amounting to 16 lb. wt. per ton. What is the acceleration of the train when its velocity is 30 m.p.h. ?

At what steady speed, with the same horse-power, can the train travel up an incline of 1 in 100 against the same resistances ?

(C.W.B.)

§ 101. Force-space Curve.

This curve is obtained by plotting the distance s moved by the point of application of the force along an axis OX, and the values of the force for different values of s parallel to a perpendicular axis OY.

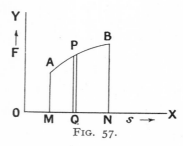

FIG. 57.

Let APB (Fig. 57) be a curve obtained in this way.

The area of a strip PQ of breadth ds is PQds, or Fds, where F is the value of the force when $s = $ OQ.

Now the work done by the force is $\int Fds$, taken between the initial and final values of s.

If OM $= s_1$, ON $= s_2$, the work done between these limits is

$$\int_{s_1}^{s_2} Fds,$$

but this is the area under the curve APB.

Hence the area under the force-space curve gives the work done by the force.

We have assumed here that the curve AB is traced in the direction from A to B, i.e. that s is increasing. If it is traced in the opposite direction, so that s is decreasing, the work given by the areas ABNM is done *against* the force (by other forces), and we must then reckon it as negative work as far as the force F is concerned.

§ 102.
Suppose the force-space curve is closed, as in Fig. 58, and traced in the direction shown by the arrows.

Starting from A, the upper portion of the curve APB represents the magnitude of the force as its point of application moves in the

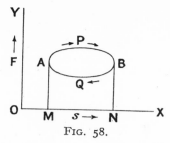

FIG. 58.

direction of the force a distance represented by MN ; and the area APBNM represents the positive or useful work done by the force. The lower portion of the curve BQA represents the magnitude of the force as its point of application is being pushed back through the distance represented by MN ; the area AQBNM represents the work done against the force.

The total positive or useful work done by the force while its point of application has moved from M to N and back is represented by the *difference* between the areas APBNM and AQBNM, i.e. by the area of the closed curve APBQ.

§ 103. Indicator Diagrams.

To obtain a measure of the amount of work done by the steam pressure in a steam engine during a complete stroke of the piston an indicator is attached to the cylinder of the engine. The indicator consists of a small cylinder containing a light piston controlled by a spiral spring, so that the vertical displacement of the piston is proportional to the steam pressure in the main cylinder. The indicator piston actuates a pencil which traces a curve on a sheet of paper placed on a rotating drum.

The engine is thus made to trace its own force-space diagram. The curve is a closed one, and its area gives a measure of the work done by the engine at each stroke.

§ **104.** The following examples are of a rather harder type, and include cases where the resistance to motion is not constant.

EXAMPLE (i).

The resistance which a train experiences, when moving at V m.p.h., is equal to

$$\left(6 + \frac{V^2}{100}\right)$$

lb. wt. per ton weight of the train. If a train of weight 150 tons is drawn up a slope of 1 in 140 by an engine of 372 horse-power, show that the maximum speed attainable is 30 m.p.h. Also find the maximum speed down the slope with steam shut off.   (Ex.)

At speed V m.p.h. the resistance is

$$\left(6 + \frac{V^2}{100}\right) 150 \text{ lb. wt.},$$

the component of weight is

$$\frac{150 \times 2240}{140} \text{ lb. wt.}$$

The total force resisting motion is

$$150\left(6 + \frac{V^2}{100} + \frac{224}{14}\right) \text{ lb. wt.}$$

The work per second is

$$150\left(6 + 16 + \frac{V^2}{100}\right)\frac{88V}{60} \text{ ft. lb.},$$

$$\therefore 150\left(22 + \frac{V^2}{100}\right)\frac{88V}{60} = 372 \times 550,$$

$$\therefore \left(\frac{V^2}{100} + 22\right)V = \frac{372 \times 550 \times 60}{150 \times 88} = 930,$$

$$\therefore V^3 + 2200V - 93000 = 0,$$

and it can be seen that $V = 30$ satisfies this equation.
    The factors of the left-hand side are

$$(V - 30)(V^2 + 30V + 3100),$$

so that the other roots of the equation are imaginary.
    In running down the slope, with steam shut off, the resistance increases with the speed until it becomes equal to the weight component down the slope, and then

$$\left(6 + \frac{V^2}{100}\right)150 = \frac{150 \times 2240}{140},$$

$$\therefore 6 + \frac{V^2}{100} = 16,$$

$$\therefore \frac{V^2}{100} = 10,$$

$$\therefore V^2 = 1000, \text{ or } V = 10\sqrt{10} \text{ m.p.h.}$$

EXAMPLE (ii).

A cyclist and his machine together weigh 200 lb. Riding along a certain road he observes that, when he is free-wheeling down a slope of 1 in 40, his speed, when it has become uniform, is 20 m.p.h., and is 30 m.p.h. when he is free-wheeling down a slope of 1 in 20. If the air resistance varies as the square of the speed, and other resistances remain constant, find in horse-power the rate at which he must work to maintain a speed of 15 m.p.h. on the level. (H.C.)

    Let the air-resistance be kv^2 lb. wt. where v is the speed in feet per second, and k is a constant; and let the other resistances be R lb. wt. In free-wheeling down a slope at uniform speed the total resistance must equal the component of weight down the slope.

Now, 20 m.p.h. $= \frac{88}{3}$ ft./sec., and 30 m.p.h. $= 44$ ft./sec. Hence we have

$$R + k\frac{88^2}{9} = \frac{200}{40} = 5 \qquad . \quad . \quad . \quad . \quad \text{(i)}$$

and

$$R + k \cdot 44^2 = \frac{200}{20} = 10 \qquad . \quad . \quad . \quad . \quad \text{(ii)}$$

whence

$$k = \frac{9}{44^2}.$$

Substituting in (ii),

$$R = 10 - 9 = 1.$$

Hence the resistance at a speed of v ft./sec. is

$$\left(1 + \frac{9v^2}{44^2}\right) \text{lb. wt.},$$

15 m.p.h. $= 22$ ft./sec., and at this speed the total resistance is

$$1 + \frac{9 \times 22^2}{44^2} = \frac{13}{4} \text{ lb. wt.}$$

The work per second $= \frac{13}{4} \cdot 22$ ft. lb.,

$$\therefore \text{ the horse-power} = \frac{13 \times 22}{4 \times 550} = \cdot 13.$$

EXAMPLE (iii).

The pressure in the boiler of a two-cylinder locomotive is p lb. wt. per square inch ; the diameter of the piston is a inches, and the diameter of the driving wheel is b inches ; prove that if the length of the stroke is l inches, the tractive power of the engine is not more than

$$\frac{pa^2l}{b}. \qquad \text{(I.E.)}$$

In one revolution the driving wheel moves πb inches, and if F is the tractive force, the work done is

$$F\pi b \text{ in. lb.}$$

Now the pressure on the piston is $\frac{\pi a^2 p}{4}$ lb. wt., and since there are two cylinders, the total distance travelled by the pistons is $4l$ inches,

$$\therefore \text{ the work done} = \pi a^2 pl \text{ in. lb.,}$$

$$\therefore F = \frac{a^2 pl}{b} \text{ lb. wt.,}$$

and this is the maximum value for F.

EXAMPLES XV.

1. A motor-cycle and its rider together weigh 412 lb., and the cycle is being driven up a gradient of 1 in 10 at 30 m.p.h. If the air resistance is $0 \cdot 005 V^2$ lb. wt., where V is the speed in ft. sec. units, and if the resistance of the road surface is $0 \cdot 01$ of the total weight, find the effective horse-power developed by the engine.

2. A cyclist riding on a level road at 15 m.p.h. is working at the rate of 0·1 H.P. Assuming that the resistance in lb. wt., apart from gravity, varies as the square of the speed in ft./sec., find the steepest gradient on the same road up which he can ride at $7\frac{1}{2}$ m.p.h., working at the same rate, the cyclist and his machine weighing together 245 lb.   (H.S.C.)

3. The resistance to the motion of a train is K (speed)^2; the maximum power of the engine is H, and the maximum speed is V. Show that the resistance at unit speed is $\dfrac{H}{V^3}$.

If $V = 60$ m.p.h., $H = 700$ H.P., the total weight 500 tons, and the tractive force constant, find the starting acceleration, and show that it is $\frac{4}{3}$ of the value at half-speed.

u and v being two speeds and f the average acceleration during the change, show that the distance is given approximately by

$$\frac{u^2 - v^2}{2f}.$$

                                                           (I.E.)

4. A train of total weight 400 tons is travelling on the level at 60 m.p.h., the engine working at 800 H.P. If the resistances, apart from air resistance, are 10 lb. wt. per ton, find in lb. wt. the magnitude of the air resistance.

If air resistance varies as the square of the speed, find the rate at which the engine is working when drawing the same train up a gradient of 1 in 200 at a steady rate of 30 m.p.h.; and find the acceleration which the train would have on this gradient at this speed if the engine were working at 800 H.P.   (H.C.)

5. A motor car is running at a constant speed of 60 ft./sec. It is found that the effective horse-power at the road wheels is 18. Find the resistance to motion.

Assuming that the resistance varies as the square of the speed, and that the effective horse-power at the road wheels remains constant and equal to 18, prove that the distance required for the car to accelerate from 20 ft./sec. to 40 ft./sec. is

$$750 \log_e \tfrac{2\,6}{1\,9} \text{ ft.}$$

The car weighs 3300 lb., and in both cases the road is level.   (C.S.)

6. An engine of weight W tons can exert a maximum tractive effort of P tons weight and develop at most H H.P. The resistances to motion are constant and equal to R tons weight. Show that, starting from rest, the engine will first develop its full horse-power when its velocity is

$$\frac{55H}{224P} \text{ ft./sec.}$$

after at least

$$\frac{55WH}{224Pg(P - R)} \text{ seconds.}$$

What is the greatest velocity which the engine can attain?
                                                           (C.S.)

7. An engine weighing 96 tons, of which 40 tons are carried by the driving wheels, exerting a uniform pull gives a train a velocity of 25 m.p.h. after travelling for 50 seconds from rest against a resistance of 10·5 lb. wt. per ton. If the friction between the driving

wheels and the rails is 0·2 times the pressure, find the tension in the coupling between the engine and the first carriage. (Tractive force = friction between driving wheels and rails.) (C.S.)

8. A motor bicycle which with its rider weighs 3 cwt. is found to run at 30 m.p.h. up an incline of 1 in 20, and at 50 m.p.h. down the same incline. Assuming that the resistance is proportional to the square of the velocity, and that the engine is working at the same horse-power, find the speed that would be attained on the level, and show that the horse-power is 2⅓ nearly. (C.S.)

9. A train weighing 300 tons drawn by an engine weighing 100 tons attains a speed of 60 m.p.h. on the level when the engine is working at the rate of 1200 H.P. Determine the resistance. Assuming that the resistance varies as the square of the velocity, and that the engine is working at the same rate, determine the retardation when the speed of the train up an incline of 1 in 100 has dropped to 40 m.p.h. (C.S.)

10. A locomotive weighing 40 tons can pull 210 ten-ton trucks at 20 m.p.h. on the level. The trucks will just run at 20 m.p.h. down an incline of 1 in 320. How many trucks can the locomotive pull at that speed up the same incline ?
    If the frictional resistance of the engine is 300 lb. wt., what is its horse-power ? (C.S.)

11. An engine moves at a steady velocity v along level ground when working at a constant horse-power H. When moving up a plane inclined at a small angle to the horizontal its steady velocity under the same horse-power is v'.
    If the engine starts down the same incline with velocity v' and moves for t seconds with a constant acceleration until it reaches its steady velocity down the plane corresponding to the same horse-power H, show that the distance travelled in these t seconds is

$$\frac{v'^2 t}{2v' - v}.$$

Assume that the frictional resistance is constant throughout. (C.S.)

12. A motor car weighing 1 ton attains a speed of 40 m.p.h. when running down an incline of 1 in 20 with the engine cut off. It can attain a speed of 30 m.p.h. up the same incline when the engine is working. Assuming that the resistance varies as the square of the velocity, find the horse-power developed by the engine. (C.S.)

13. An engine of mass 100 tons is allowed to run down a bank, whose slope is 1 in 30, with steam shut off, and is observed to attain a maximum speed of 80 m.p.h., air and frictional resistances being assumed proportional to the square of the speed.
    If the engine can develop 1000 H.P., show that its maximum speed up the bank, under its own steam, is 40 m.p.h. (= 59 ft./sec.) nearly. (Q.E.)

14. A fast cruiser is propelled at a speed of 40 m.p.h. by means of engines whose effective horse-power is 40,000. Calculate the resistance to the motion of the ship, and assuming that the resistance varies as the square of the speed, what horse-power would be required for a speed of 45 m.p.h. (Q.E.)

15. A 10-ton electric tramcar runs on a 12-mile route which rises uniformly to a height of 200 feet above the starting-point. The average frictional resistance is 25 lb. per ton, and the car has fifteen stops from a speed of 15 m.p.h. The stops are effected by first cutting off the current and then bringing the car to rest in 100 feet by applying the brakes. Find the energy consumed in horse-power hours on the run. (Q.E.)

16. A uniformly loaded goods train of mass 400 tons is being hauled up a gradient of 1 in 161, by an engine of mass 100 tons in front, assisted by an engine of mass 80 tons at the rear. When the speed is 15 m.p.h., the front and rear engines deliver 500 and 300 H.P. respectively at their wheels. If the frictional resistance to motion be taken as 12 lb. wt. per ton, find the acceleration of the train and the tension in the coupling at the centre of the train. (Q.E.)

17. A motor lorry, when loaded, weighs 5 tons, and is designed just to attain a maximum speed of 15 m.p.h. up a hill of 1 in 20. The road and wind resistance at this speed is 32 lb. per ton. Find the maximum horse-power required by the lorry. If the resistance to motion varies as the square of the speed, what would be the speed of the lorry on a level road for the same horse-power ? (Q.E.)

18. A railway wagon weighing 10 tons is pulled along a straight level track by a horse, the direction of the pull being horizontal, and inclined to the track at an angle of 30°. If the pull is constant and equal to 200 lb. wt. and the resistance to motion 100 lb. wt., find the horse-power being supplied by the horse when the wagon has moved 20 feet from rest. (Q.E.)

19. It is found that to drive a car at a uniform speed of (i) 20, (ii) 40, (iii) 60 ft./sec. on a level road the engine must work at (i) 2, (ii) 5, (iii) 10 H.P. Show that these facts are consistent with the assumption that the forces which retard the motion of the car are a constant force, together with a force proportional to the square of the speed. Regarding this assumption as correct, find the horse-power for a speed of 80 ft./sec. (H.S.D.)

20. The diameter of the low-pressure cylinder of a marine engine is 46 inches, the average speed of the piston is 800 feet per minute, and the average pressure of the steam on the piston is 32 lb. wt. per square inch. What is the indicated horse-power of the engine ? (I.E.)

21. An engine, whose mass is 100 tons, and of 1500 H.P., draws a train of mass 350 tons. The resistance to motion being $0.009 \, V^2$ lb. wt. per ton at speed V m.p.h., find the greatest speed of the train on the level. (Q.E.)

22. A train, of weight 200 tons, is running at 24 m.p.h., and accelerating at $\frac{1}{2}$ ft./sec.^{2}, the resistances to motion being at that moment 14 lb. per ton. Find the rate of working of the engine in horse-power, and if the engine continues to work at that rate while the resistance increases proportionally to the speed, find the maximum speed of the train. (Ex.)

23. The resistance to the motion of a cyclist may be assumed to be $8 + 0.006 \, v^2$ lb. wt. when his speed relative to the air is v miles per hour. If he can work at 0.15 H.P., and the least speed at which he can ride is 2 m.p.h., show that the gradient of the steepest incline

up which he can ride against a head wind blowing at 20 m.p.h. is about 1 in 11, the total weight of the cycle and the rider being 190 lb.

(N.U.4)

§ 105. The following examples depend on the same principles as those in the preceding paragraphs, but require the use of the calculus for their solution.

In the cases considered so far the accelerating force has either been constant, or, if the resistance has depended on the velocity, we have not found the *time taken* to describe a certain distance or acquire a certain velocity.

For a variable acceleration we have the expressions $\frac{d^2x}{dt^2}$, $\frac{dv}{dt}$, and $v\frac{dv}{ds}$, the last two being those most commonly used in problems of the kind we are dealing with.

The fundamental equation $mf = P$, now becomes

$$m\frac{dv}{dt} = \text{accelerating force,}$$

or

$$mv\frac{dv}{ds} = \text{accelerating force.}$$

The accelerating force is usually some function of v, s, or t, and after inserting its value in the right-hand side of one of these equations, we have to integrate and find v.

Suppose the tractive force of an engine is constant, but the resistance is proportional to the square of the speed.

Then if P is the constant tractive force, and kv^2 the resistance,

$$m\frac{dv}{dt} = P - kv^2,$$

or

$$mv\frac{dv}{ds} = P - kv^2.$$

The first equation enables us to find the velocity acquired after a given time. We write the equation

$$m\frac{dv}{P - kv^2} = dt,$$

and integrate both sides, adding a constant to the right-hand side and determining its value from the initial conditions. (Example (iii).)

The second equation enables us to find the velocity acquired after travelling a given distance. The equation is written

$$m\frac{v\,dv}{P - kv^2} = ds,$$

8 *

and both sides are integrated, a constant being added and its value
determined from the initial condition.

If the tractive force p decreases uniformly with the distance
s travelled

$$\frac{dp}{ds} = - k,$$

$$\therefore p = - ks + c,$$

the value of c is obtained as the value of p when $s = 0$, i.e. at the
start.

If p decreases uniformly with the time t,

$$\frac{dp}{dt} = - k,$$

$$\therefore p = - kt + c,$$

and c is the initial value of p.

If the horse-power is constant, then if p is the tractive force
(in lb. wt.) and v the speed (in ft./sec.)

$$\left(pv = H, \text{ and } p = \frac{H}{v} \right).$$

Example (i).

*Two particles, moving in straight lines, the first acted on by a constant
force, the second acted on by a force doing work at a constant rate, each
have their velocities increased from V to $2V$, after traversing a distance a.
Show that the time taken by the second is $\frac{27}{28}$ of that taken by the first.*

*Show also that the velocity acquired by the second after traversing a
distance x, less than a, is greater than that acquired by the first after traversing the same distance.* (H.C.)

Let f be the constant acceleration of the first particle, then

$$4V^2 = V^2 + 2fa,$$

$$\therefore f = \frac{3V^2}{2a}.$$

Also, if t_1 be the time taken,

$$2V = V + ft_1,$$

$$\therefore t_1 = \frac{V}{f} = \frac{2a}{3V}.$$

In the case of the second, if p is the force, v the speed, and H the
constant rate of working,

$$pv = H, \text{ or } p = \frac{H}{v},$$

and now

$$mv\frac{dv}{ds} = p = \frac{H}{v},$$

$$\therefore v^2 dv = \frac{H}{m} ds,$$

$$\therefore \tfrac{1}{3}v^3 = \frac{H}{m} s + c;$$

now when $s = 0$, $v = V$,

$$\therefore c = \tfrac{1}{3}V^3,$$

and when $s = a$, $v = 2V$,

$$\therefore \tfrac{8}{3}V^3 = \frac{H}{m}\,a + \tfrac{1}{3}V^3,$$

$$\therefore \frac{H}{m}a = \tfrac{7}{3}V^3, \quad \text{or } \frac{H}{m} = \frac{7V^3}{3a}.$$

Also

$$m\frac{dv}{dt} = p = \frac{H}{v},$$

$$\therefore v\,dv = \frac{H}{m}\,dt,$$

$$\therefore \tfrac{1}{2}v^2 = \frac{H}{m}\,t + c\,;$$

now when $t = 0$, $v = V$,

$$\therefore c = \tfrac{1}{2}V^2,$$

and when $t = t_2$, $v = 2V$,

$$\therefore 2V^2 = \frac{H}{m}\,t_2 + \tfrac{1}{2}V^2,$$

$$\therefore \frac{H}{m}\,t_2 = \tfrac{3}{2}V^2,$$

$$\therefore t_2 = \frac{3V^2}{2}\cdot\frac{m}{H} = \frac{3V^2}{2}\cdot\frac{3a}{7V^3} = \frac{9a}{14V},$$

$$\therefore \frac{t_2}{t_1} = \frac{9a}{14V}\cdot\frac{3V}{2a} = \frac{27}{28}.$$

The velocities acquired after traversing a distance x are, for the first,

$$v_1{}^2 = V^2 + 2fx = V^2 + \frac{3V^2}{a}x,$$

and for the second,

$$\tfrac{1}{3}v_2{}^3 = \frac{H}{m}x + \tfrac{1}{3}V^3 = \frac{7V^3}{3a}x + \tfrac{1}{3}V^\cdot,$$

or

$$v_2{}^3 = \frac{7V^3x}{a} + V^3.$$

Now

$$v_2 > v_1 \text{ if } \left(1 + \frac{7x}{a}\right)^{\frac{1}{3}} > \left(1 + \frac{3x}{a}\right)^{\frac{1}{2}},$$

i.e. if

$$\left(1 + \frac{7x}{a}\right)^2 > \left(1 + \frac{3x}{a}\right)^3,$$

or

$$1 + \frac{14x}{a} + \frac{49x^2}{a^2} > 1 + \frac{9x}{a} + \frac{27x^2}{a^2} + \frac{27x^3}{a^3},$$

or

$$\frac{27x^3}{a^3} - \frac{22x^2}{a^2} - \frac{5x}{a} < 0,$$

or

$$27x^2 - 22ax - 5a^2 < 0,$$

or

$$(27x + 5a)(x - a) < 0,$$

and this is the case when $x < a$.

EXAMPLE (ii).

A horse pulls a wagon of 10 tons from rest against a constant resistance of 50 lb. The pull exerted is at first 200 lb., and decreases uniformly with the distance until it falls to 50 lb. after a distance of 167 feet has been covered. Show that the resulting velocity of the wagon is very nearly 6 ft./sec. (C.S.)

If p is the pull (in lb.) then, since it decreases uniformly with the distance, we have

$$\frac{dp}{ds} = -k,$$

$$\therefore p = -ks + c ;$$

Now, $p = 200g$ poundals when $s = 0$, $\therefore c = 200g$,
and $p = 50g$ poundals when $s = 167$,

$$\therefore 50g = -167k + 200g,$$

$$\therefore k = \frac{150g}{167}.$$

The accelerating force is

$$-ks + 200g - 50g = -ks + 150g,$$

$$\therefore 22400v\frac{dv}{ds} = -ks + 150g.$$

$$\therefore 11200v^2 = -\tfrac{1}{2}ks^2 + 150gs,$$

and when $s = 167$,

$$11200v^2 = -\frac{1}{2} \cdot \frac{150g}{167} \cdot 167^2 + 150g \cdot 167,$$

whence $v^2 = 35 \cdot 8,$

$$\therefore v = 6 \text{ ft./sec. nearly.}$$

EXAMPLE (iii).

The propulsive horse-power required to drive a ship of mass 16,500 tons at a steady speed of 30 ft./sec. is 18,000. Assuming that the resistance is proportional to the square of the speed, and that the engines exert a constant propulsive force on the ship at all speeds, prove that the initial acceleration, when the ship starts from rest, is $\frac{2}{7}$ ft./sec.^{2} ; and that it attains a speed of 20 ft./sec. in $\frac{7}{8} \log_e 5$ minutes. (C.S.)

If P lb. wt. is the propulsive force

$$30P = 18000 \times 550,$$

$$\therefore P = 600 \times 550g \text{ poundals.}$$

Since resistance is proportional to the square of the speed, it may be taken as kv^2, and when $v = 30$ the resistance is equal to P,

$$\therefore k \times 900 = 600 \times 550g,$$

$$\therefore k = \tfrac{2}{3} \times 550g.$$

The resultant accelerating force at speed v is

$$600 \times 550g - kv^2, .$$

$$\therefore\ 16500 \times 2240\frac{dv}{dt} = 600 \times 550g - \frac{2}{3}550g \times v^2,$$

$$= \frac{2 \times 550g}{3}(900 - v^2),$$

$$\therefore\ \frac{16500 \times 2240 \times 3}{2 \times 550 \times 32} \cdot \frac{dv}{900 - v^2} = dt,$$

$$\therefore\ \frac{900 \times 7}{2}\left(\frac{1}{30 - v} + \frac{1}{30 + v}\right)\frac{dv}{60} = dt,$$

$$\therefore\ \frac{105}{2}\log_e \frac{30 + v}{30 - v} = t + c,$$

and $v = 0$, when $t = 0$, $\therefore\ c = 0$,

hence when $v = 20$,

$$t = \frac{105}{2}\log_e\frac{50}{10} = \frac{105}{2}\log_e 5 \text{ seconds,}$$

$$= \tfrac{7}{8}\log_e 5 \text{ minutes.}$$

When $v = 0$, the accelerating force is $600 \times 550g$, and the acceleration is

$$\frac{600 \times 550 \times 32}{16500 \times 2240} = \tfrac{2}{7}\text{ ft./sec.}^2$$

EXAMPLE (iv).

Show that, by plotting a curve connecting the reciprocal of the accelera-tion of a body with its velocity, it is possible to estimate the time required for a given change in velocity.

The acceleration of a tramcar starting from rest decreases by an amount proportional to the increase of speed, from 1·5 ft./sec.² at starting to 0·5 ft./sec.² when the speed is 5 m.p.h. Find the time taken to reach 5 m.p.h. from rest. (C.S.)

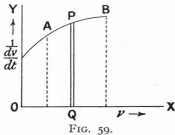

FIG. 59.

If we plot v along OX (Fig. 59) and $\dfrac{1}{\dfrac{dv}{dt}}$ along OY, the area of an elementary strip PQ is

$$\frac{1}{\dfrac{dv}{dt}} \cdot dv = dt.$$

If v_1 and v_2 are the velocities corresponding to the points A and B, the area under the curve is

$$\int_{v_1}^{v_2} \frac{dt}{dv} dv = \int_{t_1}^{t_2} dt$$

= time when velocity is v_2 — time when velocity is v_1.

= time required for increase from v_1 to v_2.

Since the acceleration is proportional to speed, and is 1·5 ft./sec.^{2} at starting

$$\frac{dv}{dt} = -kv + 1\cdot5,$$

and when v is $\dfrac{88}{12}$ or $\dfrac{22}{3}$,

$$\frac{dv}{dt} = 0\cdot5,$$

$$\therefore 0\cdot5 = -\frac{22}{3}k + 1\cdot5,$$

$$\therefore k = \frac{3}{22};$$

$$\therefore \frac{dv}{dt} = \frac{3}{2} - \frac{3}{22}v,$$

$$\therefore \frac{dv}{11 - v} = \frac{3}{22}dt,$$

$$\therefore \log_e \frac{c}{11 - v} = \frac{3}{22}t,$$

and $v = 0$ when $t = 0$,

$$\therefore c = 11,$$

$$\therefore t = \frac{22}{3} \log_e \frac{11}{11 - v}.$$

When $v = \dfrac{22}{3}$,

$$t = \frac{22}{3} \log_e 3 = 8\cdot06 \text{ seconds nearly.}$$

EXAMPLE XVI.

1. The resistance to the motion of a train is 160 lb. wt. per ton mass at all speeds. It is moving on the level with uniform speed V, and comes to an incline of 1 in 70. The engine continues to work at the same rate as before ; prove that if v is the velocity, and x the distance described up the incline in time t, then

$$v^2 = V^2 - \frac{1}{35}g(6x - 5Vt).$$

(H.C.)

2. A car is travelling at its maximum speed of 40 m.p.h. on the level, the resistance being 160 lb. wt. per ton, assumed to be independent of the speed. It then climbs a hill of 1 in 25, and the speed falls

until it is steady, the engine then working at the same effective horse-power as before. Find the steady speed up the hill.

If the tractive force increases uniformly with the distance travelled up the hill, find the distance travelled before the uniform speed is attained.   (C.S.)

3. Show that in rectilinear motion the time taken for any change in velocity is given by the area of the curve connecting the reciprocal of the acceleration and the corresponding velocity.

   A tramcar starts from rest with an acceleration of 3 ft./sec.^{2}, the relation between acceleration and speed is linear, and the acceleration is 1 ft./sec.^{2} when the speed is 5 m.p.h. Prove graphically or otherwise that the time taken to reach this speed is 4·03 seconds ($\log_{10} e = 0\cdot4343$).   (C.S.)

4. A motor car is travelling along a level road with a constant speed of V ft./sec., the resistance to motion being equivalent to a constant back pull of a lb. wt. The car then comes to a hill where the resistance to motion (including gravity) is b lb. wt., and after the velocity has again become constant, the engine works at the same constant power as on the level. If, while the velocity is varying, the tractive pull alters uniformly with the distance from its first constant value to its next constant value, show that the distance travelled along the hill before the velocity becomes constant is

$$\frac{a+b}{b^2} \cdot \frac{MV^2}{g} \text{ feet,}$$

where M is the mass of the car in lb.   (C.S.)

5. A locomotive of mass m tons starts from rest and moves against a constant resistance of P lb. wt. The driving force decreases uniformly from $2P$ lb. wt. at such a rate that at the end of a seconds it is equal to P. Find the velocity and the rate of working after t seconds ($t < a$), and show that the maximum rate of working is

$$\frac{1\cdot54 \times 10^{-5} a P^2}{m} \text{ H.P.}$$

(C.S.)

6. The force acting on a body of mass 1 lb., which is initially at rest, varies as the square of the time, and is 10 lb. wt. at the end of 10 seconds. Neglect resistances and gravity. Prove that the time-average and the space-average of the force during the first 10 seconds are $3\frac{1}{3}$ lb. wt. and $6\frac{2}{3}$ lb. wt. respectively.   (C.S.)

7. A train of weight M lb. moving at v ft./sec. on the level is pulled with a force of P lb. against a resistance of R lb. Show that in accelerating from v_0 to v_1 ft./sec., the distance in feet described by the train is

$$\frac{M}{g} \int_{v_0}^{v_1} \frac{v\,dv}{P-R}.$$

   If the resistance $R = a + bv^2$, find an expression for the distance described when the power P is shut off and the velocity decreases from v_1 to v_0.   (C.S.)

8. The acceleration of a certain racing motor car at a speed of v ft./sec. is

$$\left(3\cdot6 - \frac{v^2}{9000}\right) \text{ft./sec.}^2$$

Find the maximum speed of the car, and prove that from a standing start a speed of 150 ft./sec. is acquired in 1 minute after travelling 1800 yards. Assume that

$$\log_e 6 = 1·8 \text{ and } \log_e 11 = 2·4 \qquad \text{(C.S.)}$$

9. The resistance to an aeroplane when landing is

$$a + bv^2$$

per unit mass, v being the speed, a, b, constants. For a particular machine, $b = 10^{-3}$ ft. lb. sec. units, and it is found that if the landing speed is 50 m.p.h., the length of run before coming to rest is 150 yards. Calculate the value of the constant a. (C.S.)

10. The engine of a train of 300 tons can just attain a speed of 60 m.p.h., on the level. Assuming that the resistance varies as the square of the speed and that the horse-power is constant and equal to 1000 units, show that the train starting from rest will attain a speed of 30 m.p.h. after moving through a space of 386 yards approximately.

$$(\log_e \tfrac{8}{7} = 0·1335). \qquad \text{(C.S.)}$$

11. Show that a motor car, for which the retarding force at V m.p.h. when the brakes are acting may be expressed as

$$(1000 + 0·08V^2) \text{ lb. wt.}$$

per ton of car, can be stopped in approximately 57 yards from a speed of 50 m.p.h. ($\log_e 10 = 2·30$). (C.S.)

12. The tractive effort of a tractor weighing 6 tons is 1100 lb. wt. when at rest, and 900 lb. wt. at 10 m.p.h. ; between these values the effort varies linearly with the speed. It is proceeding up a grade of 1 in 25, and is accelerating at $\frac{1}{3}$ ft./sec.^{2} Find the speed and the horse-power at that moment, taking the frictional resistances as 40 lb. wt. per ton. (Q.E.)

13. A car moves from rest with uniformly decreasing acceleration, the initial value of which is 1·5 ft./sec.^{2} The car would attain its maximum velocity in 60 seconds, but after running for 40 seconds, brakes are applied in such a way that the retardation increases uniformly from 0·5 ft./sec.^{2}, and the car is brought to rest in 32 seconds. Find the retardation at the moment the car stops. (Q.E.)

14. The tractive force exerted by an engine hauling a train along a horizontal track, starting from rest, is constant for the first 30 seconds and equal to 16,000 lb. wt. The tractive force then diminishes uniformly with the time at a rate which would give 3000 lb. pull at 4 minutes from the start. The train resistance from all causes increases uniformly with the time, starting at 2000 lb. wt., at a rate which would give 6000 lb. wt. at the end of 4 minutes. The maximum velocity attained was 45 m.p.h. Plot the velocity-time and acceleration-time curves for the motion from the start until the maximum velocity is attained. What distance is passed over during the period ? (Q.E.)

15. The maximum speed attained by an empty truck weighing 2 tons 10 cwt. when running down an incline of 1 in 120 is found to be 30 m.p.h. If the resistance to motion from all causes is proportional to the square of the speed and is independent of the load, what would be the maximum speed of the truck when carrying a load of 6 tons down the same incline ?

Obtain in the form of an integral the time taken to acquire a given velocity by the empty truck, starting from rest on this incline.   (Q.E.)

16. A body has a constant resistance to motion of 10 lb. per ton. It is subjected to a force which increases uniformly from zero for 30 seconds and then decreases to zero at the same rate. If the greatest value of the force is such that the velocity of the body is the same at the beginning and end of this time, find the greatest change of velocity of the body.   (Q.E.)

17. A body weighing 1 ton, starting with a velocity of 10 m.p.h., moves in a straight line, the power applied (tending to increase its velocity) being constant, namely 1 H.P. Find the time that will elapse before the acceleration will be reduced to $\frac{1}{2}$ of its initial value. Find also the ratio of the initial acceleration to that of gravity.   (Q.E.)

18. A weight of 100 lb. hangs freely from the end of a rope. The weight is hauled up by means of a windlass. The pull in the rope starts at 150 lb., and then diminishes uniformly at the rate of 1 lb. for every foot of rope wound in. Find the velocity of the weight after 50 feet of rope has been wound in. The weight of the rope may be neglected.   (Q.E.)

19. A car weighing 1 ton starts from rest on a level road. The tractive force acting on it is initially 80 lb., and this falls, the decrease being proportional to the distance travelled, until its value is 30 lb. at the end of 200 yards, after which it remains constant. There is a constant frictional resistance of 30 lb. Find the speed of the car at the end of the 200 yards, and plot a curve, on a distance base, showing the gradual rise of the speed from the start.   (Q.E.)

20. The relation between the time and the acceleration of a train is as given below. The train weighs 300 tons and the tractive force required when the speed is uniform is 7500 lb. Deduce the speed-time curve, and find the total distance traversed, and the horse-power $1\frac{1}{4}$ minutes after the start.

Time in minutes	0	0·25	0·5	0·75	1·0	1·25	1·5	2·0	2·5
Acceleration in ft./sec.^{2}	0	0·17	0·26	0·31	0·33	0·33	0·3	0·2	0·14

Time in minutes	3·0	3·5	4·0	4·5	5·0
Acceleration in ft./sec.^{2}	0·09	0·07	0·05	0·04	0·035

(Q.E.)

21. Show that if V be the speed and S the distance travelled from some fixed point in the path of a moving body, the slope of the graph of $\frac{V^2}{2}$ plotted to a base of S gives the acceleration of the moving body along its path.

Observations of speed and distance from the starting-point of a car are as follows :—

V	0	12·6	16·7	19	21·4	23·2	23·6	ft./sec.
S	0	36	65	100	160	250	300	ft.

Find the initial acceleration, and the horse-power being exerted at 160 feet from the start if the car weighs 1 ton and resistance to motion is 100 lb. wt.   (Q.E.)

22. Find the measure of a force when expressed (i) by the time rate of change of momentum, and (ii) by the space rate of change of kinetic energy respectively. A shot weighs 10 lb., and its velocity changes

from 1500 ft./sec. to 500 ft./sec. in passing through a non-homogeneous target 6 inches thick in $\frac{1}{2500}$ seconds. What are the two values for the average force exerted, and how can they be reconciled ?
(Q.E.)

23. A train of mass 500 tons commences to climb a gradient at a speed of 25 m.p.h. The engine exerts a constant pull of 10,000 lb. wt., and the total resistance R due to all causes, including gravity, rises with time in accordance with the following table :—

R	2,500	3,500	5,000	7,000	9,500	12,000	16,000	lb. wt.
t	0	0·5	1·0	1·5	2·0	2·5	3·0	min.

Determine the speed of the train at the end of three minutes. (Q.E.)

24. The speed of a train of mass 100 tons varies with time in accordance with the following table :—

Time in seconds	0	10	20	30	40	50	60
Speed in m.p.h.	0	17	27	33	37	39	39·5

The train is running down an incline of 1 in 448. Find the horse-power being exerted by the engine at the end of the first half-minute if the frictional and air resistance to motion at that instant amounts to 10 lb. wt. per ton. (Q.E.)

25. A car weighing 6 tons starts from rest under the action of a force given by the following table :—

t in seconds	0	2	4	6	8	10	12	14	16	18	20
F in lb. wt.	780	750	708	620	495	420	365	324	300	280	270

If the resistances to motion are equivalent to a constant force of 40 lb. wt. per ton, draw the acceleration-time curve, and find the velocity of the car at the end of the time. (Q.E.)

26. A truck starting from rest and weighing 15 tons is drawn along the level against a constant resistance of 30 lb. wt. per ton. The draw-bar pull is found to vary with the distance travelled according to the following table :—

Distance travelled in feet	0	10	20	30	40	50
Draw-bar pull in lb. wt.	900	890	868	822	763	679

Find (i) the kinetic energy of the truck, (ii) the velocity of the truck, (iii) the work done by the force, when the truck has travelled the first 50 feet. (Q.E.)

27. A mass of 1 ton is drawn from rest up an incline of 1 in 224 by a force parallel to the ground and varying with the distance according to the following table :—

Distance in feet	0	50	100	150	200	250	300	350	400
Force in lb. wt.	115	145	150	130	100	65	35	25	10

If the frictional resistance to the motion is 25 lb. wt. per ton, find the velocity of the body after passing over 400 feet. (Q.E.)

28. A car whose mass is 2000 lb. starts from rest, and the resistance to the motion is equal to 50 lb. wt. When it has travelled a distance s feet the force exerted by the engine is F lb. wt. where

s	0	10	20	30	40	50	60
F	644	634	622	607	587	565	537

Construct the acceleration-space graph of this (continuous) motion, and find the speed of the car when it has travelled 60 feet.
(N.U.3)

29. A particle of mass 8 lb. starts from rest and is acted on by a force which increases uniformly in 5 seconds from zero to 1 lb. wt. Prove that t seconds after the body starts, its acceleration is $0.8t$ ft./sec.^{2}. Find the distance the particle moves during the first five seconds, and show that, when it has moved x feet, its speed is v ft./sec., where

$$5v^3 = 18x^2. \qquad \text{(N.U.3)}$$

30. Assuming that the acceleration of a motor car is $a - bv^2$ when the speed is v, where a and b are positive constants, prove that the speed tends to a certain maximum value V; and that, when the car is at a distance x from its starting-point, its speed is $V\sqrt{1 - e^{-2bx}}$. If a speed p is attained in a distance l after starting, and a speed q after a further distance l, prove that the maximum speed is

$$\frac{p^2}{\sqrt{2p^2 - q^2}}. \qquad \text{(N.U.4)}$$

§ 106. Units and Dimensions.

The units of mass, length, and time are called *fundamental units*, since the units of other quantities, such as speed, force, etc., can be expressed in terms of them. The unit of speed is a speed of unit distance in unit time, e.g. 1 ft./sec. or 1 cm./sec.; the unit of acceleration is an increase of unit speed in unit time, 1 ft./sec.^{2} or 1 cm./sec.^{2}

The unit of force is the product of unit mass and unit acceleration. If we denote the units of length, mass and time by L, M, T, the

unit of speed will be $\dfrac{L}{T}$,

the unit of acceleration $= \dfrac{\text{unit of velocity}}{\text{unit of time}} = \dfrac{L}{T^2}$,

the unit of force $= \dfrac{ML}{T^2}$.

the unit of work $=$ unit of force $\times$ unit of distance

$$= \frac{ML^2}{T^2}.$$

§ 107. Now the unit of area is the product of two unit lengths or L^2, and is said to be of two dimensions in length. A volume is said to be of three dimensions in length.

This idea of dimensions is extended to include mass and time, and the powers to which the fundamental units are raised to produce the unit of any quantity are called the *dimensions* of that quantity. Thus the dimensions of speed are said to be 1 in length and -1 in time, those of work are 1 in mass, 2 in length, and -2 in time.

§ 108. The dimensions of any physical quantity are easily obtained by writing down the formula for its unit in terms of M, L and T as above, by considering the way in which the quantity is defined.

Momentum is defined as the product of mass and velocity and its dimension formula is therefore

$$\frac{ML}{T}.$$

Angular velocity is obtained by dividing an angle in radians (which is merely a ratio of lengths and independent of units) by time, and its dimension formula is

$$\frac{1}{T}.$$

Power is obtained by dividing work by time, and its dimension formula is therefore

$$\frac{ML^2}{T^3}.$$

There are two important uses of dimensions which will now be considered.

§ **109.** In any equation between physical quantities each term must be of the same dimensions in the fundamental units. Just as it is impossible in ordinary arithmetic to add, say, pence and feet, so it is impossible to add any two terms of different dimensions. This often gives a useful check as to whether a formula is a possible one.

Thus, take the equation of motion

$$v^2 = u^2 + 2fs,$$

the dimensions of v^2 are $\dfrac{L^2}{T^2}$,

,,   ,, u^2 ,, $\dfrac{L^2}{T^2}$,

,,   ,, $2fs$,, $\dfrac{L}{T^2} \cdot L = \dfrac{L^2}{T^2}$

so that all the terms are of the same dimensions, namely $\dfrac{L^2}{T^2}$.

In § 80 we obtained a formula for the tension in a string over a pulley connecting two masses,

$$T = \frac{2m_1 m_2}{m_1 + m_2} g.$$

The dimensions of the right-hand side are that of a mass multiplied by an acceleration or $\dfrac{ML}{T^2}$, and are therefore those of a force, as they should be.

If the formula had only one mass in the numerator it could not represent a force, as its dimensions would be $\frac{L}{T^2}$ those of an acceleration.

In § 83 Example (iii) we obtained an expression for the acceleration of a wedge

$$\frac{mg \sin^2 \alpha \cos \alpha}{M + 3m \sin^2 \alpha}.$$

Now the dimensions of a trigonometrical ratio are zero, and as each term in the numerator and denominator contains a mass, the dimension in mass is zero. Hence the dimensions of the whole expression are those of g, an acceleration, and this is correct.

If the mass were missing from any one of the terms, the expression could not represent an acceleration.

A result, such as $\frac{V^2}{g}$, where V is a velocity, is of dimensions

$$\frac{L^2}{T^2} \cdot \frac{T^2}{L} = L,$$

and therefore represents a length.

$\frac{V}{g}$ is of dimensions $\frac{L}{T} \cdot \frac{T^2}{L} = T,$

and therefore represents a time.

§ 110. Dimensional formulæ can also be used to find the change in a unit due to changes in the fundamental units.

Let M, L, T be the units of mass, length, and time in one system, M', L', T' those in a second system.

Then if the units of, say, force in these two systems are F and F',

$$F : F' = \frac{ML}{T^2} : \frac{M'L'}{T'^2},$$

$$\text{or } \frac{F}{F'} = \frac{MLT'^2}{M'L'T^2}.$$

Thus, if M, L, T are F.P.S. units, and M', L', T' are C.G.S. units, taking 1 lb. = 453 gm. and 1 foot = 30·5 cm., we have

$$\frac{1 \text{ poundal}}{1 \text{ dyne}} = 453 \times 30 \cdot 5 = 13816 \cdot 5,$$

$$\therefore 1 \text{ poundal} = 13816 \cdot 5 \text{ dynes.}$$

If either of the quantities is given in gravitational units it must be expressed in absolute units before applying this method. 1 lb. wt. is the unit obtained by taking 32 lb. as the unit of mass, and in the above example the ratio M to M' would become 32×453.

EXAMPLE.

Taking 1 *lb.* = 453 *gm.*, 1 *foot* = 30·5 *cm.*, *and* g = 32 *ft./sec.*², *find the number of ergs in a foot-pound.*

The dimensions of work are,

$$\frac{ML^2}{T^2},$$

where M is 32 lb., L is 1 foot, and T is 1 second,

$$\therefore \frac{1 \text{ ft. lb.}}{1 \text{ erg}} = \frac{ML^2T'^2}{M'L'^2T^2},$$

where M', L', T' are 1 gm., 1 cm., and 1 second,

$$\therefore \frac{1 \text{ ft. lb.}}{1 \text{ erg}} = 32 \times 453 \times (30\cdot5)^2,$$

$$= 1\cdot348 \times 10^7,$$

$$\therefore 1 \text{ ft. lb.} = 1\cdot348 \times 10^7 \text{ ergs.}$$

EXAMPLES XVII.

1. If the units of mass, length, and time be 100 lb., 100 feet, and 100 seconds respectively, find the units of force and work.

2. Given that 1 lb. = 453 gm., 1 foot = 30·5 cm., and g = 32 ft./sec.², find the number of watts in a horse-power.

3. If the unit of mass be 1 cwt., the unit of length 42 inches, and the unit of time 7 seconds, find the unit of force.

4. If 1 cwt. be the unit of mass, a minute the unit of time, and the unit of force the weight of 1 lb., find the unit of length.

5. If the units of length, velocity, and force be each doubled, show that the units of time and mass will be unaltered, and that of energy will be increased in the ratio 1 : 4.

6. (i) Given that 1 cm. = ·3937 inches, and 1 kilo. = 2·205 lb., find the number of dynes in a poundal.
   (ii) If a second be the unit of time, the acceleration due to gravity (981 in C.G.S. units) the unit of acceleration, and a kilogram the unit of mass, find the unit of energy in ergs.   (I.S.)

7. If m is the mass of a body in lb., V its velocity in ft./sec., in what units is its kinetic energy expressed when we say that this energy is measured by $\frac{1}{2}mV^2$?   If the units of length and mass be each multiplied by 10 and the unit of time divided by 10, how will the following units be affected, (*a*) acceleration, (*b*) energy, (*c*) force, (*d*) power ?   (I.S.),

8. The kilowatt is a power which can produce 10^{10} C.G.S. units of energy per second ; prove that it is rather more than $1\frac{1}{3}$ H.P. [1 ft. = 30·48 cm., 1 lb. = 453·6 gm., and the acceleration of gravity is 981 C.G.S. units.]   (I.A.)

9. Given that 1 kilo. = 2·204 lb., 1 metre = 3·281 feet, 1 H.P. = 33,000 ft. lb. per minute, g = 981 cm./sec.², show that 3 H.P. is approximately 2·24 × 10^{10} ergs per second.   (H.S.D.)

10. Taking 1 year of 365¼ days to be the unit of time, the Earth's distance from the Sun (92,900,000 miles) to be the unit of length, and

the mass of the Earth to be the unit of mass, find the kinetic energy of the Sun relative to the fixed stars, its velocity relative to them being 11 miles per second, and its mass 332,000 times that of the Earth.

(I.C.)

11. State the dimensions of *force, power, angular velocity, pressure at a point in a fluid.*

If the force of attraction between two masses m and m_1, distant r apart, is $k\dfrac{mm_1}{r^2}$, find the dimensions of k, and its numerical value when C.G.S. units are employed. [$g = 981$ cm./sec.^{2}, radius of earth $= 6.37 \times 10^3$ kilometres, mass of earth $= 6.14 \times 10^{24}$ kilograms.]

(H.S.C.)

12. A body has mass M and volume V when the units are the foot, pound, and second. State its weight, density, and specific gravity.

State also what these become when the units are changed to the centimetre, gram, and second.

[Take 1 foot $= 30.5$ cm., 1 lb. $= 454$ gm., mass of 1 cu. foot of water $= 62.3$ lb.]

(Ex.)

CHAPTER III.

IMPULSIVE FORCES. IMPACT OF ELASTIC BODIES.

§ 111. Impulse.

The term *impulse of a force* is defined as follows :—

When the force P is constant, the impulse is the product of the force and the time during which it acts, i.e. Pt.

When the force P is variable it is the integral of the force with respect to the time, i.e.

$$\int_0^t Pdt,$$

where t is the time during which the force acts.

When P is variable, $\qquad P = m\dfrac{dv}{dt}.$

The impulse is

$$\int_0^t Pdt = \int_0^t m\frac{dv}{dt}dt = \left[m\frac{dx}{dt} \right]_0^t$$
$$= m(v - u).$$

When P is constant $Pt = m(v - u)$.

Hence in both cases,

Impulse of force = change of momentum produced.

§ 112. Impulsive Forces.

Suppose the force P is very large, but acts only for a very short time. The body will only move a very short distance whilst the force is acting, so that the change of position of the body may be neglected. The total effect of the force is measured by its impulse, or the change of momentum it produces.

Such a force is called an impulsive force.

Theoretically the force should be infinitely great and the time during which it acts infinitely small. This is, of course, never realised in practice, but approximate examples are the blow of a hammer, the impact of a bullet on a target, the collision of two billiard balls.

§ 113. Impact of Two Bodies.

If two bodies A and B impinge, then, from Newton's third law, the action of A on B is, at any rate during their contact, equal and opposite to that of B on A.

Hence the impulse of A on B is equal and opposite to that of B on A. It follows that the changes in momentum of A and B are equal and opposite, and the sum of the momenta of the two bodies, measured in the same direction, is unaltered by their impact.

This is an example of the *Principle of Conservation of Linear Momentum* (para. **76**) which is used in dealing with problems in which impacts or impulsive forces occur.

If a mass m, moving with velocity v, strike a mass M, which is free to move in the direction of m's motion, and the two move on as a single body, there is no loss of momentum.

Now the momentum of the mass m before impact is mv, and this is shared between the two masses. Hence, if V is the velocity of the two together after the impact,

$$(M + m)V = mv,$$

$$\therefore V = \frac{m}{M + m} v.$$

It should be noted that, although there is no change in momentum due to the impact, there *is* a loss of kinetic energy.

The kinetic energy before impact is $\frac{1}{2}mv^2$.

The kinetic energy after impact is

$$\tfrac{1}{2}(M + m)V^2 = \tfrac{1}{2} \frac{m^2}{M + m} v^2,$$

and this is obviously less than $\frac{1}{2}mv^2$ since $\dfrac{m}{M + m}$ is less than unity.

Since kinetic energy is lost in nearly all cases of impact the principle of energy must never be used in dealing with cases where impulsive forces occur.

§ **114.** It is also most important to realise that the principle of momentum can only be applied in a direction in which there is no *external* impulsive force acting.

Thus, if a bullet strikes a fixed target perpendicularly all the momentum of the bullet is, of course, destroyed. If the bullet hits a *smooth* target obliquely, there is no change in momentum parallel to the surface of the target, but all momentum perpendicular to the target is destroyed.

If a bullet moving horizontally hits perpendicularly the face of a block whose section is CDEF (Fig. 60), resting on a smooth

9 *

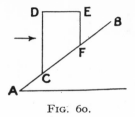

FIG. 60.

inclined plane AB, and becomes embedded in it ; then the only
direction in which we can apply the principle of momentum is
parallel to the face of the inclined plane AB. The component of
the bullet's momentum parallel to AB is shared between the bullet
and the block. The component of momentum perpendicular to AB
is destroyed by the impulsive reaction of the plane.

§ 115. Motion of a Shot and Gun.

When a gun is fired the explosive charge forms a large volume
of gas at very high pressure. This pressure acts equally on the
shot and gun in the direction of the barrel and drives the shot out.

If the gun is free to move in the direction of the barrel the
forward momentum generated in the shot at the instant it leaves
the barrel is equal to the backward momentum generated in the gun.

If the gun is placed on a smooth horizontal plane with the
barrel horizontal we can say that the momenta of the shot and gun
are equal and opposite (both will be horizontal). If, however (as
is usually the case), the barrel of the gun is elevated, the momentum
of the gun is *not* equal and opposite to that of the shot.

The horizontal momentum of the gun is equal to the horizontal
momentum of the shot, but any vertical momentum imparted to
the gun is at once destroyed by the impulsive pressure of the plane
on which it stands.

Any apparatus (such as a spring) for preventing the horizontal
recoil of the gun does not introduce an impulsive force at the instant
of firing, and does not prevent the principle of momentum being
applied. In such a case we calculate the momentum and velocity
of recoil as if the spring were absent.

The spring does not exert any force until it is compressed so
that, neglecting the time taken for the shot to leave the gun, we
consider the gun to start moving back with the velocity it would
have if the spring were absent. The spring then gradually reduces
the gun to rest.

In the same way the action of gravity is neglected in cases of
impact, this again is not an *impulsive* force, and the impact is over
before it has time to act.

§ 116. Impact of Water on a Surface.

To find the pressure due to a jet of water impinging against a fixed surface, or a continuous fall of rain on the ground, we have only to calculate the amount of momentum destroyed per second. Here we are dealing with a succession of impacts or impulsive forces. The amount of momentum destroyed per second gives us the average force on the surface, this force acting for one second would produce or destroy the given amount of momentum.

§ 117. EXAMPLE (i).

A bullet weighing 1 oz. is fired with a velocity of 500 ft./sec. into a block of wood weighing 4 lb., and lying on a smooth table. Find the velocity with which the block and bullet move after the bullet has become embedded in the block. (I.S.)

The momentum of the bullet before impact is $\frac{500}{16}$ lb. ft. units ; no momentum is lost by the impact as there is no external horizontal force acting, and as the total mass in motion is now $4\frac{1}{16}$ lb., if V is the common velocity of the two,

$$4\tfrac{1}{16}V = \frac{500}{16},$$

$$\therefore V = \frac{500}{16} \times \frac{16}{65} = 7\tfrac{9}{13} \text{ ft./sec.}$$

EXAMPLE (ii).

A shot, of mass 200 lb., is fired with a velocity of 1600 ft./sec. from a gun of mass 50 tons, which is free to recoil in the direction of the barrel ; find the resulting velocity of the gun.

The forward momentum of the shot $= 200 \times 1600$ lb. ft. units. The backward momentum of the gun is equal to the forward momentum of the shot.

Hence, if V ft./sec. is the velocity of the gun,

$$50 \times 2240\, V = 200 \times 1600,$$

$$\therefore V = \frac{200 \times 1600}{50 \times 2240} = 2\tfrac{6}{7} \text{ ft./ sec.}$$

EXAMPLE (iii).

If, in the last example, the gun is resting on an incline of 3 in 5, and the shot is fired horizontally, find the velocity of recoil of the gun.

In this case some of the horizontal momentum imparted to the gun is destroyed by the inclined plane on which it rests, and we can only say that the momentum of the gun parallel to the plane is equal to that of the shot parallel to the plane.

Now the momentum of the shot parallel to the plane is

$$200 \times 1600 \times \text{ the cosine of the slope} = 200 \times 1600 \times \tfrac{4}{5}.$$

Hence, if V is the velocity of recoil of the gun,

$$50 \times 2240 \; V = 40 \times 1600 \times 4,$$

$$\therefore V = \frac{40 \times 1600 \times 4}{50 \times 2240} = 2\tfrac{2}{7} \text{ ft./sec.}$$

EXAMPLE (iv).

A gun, of weight W, is mounted on a smooth railway, and is fired in the direction of the track. It fires a shell, of weight w, with velocity V relative to the ground. If the angle of elevation of the gun is α, prove that the initial direction of the motion of the shell is inclined to the ground at an angle.

$$\cot^{-1}\left(\frac{W \cot \alpha}{W + w}\right).$$ (H.S.C.)

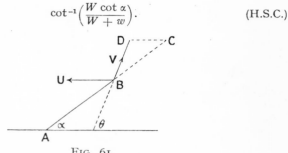

FIG. 61.

Let AB (Fig. 61) represent the barrel of the gun.

As the shot leaves the barrel the gun is moving backwards, and this imparts a backward horizontal component of velocity to the shot. The direction of the initial motion of the shot is therefore inclined to the horizontal at an angle greater than α. Let this angle be θ, and let the velocity of the gun be U.

The *horizontal* momentum of the gun is equal to the *horizontal* momentum of the shot,

$$\therefore WU = wV \cos \theta \quad . \qquad . \qquad . \qquad . \quad \text{(i)}$$

Also V is the resultant of a velocity in the direction of the barrel AB, and the horizontal velocity of the gun U.

If BD represents V, then if DC is drawn horizontal to meet AB produced in C, CD will represent U by the triangle of velocities.

Angle DCB $= \alpha$, angle DBC $= \theta - \alpha$,

and

$$\frac{CD}{\sin (\theta - \alpha)} = \frac{BD}{\sin \alpha},$$

$$\therefore \frac{\sin (\theta - \alpha)}{U} = \frac{\sin \alpha}{V} \quad . \qquad . \qquad . \qquad . \quad \text{(ii)}$$

Multiplying this equation by (i)

$$W \sin (\theta - \alpha) = w \sin \alpha \cos \theta,$$

$$\therefore W(\sin \theta \cos \alpha - \cos \theta \sin \alpha) = w \sin \alpha \cos \theta,$$

$$\therefore W(\tan \theta \cos \alpha - \sin \alpha) = w \sin \alpha,$$

$$\therefore \tan \theta \cos \alpha = \sin \alpha + \frac{w}{W} \sin \alpha,$$

$$= \frac{W + w}{W} \sin \alpha,$$

$$\therefore \tan \theta = \frac{W + w}{W} \tan \alpha,$$

$$\therefore \cot \theta = \frac{W \cot \alpha}{W + w}$$

EXAMPLE (v).

Water (of which 1 cubic foot weighs $62\frac{1}{2}$ lb.) issues from a circular pipe of 3 inches diameter with a velocity of 15 ft./sec. ; find the weight of water discharged per minute. If the water impinges directly upon a plane, and its momentum is thereby wholly destroyed, what is the pressure of the jet upon the plane ? (I.A.)

The area of the cross-section of the pipe is $\frac{\pi}{4} \times \frac{1}{16}$ square feet, and a column 15 feet long is discharged every second.

The volume per minute

$$= \frac{\pi}{64} \times 15 \times 60 \text{ cu. feet,}$$

and its mass

$$= \frac{\pi \times 15 \times 60 \times 125}{64 \times 2} \text{ lb.,}$$

$$= 2762 \text{ lb. nearly.}$$

The mass discharged per second

$$= \frac{\pi \times 15 \times 125}{128} \text{ lb.,}$$

and its velocity is 15 ft./sec.

$$\therefore \text{ the momentum destroyed per second}$$

$$= \frac{\pi \times 15 \times 15 \times 125}{128} \text{ lb. ft. units.}$$

The pressure

$$= \frac{\pi \times 225 \times 125}{128} \text{ poundals} = 21 \cdot 58 \text{ lb. wt.}$$

EXAMPLE (vi).

A pile driver of mass 3 tons falls through a height of 16 feet on to a pile of mass 1 ton ; if the pile is driven 6 inches into the ground, find the resistance of the ground (supposed uniform) in tons weight.

The velocity of the pile driver after falling 16 feet is

$$\sqrt{2 \times 32 \times 16} = 32 \text{ ft./sec.,}$$

and its momentum is $3 \times 2240 \times 32$ lb. ft. units.

After the impact the total mass in motion is 4 tons, and if V is the common velocity of the driver and pile

$$4 \times 2240 \ V = 3 \times 2240 \times 32,$$
$$\therefore V = 24 \text{ ft./sec.}$$

Now this velocity is destroyed in $\frac{1}{2}$ foot, and if f is the retardation,

$$0 = 24^2 - 2f \cdot \tfrac{1}{2},$$
$$\therefore f = 24^2 \text{ ft./sec.}^2,$$

and the retarding force is $4 \times 2240 \times 24^2$ poundals,

$$= 4 \times 70 \times 24^2 \text{ lb. wt.}$$

The resistance of the ground R must equal the retarding force $+$ the weight of the driver and pile,

$$\therefore R = (4 \times 70 \times 24^2 + 4 \times 2240) \text{ lb. wt.},$$
$$= \left(\frac{4 \times 70 \times 24^2}{2240} + 4 \right) \text{ tons wt.},$$
$$= 76 \text{ tons wt.}$$

EXAMPLES XVIII.

1. A bullet of mass $\frac{1}{2}$ oz. is fired with a velocity of 2568 ft./sec. into a block of wood weighing 10 lb. and resting on a smooth horizontal table. Find the common velocity of the bullet and block after the bullet has become embedded in the block.

2. A bullet of mass 20 gm. is fired with a velocity of 4020 cm./sec. into a block of wood weighing 4 kilograms and resting on a smooth horizontal table. Find the common velocity of the bullet and block after the bullet has become embedded in the block.

3. A gun of mass 10 tons free to recoil in the direction of the barrel, fires a shot of mass 200 lb. with a velocity of 1400 ft./sec. Find the velocity of recoil of the gun.

    If the recoil is resisted by a constant force so that the gun only moves back 5 inches, find the magnitude of this force in tons weight.

4. A gun of mass 20 tons, resting on an inclined plane of slope 30°, fires a shot of mass 400 lb. horizontally with a velocity of 2100 ft./sec. Find the velocity of recoil of the gun, and the distance it moves up the incline before coming to rest.

5. Find the average pressure per square foot on the ground due to a rainfall of $\frac{1}{2}$ inch in 2 hours. The velocity of the rain on striking the ground is equal to that acquired in falling freely through 900 feet, and 1 cu. foot of rainwater weighs $62\frac{1}{2}$ lb.

6. A pile driver of mass 5 tons falls from a height of 9 feet on to a pile weighing 1 ton ; if the pile is driven in 3 inches, find the average resistance of the ground in tons weight.

7. An inelastic vertical pile weighing $\frac{1}{2}$ ton is driven 2 feet into the ground by 30 blows of a hammer, weighing 2 tons, falling through 5 feet. Show that the resistance of the ground, supposed uniform, is $122\frac{1}{2}$ tons. (I.S.)

8. A hammer weighing 2 lb., moving with a velocity of 20 ft./sec., drives a nail weighing 1 oz. 1 inch into a fixed piece of wood. Find the common velocity of the nail and hammer just after impact, the percentage loss of energy, the time of motion of the nail, and the force of resistance of the wood assuming it to be constant. (I.E.)

9. A pile driver falls through h feet on to a pile of weight W tons ; if the resistance to penetration be R tons, and the desired penetration

h inches, find the proper weight of the driver. How much energy is
lost each fall if $h = 6$, $W = 2$, $R = 30$?
(I.E.)

10. If a gun of mass M fires horizontally a shot of mass m, find the ratio
of the energy of recoil of the gun to the energy of the shot. If a
½-ton gun discharges a 50-lb. shot with a velocity of 1000 ft./sec.,
find the uniform resistance necessary to stop the recoil of the gun
in 6 inches.
(I.S.)

11. A shot of mass m is fired from a gun of mass M, placed on a smooth
horizontal plane and inclined at an angle α to the horizontal. If
v is the velocity of the gun's recoil at the instant when the shot
leaves it, prove that the horizontal component of the impulsive
pressure on the shot is Mv, and that the component at right angles
to the gun's length is $mv \sin \alpha$. (It is assumed in each case that the
impulsive pressure is resolved into two components at right angles.)
    Prove that the initial direction of the shot's motion is inclined
at $\tan^{-1}\left[\left(1 + \dfrac{m}{M}\right) \tan \alpha \right]$ to the horizontal.   (H.C.)

12. A shot weighing 18 lb. is fired horizontally from a gun weighing
9 cwt. If the muzzle velocity of the shot is 1680 ft./sec., calculate
that of the gun.
    Calculate the total kinetic energy produced (in the shot and gun)
in foot-tons ; and if the distance travelled along the bore of the gun
is 7 feet, prove that the average force applied to the shot is a little
over 51 tons. How far will the gun have moved when the shot
leaves the muzzle ?
(H.C.)

13. A shot of mass m is fired from a gun of mass M which is suspended
by ropes of length l. If the total kinetic energy is the same as it
would be if the shot left the muzzle of a fixed gun with velocity v,
find the actual velocities of the shot and gun at the moment of
separation, and find to what height the gun will rise at the recoil.
(H.E.)

14. In making a steel stamping a weight of 200 lb. falls on to the steel
through a distance of 4 feet, and is brought to rest after traversing
a further distance of ½ inch.
    Assuming that a uniform resistance is exerted by the steel, find
the magnitude of this resistance in lb. wt.   (H.S.C.)

15. A bullet of mass m lb. is fired horizontally with a velocity of v ft./sec.
into a block of wood of mass M lb. suspended by a light cord. It is
noted that the wood and embedded bullet swing until a height of
h feet above the original position is reached. Show that $mv =
(M + m) \sqrt{2gh}$; it being given that the whole motion takes place
in one vertical plane. If an aeroplane rises vertically at 20 ft./sec.
and drops an object weighing 18 lb. from a height of 600 feet,
calculate the magnitude of the impulse with which the object strikes
the ground, stating clearly the unit of impulse employed. (H.S.D.)

16. A bullet of mass m, moving with velocity v, strikes a block of mass
M, which is free to move in the direction of the motion of the bullet,
and is embedded in it. Show that the loss of kinetic energy is

$$\frac{Mmv^2}{2(M + m)}.$$

If the block is afterwards struck by an equal bullet moving in the same direction with the same velocity, show that there is a further loss of energy equal to

$$\frac{M^2mv^2}{2(M + 2m)(M + m)}.$$ (I.S.)

17. A block of wood weighing 1 lb. is placed on a rough horizontal floor, the coefficient of friction between the block and floor being 0·4. A bullet of mass 1 oz. is fired with a velocity of 510 ft./sec. into the block. Find (a) the velocity with which the block and bullet begin to move together after the impact ; (b) the distance which the block moves along the floor ; (c) the ratio of the energy lost during the impact to that lost through friction with the floor.   (I.S.)

18. From a gun of mass M lb., which can recoil freely on a horizontal platform, is fired a shell of mass m lb., the elevation of the gun being α. Show that the angle (ϕ) which the path of the shell initially makes with the horizontal is given by the equation

$$\tan \phi = \left(1 + \frac{m}{M}\right)\tan \alpha ;$$

and further, assuming that the whole energy of the explosion is transferred to the shell and the gun, show that the muzzle energy of the shell is less than it would be if the gun were fixed in the ratio $M : (M + m\cos^2\phi)$.   (Q.E.)

19. A jet of water issues vertically at a speed of 30 ft./sec. from a nozzle 0·1 sq. inch section. A ball weighing 1 lb. is balanced in the air by the impact of the water on its underside. Show that the height of the ball above the level of the jet is 4·6 feet approximately. (Q.E.)

20. The penetration of a half-ounce bullet, fired at 1000 ft./sec., into a fixed block of wood is 3 inches.
   If the bullet is fired at the same speed into a block of the same wood 2 inches thick (weighing 3 lb.) which is free to move, prove that the block will be perforated ; and find the velocity with which the bullet emerges.   (Q.E.)

21. A fire engine is directing a horizontal jet through a nozzle 1 inch in diameter fixed to the engine. It is delivering 60 cu. feet of water per minute. What is the reaction in lb. wt. on the fire engine ?   (Q.E.)

22. A racing motor offers 16 sq. feet of area to wind pressure. If the density of air is 0·078 lb. per cu. foot., calculate the horse-power absorbed in overcoming wind resistance when the car is travelling at 70 m.p.h. against a head wind of 10 m.p.h.   (Q.E.)

23. A machine gun is fired backwards from the rear of an armoured car at the rate of 600 rounds per minute. The mass of each bullet is ½ oz. and the muzzle velocity 2200 ft./sec. Find the driving power added to that of the car when the car is travelling at 40 m.p.h.   (Q.E.)

24. A railway truck of mass 10 tons moving with a velocity of 6 m.p.h. strikes, and is at the same moment coupled to, another truck of mass 5 tons previously at rest. The second truck has its wheels locked by brakes, the coefficient of friction between the wheels and the rails being 0·2. Find how far the trucks move after the impact.   (Q.E.)

25. A pile weighing 1 ton is being driven into the ground by blows from a weight of 10 cwt. which falls freely a distance of 8 feet on to the pile without rebounding. The pile is driven in 6 inches by one blow.

If the resistance of the ground is uniform, what is the amount of this resistance, and what is the time of penetration ? (Q.E.)

26. A shell of mass m is fired from a gun of mass M which can recoil freely on a horizontal base, and the elevation of the gun is α. Prove that the initial inclination of the path of the shell to the horizon is

$$\tan^{-1}\left[\left(1 + \frac{m}{M}\right)\tan\alpha\right].$$

Prove also that the energy of the shell on leaving the gun is to that of the gun as

$$[M^2 + (M + m)^2\tan^2\alpha] : Mm,$$

assuming that none of the energy of the explosion is lost. (I.S.)

27. A shell, lying in a straight smooth horizontal tube, suddenly explodes and breaks into two portions of masses m and m'. If s is the distance apart, in the tube, of the masses after a time t, show that the work done by the explosion is

$$\frac{1}{2}\frac{mm'}{m + m'}\cdot\frac{s^2}{t^2}. \qquad \text{(H.S.D.)}$$

28. Prove that if a horizontal jet of water could be made to issue through a nozzle of 1 sq. inch orifice at the rate of 170 cu. feet per minute, it would exert a force about equal to the weight of a ton against an obstacle placed in its path ; and find the horse-power required to produce the jet. (A cubic foot of water weighs 62·3 lb.) (H.S.C.)

29. A target of mass M is moving in a straight line with uniform velocity V. Shots of mass m are fired with velocity v in the opposite direction so as to strike the target, becoming embedded in it. Find how many shots must be fired in order to make the target begin to move back. Find also the kinetic energy lost when the first shot strikes the target. (I.S.)

30. A train of trucks is being started from rest, and just before the last coupling becomes taut the front part has acquired a velocity of 15 m.p.h. If the part of the train now in motion weighs 72 tons and the last truck weighs 6 tons, find the jerk in the coupling in ft.-lb.-sec. units. (I.S.)

31. A gun weighing 64 tons fires a shell weighing 800 lb. with a horizontal muzzle velocity of 2100 ft./sec. What is the kinetic energy in ft. lb. of the gun as the shot leaves the muzzle ? What uniform retarding force in lb. wt. is required to check the recoil of the gun in 6 feet? (H.S.D.)

32. A jet of water of cross-section 3 sq. inches and velocity 40 ft./sec., impinges normally on a plane inelastic wall, so that the velocity of the water is destroyed on reaching the wall. Calculate in lb. wt. the thrust on the wall. (I.S.)

33. A bullet weighing 0·025 lb., when fired from a gun weighing 20 lb., has a muzzle velocity of 2400 ft./sec. What is the velocity of recoil of the gun and what is the total energy of the gun and bullet ? If the same bullet were fired from a gun weighing 10 lb., and if the total energy were the same as in the previous case, show that the muzzle velocity of the bullet would be about 1·5 ft./sec. less than before. (I.E.)

34. A bullet of mass m is fired with velocity v at a body of mass M, which is retiring from it with velocity V ; the bullet perforates the body

and emerges with velocity u. Show that the subsequent velocity of the body is

$$V + \frac{m(v - u)}{M}.$$

Find also the energy liberated and the resistance of the body to penetration; assuming this to be uniform and the thickness of the body ·to be a.   (H.S.D.)

35. A gun of mass M fires a shell of mass m horizontally, and the energy of the explosion is such as would be sufficient to project the shell vertically to a height h. Show that the velocity of recoil of the gun is

$$\left[\frac{2m^2gh}{M(M + m)} \right]^{\frac{1}{2}} \qquad \text{(C.S.)}$$

36. A block of mass M rests on a smooth horizontal table and a bullet of mass m is fired horizontally into it. The penetration of the bullet is opposed by a constant resisting force. If the experiment is repeated with the block firmly fixed, show that the depth of penetration of the bullet and the time which elapses before the bullet is at rest relatively to the block are in each case increased in the ratio $1 + \dfrac{m}{M}$.

37. A pile weighing 1 ton is driven into the bed of a river by means of a falling weight of 112 lb., which is allowed to fall through 8 ft. If the pile penetrates 4 inches at each blow, find the mean resistance to penetration of the bed of the river.

38. A shell of mass m is ejected from a gun of mass M by an explosion which generates kinetic energy E. Prove that the initial velocity of the shell is

$$\sqrt{\left(\frac{2ME}{(M + m)m} \right)}.$$

[You may assume that at the instant of explosion the gun is free to recoil.]   (N.U.3)

§ 118. Impulsive Tensions in Strings.

Suppose two particles, A and B (Fig. 61a), to be connected by an inextensible string and to lie on a smooth horizontal table.

Fig. 61a.

Then, if an impulse P is applied to one of them (say B), we cannot tell at once in what direction B will move (unless the direction of P is along or perpendicular to AB), as an impulsive tension is produced in the string and this also acts on B, which is therefore subject to *two* impulsive forces. We do know, however, that A must start to move in the direction of the string AB, and that its velocity is equal to the component of B's velocity in this direction.

We know also that the resultant momentum of A and B in the direction of the blow is equal to P, while the resultant at right angles to this direction is zero.

EXAMPLE.

Two balls A and B of masses 4 lb. and 2 lb. respectively, lie on a smooth horizontal plane and are connected by a taut inextensible string ; B is due E. of A.   B is struck in such a manner that, if it were free, it would move N.E. with a velocity of 21 ft./sec.   Prove that B actually moves with a velocity of about 15·65 ft./sec. in a direction about 71° 34′ N. of E.   Also compare the magnitude·of the impulsive tension in the string with that of the blow.

(I.E.)

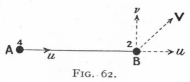

FIG. 62.

The magnitude of the blow is 42 units of impulse, and its direction N.E.   Let u, v be the components of B's velocity along and perpendicular to AB (Fig. 62).   The velocity of A is then u along AB.

The momentum in the direction AB is equal to the component of the blow in that direction, i.e. $\dfrac{42}{\sqrt{2}}$,

$$\therefore\ 4u + 2u = \frac{42}{\sqrt{2}},$$

the momentum perpendicular to AB is equal to the component of the blow perpendicular to AB, i.e.

$$\frac{42}{\sqrt{2}},$$

$$\therefore\ 2v = \frac{42}{\sqrt{2}},$$

$$\therefore\ u = \frac{7}{\sqrt{2}} \text{ ft./sec.}$$

$$v = \frac{21}{\sqrt{2}} \text{ ft./sec.}$$

It V is the resultant velocity of B,

$$V^2 = \frac{49}{2} + \frac{441}{2} = \frac{490}{2} = 245,$$

$$\therefore\ V = 15\cdot65 \text{ ft./sec.}$$

If θ is the angle the direction of V makes with the east,

$$\tan \theta = \frac{v}{u} = 3,$$

$$\therefore\ \theta = 71° 34′ \text{ nearly.}$$

The impulsive tension in the string generates a velocity u in A, i.e. a velocity of $\dfrac{7}{\sqrt{2}}$ ft./sec. in a mass of 4 lb. :

$$\therefore \text{ the tension is } \frac{28}{\sqrt{2}} \text{ units of impulse,}$$

$$\therefore \frac{\text{impulsive tension}}{\text{blow}} = \frac{28}{42\sqrt{2}} = \frac{\sqrt{2}}{3}.$$

§ 119. When two masses, connected by an inextensible string passing over a smooth pulley, are in motion, and the descending one is stopped, we know that the other goes on moving freely under gravity until the string again becomes taut. This was illustrated by examples in the last chapter. We have now to consider what happens *after* the string becomes taut again. The common velocity of the two masses after the jerk is less than that of the single mass which was moving before the string became taut, since the momentum of this mass has to be shared between the two.

We can also calculate the change in velocity produced when one of the masses picks up an extra mass previously at rest.

§ 120. EXAMPLE (i).

Two masses of m and $2m$ lb. are connected by a light inextensible string passing over a smooth pulley. Find the acceleration of the system. If the mass $2m$ hits the ground (without rebounding) after the masses have been moving for 3 seconds, find how much time elapses from the instant this happens until the system is instantaneously at rest with the string taut.

If f be the common acceleration, and T the tension in the string,

$$2mg - T = 2mf,$$
$$T - mg = mf,$$
$$\therefore 3mf = mg, \text{ or } f = \frac{g}{3}.$$

After 3 seconds the common velocity v is given by

$$v = \frac{g}{3} \cdot 3 = 32 \text{ ft./sec.}$$

The m lb. mass moves freely under gravity, starting with this velocity, and the time (t) taken to go up and return to its initial position is given by

$$0 = 32t - \tfrac{1}{2} \cdot 32t^2,$$
$$\therefore t = 2 \text{ seconds.}$$

When the string again becomes taut its velocity is again 32 ft./sec., and its momentum is $32m$.

Hence, if V is the common velocity after the jerk,

$$3mV = 32m,$$
$$\therefore V = \frac{32}{3} \text{ ft./sec.}$$

The system starts moving with this velocity, but, as the heavier mass is moving upwards, there will be a retardation of $\frac{g}{3}$, equal to the original acceleration.

Hence the time t' taken to come to rest is given by

$$0 = \frac{32}{3} - \frac{g}{3} t',$$

$$\therefore t' = 1 \text{ second.}$$

Hence the total interval between the impact of the $2m$ mass and the system coming to rest is

$$t + t' = 3 \text{ seconds.}$$

Note.—If the masses are left to themselves, the heavier one will descend and hit the plane again and the motion will be repeated indefinitely. The time taken for it to hit the plane the second time is, however, only $\frac{1}{3}$ of the original time, since it has only to acquire $\frac{1}{3}$ of the velocity it had in the first case. When the heavier mass is jerked up again the common velocity is again divided by 3, and so the time to rest will also be divided by 3. The interval from the instant when the heavier mass begins to descend until the system is again at rest in each repetition of the motion is $\frac{1}{3}$ of that in the preceding case. The total time until the heavier mass remains in contact with the ground is an infinite G.P. of common ratio $\frac{1}{3}$.

EXAMPLE (ii).

Two weights of 9 and 7 lb. are fastened to the ends of a light thread which passes over a smooth pulley, the two portions of the string being vertical. The system is released from rest, and after moving for 2 seconds, a weight of 5 lb. at rest is suddenly attached to the 7 lb. weight. Find when the system will come to rest again. How far will the original weights have moved altogether?

(I.S.)

Let f be the acceleration of the system, and T the tension in the string, then

$$9g - T = 9f,$$
$$T - 7g = 7f,$$
$$\therefore 16f = 2g,$$
$$\therefore f = \tfrac{1}{8}g.$$

After 2 seconds the velocity v is

$$v = \tfrac{1}{8}g \cdot 2 = 8 \text{ ft./sec.}$$

The momentum is

$$16 \times 8 = 128 \text{ lb. ft. units.}$$

If V is the common velocity after picking up the 5 lb. mass,

$$21V = 128,$$
$$\therefore V = \frac{128}{21} \text{ ft./sec.}$$

The masses are now 9 and 12 lb., and if F is the retardation,

$$12g - T' = 12F,$$
$$T' - 9g = 9F,$$
$$\therefore 21F = 3g,$$
$$\therefore F = \tfrac{1}{7}g.$$

The time, t, taken for the system to come to rest is given by

$$0 = \frac{128}{21} - \frac{g}{7}\,t,$$
$$\therefore t = \frac{128}{21} \times \frac{7}{32} = \frac{4}{3} \text{ seconds.}$$

During the first 2 seconds the original weights move s_1 feet where

$$s_1 = \frac{1}{2} \times \frac{1}{8}\, g \times 4 = 8 \text{ feet.}$$

During the last $\frac{4}{3}$ seconds, they move s_2 feet where,

$$s_2 = \frac{128}{21} \times \frac{4}{3} - \frac{1}{2} \times \frac{32}{7} \times \frac{16}{9} = 4\tfrac{4}{63} \text{ feet.}$$

Hence the total distance moved is $12\tfrac{4}{63}$ feet.

EXAMPLE (iii).

A body of weight W lb., moving due N. at u ft./sec., is suddenly caused to move N.W. at a speed of v ft./sec. What is the blow or impulse it has received? If the change in velocity had been gradual under a constant force and had taken a time T to effect the change, find the acceleration, and show that, if $v = \dfrac{u}{\sqrt{2}}$, and x and y be the displacements N and W at any time, $(y + x)^2 = 4uTy$. (I.E.)

In this problem it will be best to consider the *components* of the impulse in directions N. and W.

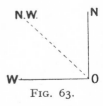

FIG. 63.

Let ON (Fig. 63) represent north and OW west.

The velocity v in direction north-west has components $\dfrac{v}{\sqrt{2}}$ north and $\dfrac{v}{\sqrt{2}}$ west.

The change in velocity in direction ON is $\dfrac{v}{\sqrt{2}} - u$, and in direction OW is $\dfrac{v}{\sqrt{2}}$.

Hence the components of impulse are,

$$\frac{W}{g}\left(\frac{v}{\sqrt{2}} - u\right) \text{ and } \frac{W}{g} \cdot \frac{v}{\sqrt{2}}.$$

The resultant impulse is

$$\frac{W}{g}\sqrt{\frac{v^2}{2} + u^2 - \frac{2uv}{\sqrt{2}} + \frac{v^2}{2}},$$

$$= \frac{W}{g}\sqrt{u^2 + v^2 - \frac{2uv}{\sqrt{2}}}.$$

If F_1, F_2 are the components of the constant force along ON and OW respectively,

$$F_1 T = \frac{W}{g}\left(\frac{v}{\sqrt{2}} - u\right), \text{ and } F_2 T = \frac{W}{g} \cdot \frac{v}{\sqrt{2}}.$$

The component accelerations are

$$\frac{F_1 g}{W}, \text{ and } \frac{F_2 g}{W}.$$

or

$$\frac{1}{T}\left(\frac{v}{\sqrt{2}} - u\right) \text{ and } \frac{1}{T} \cdot \frac{v'}{\sqrt{2}}.$$

The resultant acceleration is

$$\frac{1}{T}\sqrt{\frac{v^2}{2} + u^2 - \frac{2uv}{\sqrt{2}} + \frac{v^2}{2}},$$

$$= \frac{1}{T}\sqrt{v^2 + u^2 - \frac{2uv}{\sqrt{2}}}.$$

At time t the displacements x and y are given by

$$x = ut + \frac{1}{2} \cdot \frac{1}{T}\left(\frac{v}{\sqrt{2}} - u\right)t^2,$$

$$y = \frac{1}{2} \cdot \frac{1}{T} \cdot \frac{v}{\sqrt{2}} t^2,$$

and if

$$v = \frac{u}{\sqrt{2}}, \ x = ut - \frac{u}{4T} t^2,$$

$$y = \frac{u}{4T} t^2,$$

$$\therefore y + x = ut,$$

$$\therefore (y + x)^2 = u^2 t^2 = 4uTy.$$

EXAMPLES XIX.

1. Two masses of 10 oz. and 8 oz. are connected by a light string passing over a smooth fixed pulley. The system starts from rest and the 8 oz. mass, after it has risen 3 inches, passes through a fixed ring on which rests a bar of mass 4 oz., and so carries the 4 oz. mass on with it. Show that the 4 oz. mass will be carried nearly $2\frac{1}{2}$ inches above the ring.
(I.A.)

2. Two particles m_1 and m_2 $(m_1 > m_2)$, connected by a light inextensible string passing over a smooth fixed pulley, are left free. If the

VOL. I.—10

heavier particle reaches the ground after descending a distance a feet, after how many seconds will it be jerked off the ground, and with what velocity will it begin to rise ?   (I.S.)

3. Two masses, each of 2 lb. connected by a string passing over a smooth pulley, are moving vertically with a velocity of 2 ft./sec. The ascending mass passes through a fixed ring without touching it, and removes from the ring a mass of 4 oz. which it carries with it. Find the height to which the 4 oz. mass is carried, and the time that elapses before it is again left on the ring.   (I.A.)

4. Two masses $3M$ and M are connected by a cord passing over a pulley, and the whole is at rest with the former on the ground. A third mass M falls through a height h, strikes the second mass, adheres to it, and sets the whole in motion. Prove that the mass $3M$ will rise from the ground to a height $\dfrac{h}{5}$.   (I.A.)

5. Two masses of 3 lb. and 5 lb. are tied to the ends of a string 13 feet long. The string passes over a smooth peg 8 feet above a horizontal table, the 5 lb. mass lying on the table, the 3 lb. mass being held close to the peg. If the 3 lb. mass is allowed to fall, show that it will not reach the table.

    Find also the greatest height reached by the 5 lb. mass and the time it is in motion before it reaches the table a second time.   (I.A.)

6. Two masses m and M are connected by a light string passing over a smooth weightless pulley vertically above a smooth inelastic horizontal plane, M being held so as to prevent motion. If M is released and takes t seconds to reach the plane, show that the system will first be at rest instantaneously (with the string taut) after a time

$$\frac{3Mt}{M + m},$$

and that the system will be finally at rest with M on the plane after a time $3t$.   (Ex.)

7. Two particles of masses 3 oz. and 5 oz. are connected by an inextensible string of length 14 feet which passes over a small smooth pulley at a height of 10 feet above a table on which the heavier particle rests, vertically beneath the pulley. The other particle is raised to the pulley and allowed to fall. Find the velocity of the system after the jerk, and the time at which it will first come to rest.   (I.S.)

8. Two masses of 2 lb. and 3 lb. are fastened to the ends of a light string of length 2 feet, and placed on a smooth horizontal shelf 5 feet above the ground. The 2 lb. mass is placed at the edge of the shelf, and the 3 lb. mass 1 foot away from the edge, the line joining the two masses being perpendicular to the edge. If the 2 lb. mass is gently pushed over the edge, find the time that elapses before the 3 lb. mass strikes the ground.   (H.S.D.)

9. Two equal masses (M) are connected by a light inextensible string which passes over a smooth peg, the masses hanging freely under gravity. A rider of mass m is placed on one of these masses. When this mass has descended through a distance h the rider is raised off the mass. At the same instant the other mass picks up from rest a precisely similar rider. Show that the system will next come to rest when the first mass has descended a further distance

$$\frac{4M^2h}{(2M + m)^2}.$$
        (H.S.C.)

10. Masses A, of 3 lb. and B, of 2 lb., are connected by an inelastic string
    2 feet long, which passes over a small smooth pulley fixed at the top
    of a smooth inclined plane of length 2 feet (measured along the slope)
    and height 4 inches ; A being on the plane at its highest point and
    B on the ground vertically below the pulley with the string slack.
    Prove that, if A is let go, the system will come to rest again when A
    has reached the bottom of the inclined plane.   (H.S.D.)

11. A mass A of weight W lb. lying on a smooth table, a feet from the
    edge, is pulled off by means of a light inextensible cord, attached to
    it and passing over the edge (at right angles to the edge) and having
    a mass B of weight w lb. hanging from its lower end. Find the
    velocities of the weights when the edge is just reached and also just
    after A has left the table.   (H.S.C.)

12. A particle of 2 oz. mass moving at 5 ft./sec. in a given direction is
    struck by a blow which deflects its direction of motion through 60°
    and doubles its velocity.   If a particle at rest, of 9 oz. mass, were
    struck an equal blow, in what direction relative to the direction of
    the first particle, and with what velocity would it begin to move ?
    Also, if the velocity of the former particle were reversed before the
    blow, what would be its velocity and direction after the blow ? (I.E.)

13. A mass M rests on a smooth table and is attached by two inelastic
    strings to masses m, m' $(m' > m)$, which hang over smooth pulleys
    at opposite edges of the table.   The mass m', after moving a distance
    x from rest, comes in contact with the floor (supposed inelastic).
    Show that m will continue to ascend through a distance y given
    by

    $$\frac{y}{x} = \frac{(m' - m)(M + m)}{m(M + m + m')}.$$

    Show further that when m' is jerked into motion again as m falls it
    will ascend a distance

    $$\frac{x(M + m)^2}{(M + m + m')^2}.$$ (C.S.)

14. A battleship of symmetrical form and mass 30,000 tons is moving at
    10 m.p.h. and fires a salvo of all its eight guns in a direction perpen-
    dicular to its motion.   If the shells weigh 15 cwt. each, have a
    muzzle velocity of 2000 ft./sec., and are fired at an elevation of 30°,
    show that the motion immediately after firing makes an angle of
    about 1° 21′ with that before.   (C.S.)

15. A train consists of an engine and tender, of mass M tons, and two
    coaches, each of mass m tons.   At the start the buffers are in con-
    tact, and when the coupling chains are tight the buffers are a feet
    apart.   The train starts with the engine exerting a constant tractive
    force F tons weight.   Neglecting resistance, show that the second
    coach starts with velocity v ft./sec., where

    $$v^2 = 2ga \cdot \frac{F(2M + m)}{(M + 2m)^2}.$$ (C.S.)

16. Three equal particles A, B, C of mass m are placed on a smooth
    horizontal plane.   A is joined to B and C by light threads AB, AC,
    and the angle BAC is 60°.
       An impulse I is applied to A in the direction BA.   Find the
                                                          10 *

initial velocities of the particles and show that A begins to move in a direction making an angle

$$\tan^{-1}\frac{\sqrt{3}}{7},$$

with BA.   (C.S.)

17. A particle of mass m lies on a smooth horizontal plane and is connected by smooth light inextensible strings, both taut, with particles of masses m' and m'' lying on the plane, the angle between the strings being 2α. A blow is given to m in a direction bisecting the angle 2α so as to jerk the other masses into motion. Show that the mass m begins to move in a direction

$$\tan^{-1}\left[\frac{(m'-m'')\sin\alpha\cos\alpha}{m+(m'+m'')\sin^2\alpha}\right]$$

with the bisector of the angle between the strings. Also find the kinetic energy of the system.   (C.S.)

18. Four equal particles of mass m at the corners of a square are connected by light strings forming the sides of the square. If one particle receives a blow P along a diagonal outwards, show that its initial velocity is

$$\frac{P}{2m},$$

and find the initial velocities of the other particles.   (C.S.)

19. A mass m is connected by a string passing over a smooth pulley with a mass m' which is also joined by a string of length c to a mass m'' ; the system is at rest and is released when m'' is in contact with m' so that m'' begins to fall freely and the masses m and m' move as in Attwood's machine ; show that the velocity with which all the masses will move after both strings become taut is

$$\frac{m-m'-m''}{m+m'+m''}\sqrt{gc\frac{m+m'}{m}}$$

given that $m > m'+m''$.   (H.S.D.)

20. Three masses m_1, m_2, and m_3 lie at points A, B, and C upon a smooth horizontal table ; A and B, B and C are connected by light inextensible strings, and the angle ABC is obtuse. An impulse I is applied to the mass m_3 in the direction BC ; find the initial velocities of the masses and show that the mass m_2 begins to move in a direction making an angle θ with AB where

$$m_2\tan\theta+(m_1+m_2)\tan B=0.$$ (C.S.)

21. Three small bodies of masses 4, 5, 6 oz. respectively lie in order in a straight line on a large smooth table, the distance between consecutive bodies being 6 inches. Two slack strings, each 2 feet in length, connect the first with the second, and the second with the third. The third body is projected with a speed of 15 ft./sec. directly away from the other two. Find the time which elapses before the first begins to move and the speed with which it starts. Find also the loss of kinetic energy.   (H.C.)

22. A set of n trucks with s feet clear between them are inelastic and are set in motion by starting the end one with velocity V towards the next. Find how long it takes for the last truck to start, and the value of the final velocity.   (C.S.)

23. Two particles of masses 8 lb. and 6 lb. are lying on a smooth table and are connected by a slack string. The first particle is projected along the table with a velocity of 56 ft./sec. in a direction directly away from the second particle. Find the velocity of each particle after the string has become taut, and also find the difference between the kinetic energies of the system when the string is slack and when it is taut.

If the second particle is attached to a third particle of unknown mass by another slack string, and if the velocity of the system after both strings have become taut is 28 ft./sec., find the magnitude of the unknown mass. (N.U.3)

24. What do you understand by the statement "momentum is a vector"? In a square ABCD, the middle point of CD is X. Bodies whose masses are 3, 2, 4, 1 lb. moving along AX, BX, CX, DX respectively with speeds 5, 6, 3, 8 ft./sec. collide simultaneously at X and remain united. Determine, preferably by graphical methods, the new velocity and also the loss of kinetic energy.

If only the first three bodies remain united after the collision, and the fourth moved off in the direction BD with a speed 6 ft./sec., find the final velocity of the composite body. (N.U.4)

§ 121. Impact of Elastic Bodies.

When two spheres of any hard material collide they separate again, and, in many cases, if they are moving in opposite directions before impact, the velocity of one of them is reversed.

The balls are slightly compressed, and, as they generally tend to return to their original shape, they rebound.

The time during which they are in contact may be divided into two parts, (i) the period of compression, and (ii) the period of restitution, during which they are recovering their shape. The property which causes bodies to recover their shape and here causes the rebound after collision is called *Elasticity*. If a body does not tend to recover its shape it will cause no force of restitution, and such a body is said to be *Inelastic*.

In dealing with the impact of elastic bodies we shall consider that they are smooth, so that the only mutual action they can have on each other will be along the common normal at the point where they touch.

Usually the bodies are considered to be smooth spheres, and the mutual action between them is then along the line joining their centres.

When the direction of motion of each body is along the common normal at the point where they meet the impact is said to be *direct*.

When the direction of motion of either, or both, is not along the common normal, the impact is said to be *oblique*.

Suppose two bodies of masses m_1 and m_2, moving with velocities u_1 and u_2 respectively, impinge directly.

If v_1 and v_2 are the velocities after impact, the principle of momentum gives us the equation

$$m_1v_1 + m_2v_2 = m_1u_1 + m_2u_2 \qquad . \qquad . \qquad . \quad \text{(i)}$$

In the cases dealt with previously, the bodies have kept together after impact, so that $v_1 = v_2$, and one equation is sufficient to determine this velocity.

When the bodies separate after impact this one equation is not sufficient to determine v_1 and v_2.

This is only to be expected as the values of v_1 and v_2 will depend on the material of the bodies, and the principle of momentum takes no account of this.

There is no way of calculating the effect of the elasticity of the bodies, and we have to fall back on the results of experiments. Newton investigated the rebound of elastic bodies experimentally, and the result of these experiments is embodied in the following law :—

§ 122. Newton's Experimental Law.

When two bodies made of given substances impinge directly, the relative velocity after impact is in a constant ratio to the relative velocity before impact, and in the opposite direction. If the bodies impinge obliquely, the same result holds for the component velocities along the common normal.

Hence, if u_1, u_2 be the velocities before, and v_1, v_2 the velocities after impact, *all measured in the same direction*,

$$\frac{v_1 - v_2}{u_1 - u_2} = - e,$$

where e is a constant depending on the material of which the bodies are made, and is called the *coefficient of restitution* (sometimes called the *coefficient of elasticity*).

This law, therefore, gives us a second equation,

$$v_1 - v_2 = - e(u_1 - u_2) \qquad . \qquad . \qquad . \quad \text{(ii)}$$

and by means of this and equation (i) (§ 121) we can find v_1 and v_2.

The value of e differs considerably for different bodies ; for two glass balls it is about 0·9 ; for ivory 0·8 ; whilst for lead it is about 0·2.

Bodies for which e is zero are said to be inelastic, whilst for *perfectly elastic* bodies $e = 1$.

Note.—Newton's Law, like many experimental laws, is not accurately true. The value of e for given bodies does alter slightly for very large velocities, and in any case the law must only be regarded as an approximate one.

§ 123. Direct Impact of Two Spheres.

Let m_1, m_2 be the masses, u_1, u_2 the velocities before impact, v_1, v_2 the velocities after impact, and e the coefficient of restitution.

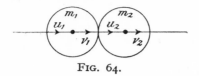

FIG. 64.

We then have as above,
by the principle of momentum,

$$m_1v_1 + m_2v_2 = m_1u_1 + m_2u_2 \quad . \qquad . \qquad . \quad \text{(i)}$$

by Newton's Law,

$$v_1 - v_2 = - e(u_1 - u_2) \qquad . \qquad . \qquad . \quad \text{(ii)}$$

Multiplying (ii) by m_2, and adding,

$$(m_1 + m_2)v_1 = (m_1 - em_2)u_1 + m_2(1 + e)u_2.$$

Multiplying (ii) by m_1, and subtracting,

$$(m_1 + m_2)v_2 = m_1(1 + e)u_1 + (m_2 - em_1)u_2.$$

These equations give v_1 and v_2.

If one sphere, say m_2, is moving originally in a direction opposite to that of m_1, we must change the sign of u_2 in each of the equations (i) and (ii).

It is most important, however, that we should assume that v_1 and v_2 are in *the same direction*. We fix on the direction we are going to call positive, usually that in which the body with greater momentum is moving, and then assume that both v_1 and v_2 are in this direction.

If either of them is really in the opposite direction, the value obtained for it will have a negative sign.

In writing down equation (ii) great care must be taken to subtract the velocities in the same order on both sides. It is best to draw a diagram showing clearly the positive direction and the directions of the velocities of both bodies.

EXAMPLE (i).

A ball of mass 10 lb., moving at 5 ft./sec., overtakes another of mass 4 lb., moving at 2 ft./sec. in the same direction. If $e = \frac{1}{2}$, find the velocities after impact.

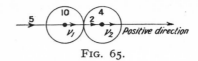

FIG. 65.

Let v_1, v_2 be the velocities of the 10 lb. and 4 lb. spheres respectively after impact. By the principle of momentum,

$$10v_1 + 4v_2 = 10 \times 5 + 4 \times 2 = 58,$$

and by Newton's Law,

$$v_1 - v_2 = -\tfrac{1}{2}(5 - 2) = -\tfrac{3}{2};$$
$$\therefore 14v_1 = 52, \text{ or } v_1 = 3\tfrac{5}{7} \text{ ft./sec.,}$$

and
$$14v_2 = 73, \text{ or } v_2 = 5\tfrac{3}{14} \text{ ft./sec.}$$

EXAMPLE (ii).

If the 4 lb. ball in the previous question be moving in a direction opposite to that of the 10 lb. ball, find the velocities after impact.

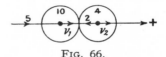

FIG. 66.

The equations now become,

$$10v_1 + 4v_2 = 10 \times 5 - 4 \times 2 = 42,$$
$$v_1 - v_2 = -\tfrac{1}{2}(5 + 2) = -\tfrac{7}{2},$$
$$\therefore 14v_1 = 28, \text{ or } v_1 = 2 \text{ ft./sec.,}$$

and
$$14v_2 = 77, \text{ or } v_2 = 5\tfrac{1}{2} \text{ ft./sec.}$$

EXAMPLE (iii).

A ball of mass 8 lb., moving with a velocity of 10 ft./sec., impinges directly on another of mass 24 lb., moving at 2 ft./sec. in the opposite direction. If $e = \tfrac{1}{2}$, find the velocities after impact.

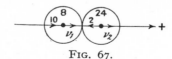

FIG. 67.

The equations here are,

$$8v_1 + 24v_2 = 8 \times 10 - 24 \times 2 = 32,$$
$$v_1 - v_2 = -\tfrac{1}{2}(10 + 2) = -6,$$
$$\therefore 32v_1 = 32 - 144 = -112,$$
$$\therefore v_1 = -\tfrac{112}{32} = -3\tfrac{1}{2} \text{ ft./sec.,}$$

also
$$32v_2 = 32 + 48 = 80,$$
$$\therefore v_2 = \tfrac{80}{32} = 2\tfrac{1}{2} \text{ ft./sec.}$$

The negative sign of v_1 shows that the direction of motion of the 8 lb. ball is *reversed*, as we took the direction left to right as positive.

and assumed v_1 to be in this direction. Since v_2 is positive, the 24 lb.
sphere moves from left to right after impact, so that its direction of
motion is also reversed.

EXAMPLE (iv).

*Three smooth spheres A, B, C, of masses $3m$, m, $2m$ respectively, lie
on a smooth table with their centres in a straight line. A is projected to
impinge on B ; show that, if the coefficient of restitution is $\frac{1}{2}$, B is reduced
to rest after its first impact with C ; and further, that impacts will cease
with the second impact of B on C.*
(I.S.)

Let u be the initial velocity of A, v_1 and v_2 the velocities of A and
B after impact, then

$$3mv_1 + mv_2 = 3mu,$$
$$v_1 - v_2 = -\tfrac{1}{2}u ;$$
$$\therefore 4v_1 = 2\tfrac{1}{2}u, \text{ or } v_1 = \tfrac{5}{8}u,$$

also,
$$4v_2 = \tfrac{9}{2}u, \text{ or } v_2 = \tfrac{9}{8}u ;$$

B moves on faster than A, and strikes C. If v_2', v_3' be the velocities of
B and C after impact,

$$mv_2' + 2mv_3' = \tfrac{9}{8}mu,$$
$$v_2' - v_3' = -\tfrac{1}{2}\cdot\tfrac{9}{8}u,$$
$$\therefore 3v_2' = 0,$$

i.e. B is reduced to rest,

also
$$3v_3' = (\tfrac{9}{8} + \tfrac{9}{16})u = \tfrac{27}{16}u,$$
$$\therefore v_3' = \tfrac{9}{16}u.$$

After the first impact A moves on with velocity $\tfrac{5}{8}u$, and strikes B
again after the latter has been reduced to rest. If V_1, V_2 be the velocities of A and B after impact,

$$3mV_1 + mV_2 = 3m \cdot \tfrac{5}{8}u,$$
$$V_1 - V_2 = -\tfrac{1}{2}\cdot\tfrac{5}{8}u,$$

These equations give,

and
$$V_1 = \tfrac{25}{64}u,$$
$$V_2 = \tfrac{45}{64}u.$$

The latter is greater than the velocity of C $(\tfrac{9}{16}u)$, so that B overtakes
C again, if V_2', V_3' be their velocities after impact,

$$mV_2' + 2mV_3' = \tfrac{45}{64}mu + \tfrac{9}{16}2mu = \tfrac{117}{64}mu,$$
$$V_2' - V_3' = -\tfrac{1}{2}(\tfrac{45}{64} - \tfrac{9}{16})u = -\tfrac{9}{128}u.$$

These equations give

$$V_2' = \tfrac{36}{64}u, \text{ and } V_3' = \tfrac{87}{128}u.$$

The velocities of A, B, C are now

$$\tfrac{25}{64}u, \text{ or } \tfrac{50}{128}u, \tfrac{36}{64}u, \text{ or } \tfrac{72}{128}u, \text{ and } \tfrac{87}{128}u,$$

in the same direction, and no more impacts can occur.

§ 124. Loss of Kinetic Energy due to Direct Impact.

Let m_1, m_2 be the masses, u_1 and u_2, v_1 and v_2 their velocities
before and after impact, and e the coefficient of restitution.

We have, as before,

$$m_1 v_1 + m_2 v_2 = m_1 u_1 + m_2 u_2 \qquad . \qquad . \qquad . \qquad \text{(i)}$$
$$v_1 - v_2 = -e(u_1 - u_2) \qquad . \qquad . \qquad . \qquad \text{(ii)}$$

Square both equations, multiplying the square of the second by $m_1 m_2$, and add the results ; we get

$$(m_1{}^2 + m_1 m_2) v_1{}^2 + (m_2{}^2 + m_1 m_2) v_2{}^2 = (m_1 u_1 + m_2 u_2)^2 + e^2 m_1 m_2 (u_1 - u_2)^2.$$

$$\therefore m_1(m_1 + m_2) v_1{}^2 + m_2(m_2 + m_1) v_2{}^2 = (m_1 u_1 + m_2 u_2)^2$$
$$+ m_1 m_2 (u_1 - u_2)^2 + e^2 m_1 m_2 (u_1 - u_2)^2 - m_1 m_2 (u_1 - u_2)^2,$$

$$\therefore (m_1 + m_2)(m_1 v_1{}^2 + m_2 v_2{}^2) = (m_1 + m_2)(m_1 u_1{}^2 + m_2 u_2{}^2)$$
$$- m_1 m_2 (u_1 - u_2)^2 (1 - e^2),$$

$$\therefore \tfrac{1}{2} m_1 v_1{}^2 + \tfrac{1}{2} m_2 v_2{}^2 = \tfrac{1}{2} m_1 u_1{}^2 + \tfrac{1}{2} m_2 u_2{}^2 - \tfrac{1}{2}\frac{m_1 m_2}{m_1 + m_2}(u_1 - u_2)^2 (1 - e^2).$$

and

$$\tfrac{1}{2} m_1 v_1{}^2 + \tfrac{1}{2} m_2 v_2{}^2$$

is the kinetic energy after impact, while

$$\tfrac{1}{2} m_1 u_1{}^2 + \tfrac{1}{2} m_2 u_2{}^2$$

is the kinetic energy before impact,

$\therefore$ the loss in kinetic energy is

$$\tfrac{1}{2}\frac{m_1 m_2}{m_1 + m_2}(u_1 - u_2)^2 (1 - e^2).$$

We see that there is always a loss unless $e = 1$, when this expression vanishes.

In many numerical examples it is easier to find the velocities after impact, and subtract the kinetic energy after impact from that before. The above is the shortest way of obtaining the value for the loss in the general case.

EXAMPLE (i).

A sphere of mass 1 lb., moving at 10 ft./sec., overtakes another sphere of mass 5 lb. moving in the same line at 3 ft./sec. Find the loss of kinetic energy during impact, and show that the direction of motion of the first sphere is reversed. (Coefficient of restitution = 0·75.) (H.S.C.)

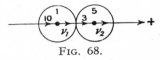

FIG. 68.

If v_1 and v_2 be the velocities of the 1 lb. and 5 lb. spheres after impact,

$$v_1 + 5v_2 = 10 + 15 = 25,$$
$$v_1 - v_2 = -\tfrac{3}{4}(10 - 3) = -\tfrac{21}{4},$$
$$\therefore 6v_1 = 25 - \tfrac{105}{4} = -\tfrac{5}{4}, \text{ or } v_1 = -\tfrac{5}{24} \text{ ft./sec.,}$$

and

$$6v_2 = 25 + \tfrac{21}{4} = \tfrac{121}{4}, \text{ or } v_2 = \tfrac{121}{24} \text{ ft./sec.}$$

The value of v_1 is negative, showing that the direction of motion of the first sphere is reversed.

It must be remembered that the direction of motion does not affect the value of the kinetic energy. In this case the kinetic energy after impact is the same as if both spheres were moving in the original direction. Algebraically, the value of v^2 is the same whether v is positive or negative.

The kinetic energy before impact is

$$\tfrac{1}{2} \cdot 1 \cdot 10^2 + \tfrac{1}{2} \cdot 5 \cdot 3^2 = 50 + \frac{45}{2} = \frac{145}{2} \text{ ft. pdls.}$$

The kinetic energy after impact is

$$\tfrac{1}{2} 1 \cdot \frac{25}{24^2} + \tfrac{1}{2} \cdot 5 \cdot \frac{121^2}{24^2} = \frac{5}{2 \cdot 24^2}(5 + 14641) = 63\frac{109}{192} \text{ ft. pdls.}$$

The loss

$$= 72\tfrac{1}{2} - 63\frac{109}{192} = 8\frac{179}{192} \text{ ft. pdls.}$$

EXAMPLE (ii).

Two masses, m and n, are moving in the same straight line, prove that their kinetic energy is

$$\tfrac{1}{2}(m + n)V^2 + \tfrac{1}{2}\frac{mn}{m + n}v^2,$$

where V is the velocity of their centre of mass, and v is their relative velocity.

If there is a direct impact between the masses, prove that their loss of kinetic energy is

$$\tfrac{1}{2}\frac{mn}{m + n}(1 - e^2)v^2.$$

where e is their coefficient of restitution. (I.S.)

If u_1 and u_2 are the velocities of m and n, the velocity V of their centre of mass is given by

$$V = \frac{mu_1 + nu_2}{m + n},$$

and their relative velocity $v = u_1 - u_2$.

If E is their kinetic energy

$$E = \tfrac{1}{2}mu_1^2 + \tfrac{1}{2}nu_2^2,$$
$$\therefore (m + n)E = \tfrac{1}{2}m^2u_1^2 + \tfrac{1}{2}n^2u_2^2 + \tfrac{1}{2}mn(u_1^2 + u_2^2),$$
$$= \tfrac{1}{2}(mu_1 + nu_2)^2 + \tfrac{1}{2}mn(u_1^2 + u_2^2) - mnu_1u_2,$$
$$= \tfrac{1}{2}(mu_1 + nu_2)^2 + \tfrac{1}{2}mn(u_1 - u_2)^2,$$
$$\therefore (m + n)E = \tfrac{1}{2}(m + n)^2V^2 + \tfrac{1}{2}mnv^2,$$
$$\therefore E = \tfrac{1}{2}(m + n)V^2 + \tfrac{1}{2}\frac{mn}{m + n}v^2.$$

Now the velocity of the centre of mass is unaffected by impact between the masses, hence the first term remains unaltered. By Newton's Law the relative velocity v is multiplied by e and reversed, i.e. it becomes $- ev$.

Hence, the second term becomes, after the impact,

$$\tfrac{1}{2}\frac{mn}{m+n}e^2 v^2,$$

and the loss in kinetic energy is

$$\tfrac{1}{2}\frac{mn}{m+n}v^2(1-e^2).$$

EXAMPLES XX.

1. A sphere of mass 6 lb., moving at 4 ft./sec., overtakes another sphere of mass 4 lb., moving in the same direction with velocity 2 ft./sec. If $e=\tfrac{1}{4}$, find the velocities after impact.

2. A ball of mass 10 lb., moving at 8 ft./sec., overtakes another of mass 8 lb., moving in the same direction at 5 ft./sec. If $e=\tfrac{1}{2}$, find the velocities after impact.

3. A ball of mass 10 lb., moving at 8 ft./sec., impinges directly on a ball of mass 8 lb., moving in the opposite direction at 4 ft./sec. If $e=\tfrac{1}{3}$, find their velocities after impact.

4. A ball of mass m, moving at 7 ft./sec., overtakes another of mass $2m$, moving in the same direction at 1 ft./sec. If $e=\tfrac{3}{4}$, show that the first ball will remain at rest after impact.

5. If two perfectly elastic spheres, of equal mass and moving in opposite directions, impinge directly, show that they will exchange velocities.

6. Two spheres of masses m and m', and coefficient of restitution e, impinge directly. Prove that the momentum transferred from one sphere to the other is

$$\frac{mm'}{m+m'}(1+e)\text{ (relative velocity before impact).}\qquad\text{(I.S.)}$$

7. A ball of mass m_1, moving with velocity v_1, impinges directly on a ball of mass m_2 lying at rest, and the second ball then impinges directly upon a third ball of mass m_3, which is also at rest. If the coefficient of restitution of the first pair is e, and that of the second pair is e', find the velocities of all three balls immediately after these impacts. (I.E.)

8. Two spheres of masses 2 and 3 oz. are moving in their line of centres towards each other with velocities of 24 ft./sec. and 30 ft./sec., and their coefficient of restitution is $\tfrac{3}{4}$. Find their velocities after impact, and the amount of kinetic energy transformed in the collision. (I.A.)

9. If the velocities of two spheres before direct impact are given, show that the impulse which each sphere receives varies as

$$\frac{(1+e)mm'}{m+m'},$$

where e is the coefficient of restitution, and m, m' are the masses of the spheres. (I.A.)

10. Two particles are moving in the same straight line. Express their kinetic energy in terms of their masses, their relative velocity, and the velocity of their centre of gravity; and hence, or otherwise, show that, if the particles are inelastic, kinetic energy is always

lost by their impact. Two particles of masses m and $14m$ are moving with velocities $6u$ and u respectively, and the coefficient of restitution between them is 0·5. Show that, after impact, the kinetic energy gained by one equals half that lost by the other.

(I.S.)

11. A mass of 4 lb., moving at 20 ft./sec., overtakes a mass of 3 lb. moving in the same direction at $15\frac{1}{3}$ ft./sec. Five seconds after the impact the 3 lb. mass encounters a fixed obstacle, which reduces it to rest. Assuming the coefficient of restitution between the masses to be $\frac{1}{4}$, find the further time that will elapse before the 4 lb. mass strikes the 3 lb. mass again. (H.S.D.)

12. A truck weighing 10 tons, moving at 8 ft./sec., impinges on another truck at rest which weighs 5 tons, and after impact the speed of the second truck relative to the first is 2 ft./sec. Determine in ft. lb. the loss of kinetic energy due to the impact. (I.E.)

13. A sphere of mass 3 lb., moving with a velocity of 7 ft./sec., impinges directly on another sphere, of mass 5 lb., at rest; after the impact the velocities of the spheres are in the ratio of 2 : 3. Find the velocities after impact and the loss of kinetic energy. (H.S.C.)

14. Three balls A, B, C, of masses $3m$, $2m$, $2m$, and of equal radii, lie on a smooth table with their centres in a straight line. Their coefficient of restitution is $\frac{1}{4}$. Show that, if A is projected with velocity V to strike B, there are three impacts, and that the final velocities are

$$\frac{(50, \ 57, \ 60)}{128} \ V.$$

(H.C.)

15. Two trucks, weighing respectively 5 tons and 3 tons, are standing, on the same level set of rails. If the heavier truck impinges on the lighter, which is at rest, with a speed of 5 ft./sec., and the velocity of the lighter relative to the heavier after they separate is 3 ft./sec., find the actual speeds of the two trucks after they separate, and calculate the number of foot-pounds of kinetic energy lost by the impact. (H.C.)

16. A, B, C are three exactly similar small spheres at rest in a smooth horizontal straight tube. A is set in motion and impinges on B. Show that A will impinge on B again after B has impinged on C, and show that there will be no more impacts, if e, the coefficient of restitution between the spheres, is not less than $3 - \sqrt{8}$. (H.C.)

17. Three small exactly similar spheres A, B, C are at rest in a smooth straight horizontal tube. The coefficient of restitution between any two of the spheres is 0·5. A is projected towards B with a velocity u.
Determine the velocities of the three spheres after B has impinged on C, and A has impinged a second time on B, and show that there will be no more impacts. (H.C.)

18. A truck weighing 5 tons is moving on a set of level rails at the rate of 5 ft./sec., and impinges on a second truck weighing 10 tons, which is standing at rest on the same rails. If after the impact the second truck moves on at the rate of 2 ft./sec., find the rate at which the first truck moves after the impact, and calculate in ft. lb. the amount of kinetic energy lost by the impact. (H.C.)

19. The velocities of two spheres before impact are represented in magnitude and direction by lengths OP and OQ, those after impact by Op, Oq (the points O, P, Q, p, q, being in a straight line).

    Prove that the ratio of Qq to Pp is equal to the ratio of the masses, and that the ratio QP to pq is the coefficient of restitution. (I.S.)

20. Two spheres impinge on each other directly, and the impulse between them is R. Just before impact the velocity of their common centre of gravity is U, and the velocity of the faster moving sphere relative to this centre of gravity is U_1. Show that the kinetic energy lost by this sphere is
$$\tfrac{1}{2}R[2U + (1-e)U_1],$$
where e is the coefficient of restitution between the spheres. (I.S.)

21. Two smooth spheres of masses m and m' impinge directly, their relative velocity just before impact being v, and the coefficient of restitution e.

    Prove that the loss of kinetic energy due to the impact is
$$\frac{1}{2}\frac{mm'v^2(1 - e^2)}{m + m'}. \tag{H.S.D.}$$

22. A ball overtakes another ball of m times its mass, which is moving with $\dfrac{1}{n}$th of its velocity in the same direction. If the impact reduces the first ball to rest, prove that the coefficient of restitution is
$$\frac{m + n}{mn - m},$$
and that m must be greater than $\dfrac{n}{n - 2}$. (H.S.D.)

23. Two equal spheres A, B lie in a smooth horizontal circular groove at opposite ends of a diameter. A is projected along the groove and at the end of time t_0 impinges on B. Show that the second impact will occur at a further time
$$\frac{2t_0}{e},$$
where e is the elastic coefficient. (C.S.)

24. Two equal spheres of mass $9m$ are at rest, and another sphere of mass m is moving along their line of centres between them. How many collisions will there be if the spheres are perfectly elastic ? (C.S.)

25. A railway truck is at rest at the foot of an incline of 1 in 70. A second truck of equal weight starts from rest at a point 1000 feet up the incline, and runs down under gravity. The trucks collide at the foot of the incline, the coefficient of restitution being $\tfrac{1}{5}$. Find how far each truck travels along the level, the frictional resistance for each truck being 16 lb. wt. per ton, both on the incline and on the level. Where the incline meets the level, the rails are slightly curved, each in a vertical plane, so that there is no vertical impact, and at the instant of collision both trucks are on the level. (C.S.)

26. Two imperfectly elastic spheres, of weights W and $2W$, collide directly. Just before the impact the lighter sphere is moving with velocity 9 ft./sec., and the heavier with velocity 2 ft./sec. in opposite directions. The smaller sphere is brought to rest by the impact. Find the coefficient of restitution, and the velocity of the larger sphere after the impact. (H.S.D.)

27. Three spheres of equal mass lie in a straight line. If the first sphere be given a velocity u, show that the velocities of the spheres, after two impacts have taken place, are

$$\tfrac{1}{2}(1 - e)u, \quad \tfrac{1}{4}(1 - e^2)u, \quad \text{and} \quad \tfrac{1}{4}(1 + e)^2u,$$

where e is the coefficient of restitution. (I.S.)

28. A, B, C are three small beads of equal mass threaded on a smooth horizontal circular wire, B and C being at rest and separated by $\tfrac{1}{64}$ of the circumference. A is projected along the wire and strikes B, which is driven forward along the wire and strikes C. If the coefficient of restitution between any two beads is $\tfrac{4}{5}$, show that the next impact takes place simultaneously by A overtaking B at the same instant that C overtakes A, and that C has travelled a distance equal to $\tfrac{9}{8}$ of the circumference before this happens. (Ex.)

29. Two uniform spheres of equal radii rest on a perfectly smooth horizontal table. The first, of mass m, is struck by a horizontal impulse I, whose line of action passes through the centre. After moving for a time it collides directly with the second sphere, which is of greater mass M, and which is initially at rest. Show that the loss of kinetic energy due to the impact between the spheres is

$$\tfrac{1}{2}(1 - e^2)\frac{MI^2}{m(M + m)},$$

where e is the coefficient of restitution.

30. Three bodies of masses a, b, c lie in a straight line on a smooth horizontal plane. The first is projected with a velocity u along the straight line so as to strike the second, which in turn strikes the third. If the coefficient of elasticity for each pair of bodies is e, find the velocity with which the third body is made to move. Also find the ratios $a : b : c$ so that the first and second bodies may remain at rest after the first and second impacts respectively, and in this case show that the final energy is e^2 times the original energy. (Ex.)

31. A ball is dropped, and after falling for 1 second meets another equal ball which is moving upwards with speed of 48 ft./sec. Calculate the velocity of each ball after the collision, given that the coefficient of restitution is $\tfrac{3}{4}$.
Find the percentage loss in kinetic energy due to the impact.
(N.U.3)

32. Two spheres of masses m_1 and m_2, travelling with velocities v_1 and v_2 in the same direction, collide directly and rebound. Determine the amount of momentum which is transferred between the spheres during the impact when the coefficient of restitution is e. If the velocities after impact are u_1, u_2, show that each sphere loses the same energy if

$$. \; v_1 + v_2 + u_1 + u_2 = 0. \qquad \text{(C.W.B.)}$$

§ 125. Impact of a Smooth Sphere on a Fixed Smooth Plane.

Let AB (Fig. 69) be the fixed plane, P the point at which the sphere impinges. Then if C is the centre of the sphere, CP is the normal to the plane at P. Let the velocity of the sphere at impact be u, and the direction of motion of its centre make an angle α with CP.

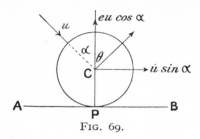

FIG. 69.

Since the plane and sphere are smooth, there is no force parallel to the plane ; hence the component of the sphere's velocity in this direction, viz. $u \sin \alpha$, is unaltered.

By Newton's experimental law, the relative velocity along the normal after impact is $- e$ times that before impact measured in the same direction.

∴ if v is the normal velocity after impact

$$v - 0 = - e(u \cos \alpha - 0) \text{ or } v = - eu \cos \alpha,$$

i.e. the normal velocity is reversed and multiplied by e.

The velocity after impact has therefore two components, $u \sin \alpha$ parallel to AB, and $eu \cos \alpha$ parallel to the normal PC.

The resultant velocity after impact $= u\sqrt{\sin^2 \alpha + e^2 \cos^2 \alpha}$. If θ be the angle between the direction of motion and the normal,

$$\tan \theta = \frac{u \sin \alpha}{eu \cos \alpha} = \frac{1}{e} \tan \alpha.$$

or $$\cot \theta = e \cot \alpha.$$

The impulse on the plane due to the impact is measured by the change of momentum along the normal. If m is the mass of the sphere, this is

$$mu \cos \alpha + me \cos \alpha = mu(1 + e) \cos \alpha.$$

If the impact be direct there is no component of velocity parallel to the plane, the sphere rebounds along the normal with velocity eu.

If $e = 1$, the velocity after impact is u, and $\theta = \alpha$, the sphere after impact rebounds so that the angle of reflection is equal to the angle of incidence.

If $e = 0$ there is no velocity along the normal after impact, and the sphere slides along the plane with velocity $u \sin \alpha$.

EXAMPLE (i).

A ball, moving with a velocity of 20 ft./sec., impinges on a smooth fixed plane in a direction, making an angle of 30° with the plane ; if the coefficient of restitution is $\frac{2}{5}$, find the velocity and direction of motion of the ball after the impact.

The component of velocity parallel to the plane is 20 cos 30°, or $10\sqrt{3}$ ft./sec., and this is unaltered by the impact.

The component of velocity perpendicular to the plane is 20 sin 30°, or 10 ft./sec., and this is reversed and multiplied by $\frac{2}{5}$.

The components of velocity along and perpendicular to the plane after impact are, therefore,

$$10\sqrt{3}, \text{ and } 4 \text{ ft./sec.}$$

If V is the resultant velocity,

$$V^2 = 300 + 16 = 316,$$
$$\therefore V = \sqrt{316} = 17{\cdot}7 \text{ ft./sec.}$$

The direction makes an angle

$$\tan^{-1}\frac{4}{10\sqrt{3}}$$

or

$$\tan^{-1}\frac{2\sqrt{3}}{15}$$

with the plane.

EXAMPLE (ii).

A particle falls from a height h upon a fixed horizontal plane ; if e be the coefficient of restitution, show that the whole distance described before the particle has finished rebounding is

$$\frac{1 + e^2}{1 - e^2} h,$$

and that the whole time taken is

$$\sqrt{\frac{2h}{g}} \cdot \frac{1 + e}{1 - e}.$$

Let u be the velocity of the particle on first hitting the plane, so that

$$u^2 = 2gh.$$

The particle rebounds with velocity eu. The velocity when it hits the plane the second time is again eu, and the velocity after the second rebound is e^2u. Similarly, the velocities after the third, fourth, etc., rebounds are e^3u, e^4u, etc.

The height to which the particle rises after the first rebound is

$$\frac{(eu)^2}{2g}$$

and after the second

$$\frac{(e^2u)^2}{2g}$$

and so on.

Also $u^2 = 2gh$, so that these distances are e^2h, e^4h, etc. Hence the whole distance described is

$$h + 2(e^2h + e^4h + \ldots \text{ to infinity}),$$
$$= h + 2h\frac{e^2}{1 - e^2} = h\frac{1 + e^2}{1 - e^2}.$$

The time of flight after the first impact is $\dfrac{2eu}{g}$, after the second $\dfrac{2e^2u}{g}$, and so on, and the time of falling originally is

$$\sqrt{\dfrac{2h}{g}}.$$

Hence, the whole time of motion

$$= \sqrt{\dfrac{2h}{g}} + \dfrac{2u}{g}(e + e^2 + e^3 + \ldots \text{ to infinity}).$$

$$= \sqrt{\dfrac{2h}{g}} + 2\sqrt{\dfrac{2h}{g}}(e + e^2 + \ldots),$$

$$= \sqrt{\dfrac{2h}{g}}\left(1 + 2\dfrac{e}{1-e}\right) = \sqrt{\dfrac{2h}{g}} \cdot \dfrac{1+e}{1-e}.$$

EXAMPLE (iii).

A sphere of mass m lies on a smooth table between a sphere of mass m' and a fixed vertical plane. It is projected towards the other sphere ; show that, if the coefficient of restitution between the two spheres and between m and the plane is $\frac{3}{5}$ in both cases, m will be reduced to rest at its second impact with m' if m' = 15m. (I.S.)

Let u be the velocity of projection of m, and v_1, v_2 the velocities of m and m' after impact, then

$$mv_1 + m'v_2 = mu,$$

$$v_1 - v_2 = -\tfrac{3}{5}u,$$

$$\therefore (m + m')v_1 = u(m - \tfrac{3}{5}m'),$$

and $$(m + m')v_2 = \tfrac{8}{5}mu.$$

Putting $m' = 15m$, these become

$$16mv_1 = u(m - 9m) = -8mu, \text{ or } v_1 = -\dfrac{u}{2}.$$

$$16mv_2 = \tfrac{8}{5}mu, \text{ or } v_2 = \tfrac{1}{10}u.$$

The velocity of m is therefore reversed, and it hits the plane, rebounding with velocity

$$\dfrac{3}{5} \cdot \dfrac{u}{2}, \text{ or } \dfrac{3}{10}u,$$

which enables it to catch m' again.

If V, V' be the velocities of m and m' after their second impact,

$$mV + m'V' = \tfrac{3}{10}mu + \tfrac{1}{10}m'u,$$

$$V - V' = -\tfrac{3}{5}(\tfrac{2}{10})u = -\tfrac{3}{25}u,$$

$$\therefore (m + m')V = \tfrac{3}{10}mu + \tfrac{1}{10}m'u - \tfrac{3}{25}m'u,$$

or putting $m' = 15m$,

$$16mV = \tfrac{3}{10}mu + \tfrac{3}{2}mu - \tfrac{9}{5}mu,$$
$$= 0,$$

$\therefore m$ is reduced to rest.

EXAMPLE (iv).

A billiard ball moving with velocity u strikes the side of a smooth billiard table, its direction making an angle α with the side of the table ; it then strikes the next side, and so on, striking each side in succession. Show that the various portions of the path are parallel to the sides of a parallelogram, and that if c_1 is the length of the path between the first and second impacts, c_2 that between the second and third, and so on,

$$c_{2n+1} - e\,c_{2n-1} = \sec \alpha'(b - a \cot \alpha),$$

where e is the coefficient of restitution, b the length of the side at which the first impact takes place, a the next side, and α' the angle between the direction of the path after the first impact and the side of length b. (H.S.C.)

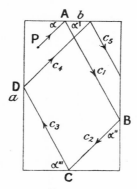

FIG. 70.

Let A (Fig. 70) be the point of the first impact, B, C, D those of the second, third, and fourth impacts. The velocity parallel to the cushion is $u \cos \alpha$, and is unaltered. The velocity perpendicular to the cushion is $u \sin \alpha$, and after impact $- eu \sin \alpha$,

$$\therefore \tan \alpha' = \frac{eu \sin \alpha}{u \cos \alpha} = e \tan \alpha.$$

Similarly,

$$\tan \alpha'' = e \cot \alpha' = \cot \alpha,$$
$$\therefore BC \text{ is parallel to } PA.$$

Also

$$\tan \alpha''' = e \cot \alpha'' = e \tan \alpha = \tan \alpha',$$
$$\therefore \alpha''' = \alpha', \text{ and } CD \text{ is parallel to } AB.$$

In the same way the path after the impact at D will be parallel to CB or PA.

Projecting AB and BC on to the side a, and BC, CD on to b,

$$c_1 \sin \alpha' + c_2 \cos \alpha'' = a,$$
and
$$c_2 \sin \alpha'' + c_3 \cos \alpha''' = b,$$
$$\therefore c_1 \sin \alpha' + c_2 \sin \alpha = a,$$
$$c_2 \cos \alpha + c_3 \cos \alpha' = b,$$
$$\therefore c_3 \cos \alpha' \sin \alpha - c_1 \sin \alpha' \cos \alpha = b \sin \alpha - a \cos \alpha,$$
$$\therefore c_3 - c_1 \frac{\tan \alpha'}{\tan \alpha} = b \sec \alpha' - a \sec \alpha' \cot \alpha,$$
$$\therefore c_3 - ec_1 = \sec \alpha'(b - a \cot \alpha) ;$$

and a similar relation evidently holds for c_3 and c_5, by projecting c_3, c_4, c_5 on to a and b.

EXAMPLES XXI.

1. A particle falls from a height of 25 feet upon a fixed horizontal plane, the coefficient of restitution being $\frac{1}{5}$. Find the height to which the particle rises after impact, and the time it takes to reach the plane again. What is the velocity after the second rebound ?

2. A ball falls from a height of 25 feet upon a fixed horizontal plane ; if it rebounds to a height of 16 feet, find the coefficient of restitution.

3. A ball moving at 40 ft./sec. impinges on a smooth fixed plane so that its direction of motion makes an angle of 30° with the plane ; if the coefficient of restitution is $\frac{1}{2}$, find the magnitude and direction of the velocity of the ball after impact.

4. A ball falls from a height of 25 feet upon an inclined plane, the coefficient of restitution being $\frac{1}{5}$. Find the magnitude and direction of the velocity of the ball after impact, when the inclination of the plane is (1) 45°, (2) 60°.

5. A billiard ball of mass 7 oz. strikes a smooth cushion when moving at 8 ft./sec. in a direction inclined at 30° to the cushion. If the coefficient of restitution is $\frac{7}{8}$, find the loss of kinetic energy due to the impact. (I.A.)

6. A marble dropped on a stone floor from a height of 12 feet is found to rebound to a height of 10 feet. Find the coefficient of restitution to the nearest hundredth. (I.A.)

7. A billiard table is 6 feet by 8 feet. Find the position of a point in the shorter side and the direction of projection, such that a ball thus struck off will describe a rectangle and return to the same spot after rebounding at each of the other three cushions, the ball being smooth, and the coefficient of elasticity being $\frac{4}{9}$. (I.S.)

8. A sphere of mass m moving with velocity u impinges on a fixed plane, the direction of motion making an angle α with the plane. If e is the coefficient of restitution between the sphere and the plane, find (i) the magnitude and direction of the velocity of the sphere after impact ; (ii) the loss of momentum ; (iii) the loss of kinetic energy. (I.S.)

9. A smooth elliptical tray is surrounded by a smooth vertical rim ; prove that a perfectly elastic particle projected from a focus along the tray in any direction will after two impacts return to the focus. (H.S.D.)

10. If sheets of paper are placed on a table, the coefficient of restitution is reduced by an amount proportional to the thickness of the paper. When a ball is dropped on to the bare table it rises after impact to three-quarters of the height of fall. When the thickness of the paper is 1 inch it rises to only one-half of the height of fall. What thickness of paper is required in order that the rebound shall be one-quarter of the height of fall ? (I.S.)

11. The line joining the centres of two equal smooth balls P and Q lying on a smooth table is perpendicular to a smooth vertical plane ; the ball P farthest from the plane slides towards Q, which is at rest, with velocity u ; after the impact Q meets the plane and a second impact occurs and so on. If e is the coefficient of restitution between the balls and e' that between Q and the plane, find the velocities of P and Q after the first impact of Q with the plane. Show that there will necessarily be a third impact of P and Q if $e' < \dfrac{(1 - e)^2}{(1 + e)^2}$.

(H.S.D.)

12. A bullet of mass 2 oz. is fired horizontally into a fixed block of wood striking it with a speed 1200 ft./sec. If the bullet penetrates to a distance 6 inches, find in lb. wt. the average force of resistance of the wood to the motion.

If the block were of metal, and the bullet rebounded instead of penetrating, find the kinetic energy which would be lost at the impact if the coefficient of restitution between the bodies were 0·3. State the units in which you give your result. (N.U.3)

§ 126. Oblique Impact of Two Spheres.

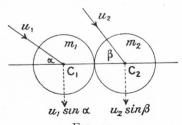

FIG. 71.

Let C_1, C_2 (Fig. 71) be the centres of the spheres, m_1, m_2 their masses, and let their velocities u_1 and u_2 be inclined at angles α and β to the line of centres C_1C_2 at the moment of impact.

The components of velocity perpendicular to C_1C_2 are $u_1 \sin \alpha$, $u_1 \sin \beta$, and these are unaltered by the impact.

Considering the motion along C_1C_2, if v_1 and v_2 are the velocities along this line after impact, we have
by the principle of momentum,

$$m_1 v_1 + m_2 v_2 = m_1 u_1 \cos \alpha + m_2 u_2 \cos \beta \quad . \quad . \quad (i)$$

by Newton's Law,

$$v_1 - v_2 = - e(u_1 \cos \alpha - u_2 \cos \beta) \quad . \quad . \quad (ii)$$

These equations give

$$v_1 = \frac{(m_1 - em_2)u \cos \alpha + m_2 u_2 \cos \beta(1 + e)}{m_1 + m_2},$$

$$v_2 = \frac{m_1 u_1 \cos \alpha(1 + e) + u_2 \cos \beta(m_2 - em_1)}{m_1 + m_2}.$$

The resultant velocity of each sphere and its direction of motion can be found from these components and the components perpendicular to $C_1 C_2$, viz. $u_1 \sin \alpha$ and $u_2 \sin \beta$.

If $m_1 = m_2$ and $e = 1$, $v_1 = u_2 \cos \beta$ and $v_2 = u_1 \cos \alpha$, i.e. the spheres interchange their velocities in the direction of the line of centres.

In many problems one of the spheres is at rest. Now, if $u_2 = 0$, the equations (i) and (ii) of the last paragraph reduce to

$$m_1 v_1 + m_2 v_2 = m_1 u_1 \cos \alpha,$$
$$v_1 - v_2 = - eu_1 \cos \alpha.$$

$$\therefore v_1 = \frac{u_1 \cos \alpha(m_1 - em_2)}{m_1 + m_2}, \text{ and } v_2 = \frac{m_1 u_1 \cos \alpha(1 + e)}{m_1 + m_2}$$

The second sphere has no velocity perpendicular to the line of centres, so that it moves off along that line.

The sphere m_1 has velocity $u_1 \sin \alpha$ perpendicular to $C_1 C_2$, so that if θ is the angle made by its direction of motion with $C_1 C_2$

$$\tan \theta = \frac{u_1 \sin \alpha}{v_1} = \frac{(m_1 + m_2) \sin \alpha}{\cos \alpha(m_1 - em_2)}.$$

If also $m_1 = m_2$, the results simplify still further, and we have

$$v_1 = \tfrac{1}{2}u_1 \cos \alpha(1 - e), \quad v_2 = \tfrac{1}{2}u_1 \cos \alpha(1 + e),$$

$$\tan \theta = \frac{2 \sin \alpha}{(1 - e) \cos \alpha}.$$

§ 127. Loss of Kinetic Energy in Oblique Impact.

The velocities perpendicular to the line of centres are unaltered. The loss of kinetic energy is therefore the same as in the case of direct impact (§ 124) if we substitute $u_1 \cos \alpha$ and $u_2 \cos \beta$ for u_1 and u_2 respectively.

The loss is therefore

$$\tfrac{1}{2} \frac{m_1 m_2}{m_1 + m_2} (u_1 \cos \alpha - u_2 \cos \beta)^2(1 - e^2).$$

§ 128. EXAMPLE (i).

A ball of mass 8 lb., moving with velocity 4 ft./sec., impinges on a ball of mass 4 lb., moving with velocity 2 ft./sec. If their velocities before impact be inclined at angles 30° and 60° to the line joining their centres at the moment of impact, find their velocities after impact when $e = \tfrac{1}{2}$.

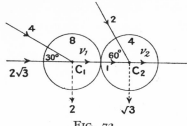

FIG. 72.

Let C_1 and C_2 (Fig. 72) be the centres of the balls.

The components of velocity perpendicular to C_1C_2 are 4 sin 30° and 2 sin 60°, or 2 and $\sqrt{3}$ ft./sec. These are unaltered by the impact.

If v_1 and v_2 be the velocities along C_1C_2 after impact, we have by momentum

$$8v_1 + 4v_2 = 8 \times 4 \cos 30° + 4 \times 2 \cos 60° = 16\sqrt{3} + 4,$$

and by Newton's Law,

$$v_1 - v_2 = -\tfrac{1}{2}(4 \cos 30° - 2 \cos 60°) = -\tfrac{1}{2}(2\sqrt{3} - 1),$$

$$\therefore 2v_1 + v_2 = 4\sqrt{3} + 1,$$

$$2v_1 - 2v_2 = -2\sqrt{3} + 1,$$

$$\therefore 3v_2 = 6\sqrt{3}, \text{ or } v_2 = 2\sqrt{3}, \text{ and } 6v_1 = 6\sqrt{3} + 3,$$

or

$$v_1 = \frac{2\sqrt{3} + 1}{2}.$$

The velocity of the 8 lb. sphere

$$= \sqrt{4 + \left(\frac{2\sqrt{3} + 1}{2}\right)^2} = \sqrt{\frac{29 + 4\sqrt{3}}{2}} \text{ ft./sec.,}$$

and if θ be the inclination to C_1C_2,

$$\tan \theta = \frac{2 \times 2}{2\sqrt{3} + 1} = \frac{4(2\sqrt{3} - 1)}{11}.$$

The velocity of the 4 lb. sphere

$$= \sqrt{3 + 12} = \sqrt{15} \text{ ft./sec.}$$

and if ϕ be the inclination to C_1C_2.

$$\tan \phi = \frac{\sqrt{3}}{2\sqrt{3}} = \frac{1}{2}.$$

EXAMPLE (ii).

A sphere of mass M, travelling with velocity u, impinges obliquely on a stationary sphere of mass M', the direction of the blow making an angle α *with the line of motion of the impinging sphere. If the coefficient of restitution is e, prove that the impinging sphere is deflected through an angle* β, *such that*

$$\tan \beta = \frac{M'(1 + e) \tan \alpha}{(M - eM') + (M + M') \tan^2 \alpha}.$$

Find the subsequent velocities if $u = $ 10 ft./sec., $\alpha = $ 30°, $M' = 2M$, and $e = $ 0·5.   (Ex.)

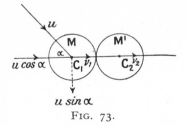

$u \sin \alpha$

FIG. 73.

Let C_1 and C_2 (Fig. 73) be the centres of M and M'.

The component velocities of M along and perpendicular to C_1C_2 are $u \cos \alpha$ and $u \sin \alpha$, and the latter is unaltered by the impact.

If v_1 and v_2 are the velocities along C_1C_2 after impact,

$$Mv_1 + M'v_2 = Mu \cos \alpha . \qquad . \qquad . \qquad . \qquad \text{(i)}$$

$$v_1 - v_2 = - eu \cos \alpha \qquad . \qquad . \qquad . \qquad \text{(ii)}$$

$$\therefore (M + M')v_1 = u \cos \alpha(M - eM'),$$

$$\therefore v_1 = \frac{(M - eM')u \cos \alpha}{M + M'}.$$

To find the angle of deflection we resolve v_1 and $u \sin \alpha$ perpendicular to and along the original direction of motion.

The sum of the components perpendicular to the original direction is

$$u \sin \alpha \cos \alpha - v_1 \sin \alpha,$$

$$= u \sin \alpha \cos \alpha - \frac{(M - eM')u \sin \alpha \cos \alpha}{M + M'} = \frac{u \sin \alpha \cos \alpha(1 + e)M'}{M + M'}.$$

The sum of the components along the original direction is

$$u \sin^2 \alpha + v_1 \cos \alpha = u \sin^2 \alpha + \frac{(M - M'e)u \cos^2 \alpha}{M + M'},$$

$$= \frac{u(M + M' \sin^2 \alpha - eM' \cos^2 \alpha)}{M + M'}.$$

$$\therefore \tan \beta = \frac{u \sin \alpha \cos \alpha(1 + e)M'}{u[M \sin^2 \alpha + M' \sin^2 \alpha + M \cos^2 \alpha - eM' \cos^2 \alpha]}$$

$$= \frac{M' \tan \alpha(1 + e)}{(M + M') \tan^2 \alpha + (M - eM')}.$$

If $u = $ 10, $\alpha = $ 30°, $M' = 2M$, $e = $ 0·5,

$$v_1 = \frac{(M - \tfrac{1}{2} 2M)u \cos \alpha}{M + 2M} = 0,$$

and $u \sin \alpha = 10 \times \tfrac{1}{2} = 5$ ft./sec.,

$\therefore$ the velocity of M is 5 ft./sec. perpendicular to the line of centres.

Also from (i) and (ii),
$$(M + M')v_2 = Mu \cos \alpha(1 + e),$$
$$\therefore v_2 = \frac{Mu \cos \alpha(1 + e)}{M + M'} = \frac{10 \cdot \frac{\sqrt{3}}{2} \cdot \frac{3}{2}}{3} = \frac{5\sqrt{3}}{2} \text{ ft./sec.}$$

EXAMPLE (iii).

A sphere is suspended from a fixed point by an inextensible string. A second sphere of small radius and equal mass m, moving downwards in a direction making an angle of 30° with the vertical, impinges directly on the first sphere with speed V. If the coefficient of restitution between the spheres is ½, prove that the initial velocity of the first sphere after impact is $\frac{3}{5}V$.

Calculate also the impulsive force in the string at the moment of impact.
(H.S.D.)

In this problem, although the impact is direct, the suspended sphere is not free to move along the line of centres. It is only free to move perpendicular to the string, i.e. horizontally, and *we can apply the principle of momentum in this direction only.*

Newton's Law is applied, as usual, along the line of centres.

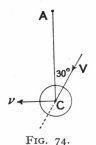

FIG. 74.

Let A (Fig. 74) be the point of suspension, and C the centre of the first sphere.

Let v be the horizontal velocity of this sphere after impact, u the velocity of the impinging sphere.

As the blow on the latter is along the line of centres, u is in the same straight line as the original direction of motion.

Equating horizontal momenta after and before impact,
$$mv + mu \cos 60° = mV \cos 60° \qquad \text{(i)}$$

From Newton's Law, along the line of centres,
$$u - v \cos 60° = -\tfrac{1}{2}V \qquad \text{(ii)}$$
$$\therefore v + \tfrac{1}{2}u = \tfrac{1}{2}V,$$
$$u - \tfrac{1}{2}v = -\tfrac{1}{2}V,$$
$$\therefore \tfrac{5}{4}v = (\tfrac{1}{2} + \tfrac{1}{4})V = \tfrac{3}{4}V,$$
$$\therefore v = \tfrac{3}{5}V.$$
Also
$$\tfrac{5}{4}u = -\tfrac{1}{4}V, \text{ or } u = -\tfrac{1}{5}V.$$

The vertical momentum before impact was $mV \cos 30° = \dfrac{\sqrt{3}}{2}mV$.

The vertical momentum after impact is

$$- \tfrac{1}{5}mV \cos 30° = - \dfrac{\sqrt{3}}{10}mV.$$

The impulsive tension in the string is equal to the change of momentum it produces, and is therefore

$$\dfrac{\sqrt{3}}{2}mV + \dfrac{\sqrt{3}}{10}mV = \dfrac{3\sqrt{3}}{5}mV.$$

EXAMPLES XXII.

1. A sphere of mass 2 lb., moving at 10 ft./sec., impinges obliquely on a sphere of mass 4 lb. which is at rest, the direction of motion of the first sphere making an angle of 60° with the line of centres at the moment of impact. Find the velocities of the spheres after impact, the coefficient of restitution being $\tfrac{1}{2}$.

2. A sphere of mass 8 lb., moving at 6 ft./sec., impinges obliquely on a sphere of mass 4 lb. which is at rest, the direction of motion making an angle of 30° with the line of centres. Find the velocities of the spheres after impact, the coefficient of restitution being $\tfrac{3}{4}$.

3. A sphere of mass 2 lb., moving with velocity 8 ft./sec., impinges on a sphere of mass 4 lb., moving with velocity 2 ft./sec.; if their velocities before impact be in like parallel directions and inclined at an angle of 30° to the line of centres at the moment of impact, find the velocities after impact, the coefficient of restitution being $\tfrac{1}{3}$.

4. If, in the last example, the spheres are moving in opposite parallel directions, find their velocities after impact.

5. Two equal balls, moving with equal speeds, impinge so that their directions of motion are inclined at 30° and 60° to the line of centres at the moment of impact ; if the balls are perfectly elastic, find their directions of motion after the impact.

6. If, in question 5, the coefficient of restitution is $\tfrac{1}{2}$, find the velocities of the balls after impact.

7. A sphere of mass m impinges obliquely on a sphere of mass M, which is at rest. Show that, if $m = eM$, the directions of motion after impact are at right angles.

8. A smooth billiard ball impinges on another equal ball at rest in a direction that makes an angle α with the line of centres at the moment of impact, and e is their coefficient of restitution. Prove that the angle, through which the direction of motion of the impinging

ball is deviated, is $\tan^{-1}\left[\dfrac{(1 + e)\tan \alpha}{1 - e + 2\tan^2 \alpha}\right]$.   (I.S.)

9. Two equal smooth billiard balls, whose coefficient of restitution is e, moving with equal velocities in opposite directions, impinge obliquely, the line of centres on impact being inclined at 45° to the direction of motion. Prove that the loss of kinetic energy is half what it would have been had the impact been direct.   (I.S.)

10. A smooth sphere, moving with velocity u, impinges on an equal smooth sphere at rest, the direction of u just before impact being inclined at an angle α to the line of centres. Find the magnitude and direction of the velocity of each sphere after impact in terms of u, α and the coefficient of restitution e. If $\tan^2 \alpha = \frac{8}{27}$, and $e = \frac{2}{3}$, show that the velocity of the first sphere is halved by the impact.
(H.S.D.)

11. A smooth sphere of mass m impinges obliquely on a sphere of mass M which is at rest. If after the impact the first sphere is moving in a direction perpendicular to that of its original motion, show that $m < eM$, where e is the coefficient of restitution. Show also that the kinetic energy of the two spheres is reduced by the impact in the ratio $1 : e$.
(H.S.D.)

12. Two equal spheres impinge obliquely, one being originally at rest and the other moving in a direction making an angle θ with the line of centres at the moment of impact. Show that the direction of motion of the second sphere is deflected through an angle α where

$$\tan \alpha = \frac{(1 + e) \tan \theta}{1 - e + 2 \tan^2 \theta},$$

e being the coefficient of restitution.

Show that θ may be so chosen that α has any given value such that

$$\tan \alpha < \frac{1}{2} \frac{1 + e}{\sqrt{2(1 - e)}}.$$
(H.S.D.)

13. A billiard ball is at rest and another equal ball is aimed at the first so that the direction of motion of the centre (when produced geometrically) just touches the first; if the coefficient of restitution is $\frac{4}{5}$, find the directions in which the balls travel after impact, and prove that the amount of kinetic energy transferred to the first ball is about 0·61 of the energy of the other before impact, while the other has about 0·26 of its original energy left.
(I.S.)

14. Two smooth spheres, masses M and m, impinge obliquely, and the latter is brought to rest. Prove that the gain of kinetic energy of the former is

$$\frac{T}{M(1 + e)} [2Me + m(e - 1)],$$

where e is the coefficient of restitution, and T the kinetic energy of the sphere m before the impact.
(I.A.)

15. Prove that, if the effect of an impact between two smooth spheres is to turn their relative velocity through a right angle, the relative velocity just before the impact must make an angle $\tan^{-1} \sqrt{e}$ with the line of centres ; e being the coefficient of restitution.
(I.S.)

16. Show that if a perfectly elastic sphere collides with another at rest, and their lines of motion after impact are at right angles, their masses must be equal.
(C.S.)

17. Two smooth spheres of equal mass whose centres are moving with equal speeds in the same plane, collide in such a way that at the moment of collision the line of centres makes an angle $90° - \beta$ with the direction bisecting the angle α between the velocities

before impact.   Show that after impact the velocities are inclined at an angle tan^{-1} (tan α cos 2β), the collision being perfectly elastic.
(C.S.)

18. A smooth sphere of mass M is suspended from a fixed point by an inelastic string, and another sphere of mass m impinges directly on it with a velocity v in a direction making an acute angle α with the vertical.   Show that the loss of kinetic energy due to the impact is

$$\frac{1}{2}\frac{mM(1 - e^2)v^2}{M + m \sin^2 \alpha},$$

where e is the coefficient of elasticity.
(C.S.)

19. Show that if a smooth sphere of mass m_1 collides with another sphere of mass m_2 at rest, and is deflected through an angle θ from its former path, the sphere of mass m_2 being set in motion in a direction ϕ with the former path of m_1, then

$$\tan \theta = \frac{m_2 \sin 2\phi}{m_1 - m_2 \cos 2\phi},$$

both spheres being perfectly elastic.
(C.S.)

20. A sphere of mass $4m$ in motion collides with a sphere of mass m at rest.   Assuming the spheres to be smooth and perfectly elastic, show that the direction of motion of the more massive sphere cannot be deflected by the collision through an angle greater than $14° \ 29'$
(C.S.)

21. A ball A impinges on an equal ball B which is at rest.   If the direction of motion of A before and after impact makes angles θ and θ' respectively with the line of centres of the balls, find θ' in terms of θ and e, the coefficient of restitution between the balls.
Show that when the deviation of A is greatest,

$$\theta + \theta' = 90°.$$
(H.C.)

22. Two uniform smooth spheres A, B, of equal radii are set in motion on a smooth horizontal table and collide with one another.   Prove that if u, u' are the components of their velocities relative to the centre of gravity, resolved along the line of centres before impact, and v, v' the corresponding velocities just after impact, then

$$mu + m'u' = 0 = mv + m'v',$$

where m, m' are the masses of the spheres.
Prove also that if e is the coefficient of resilience,

$$v' = - eu', \text{ and } v = - eu,$$

and the total energy lost in the collision is

$$\tfrac{1}{2}(1 - e^2) \ (mu^2 + m'u'^2).$$
(I.C.)

§ **129.** The following examples are of a rather harder type than those in the preceding paragraphs.

EXAMPLE (i).

A sphere of mass m is let fall on a smooth hemisphere of mass M resting with its plane face on a smooth horizontal table, so that at the moment of impact the line of centres makes an angle α with the vertical.   Find equations for determining the velocities of the bodies after impact, the velocity of the *sphere just before impact being u, and e the coefficient of restitution. Show that, when* $\alpha = 45°$, *the speed of the hemisphere after impact will equal that of the sphere just before impact if* $2M = em$.　　　　　　　　　(Ex.)

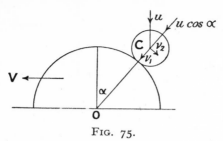

FIG. 75.

Let O (Fig. 75) be the centre of the hemisphere, and C that of the sphere.

Since the hemisphere is standing on a horizontal table we can only apply the principle of momentum horizontally.

Newton's Law is applied along the line of centres.

If V be the velocity of the hemisphere after impact (V is horizontal), v_1 and v_2 the components of the velocity of the sphere along and perpendicular to the line of centres, then, since there is no horizontal momentum initially,

$$MV + mv_1 \sin \alpha - mv_2 \cos \alpha = 0 \qquad . \qquad . \qquad \text{(i)}$$

Applying Newton's Law along the line of centres,

$$v_1 - V \sin \alpha = - eu \cos \alpha \qquad . \qquad . \qquad . \qquad \text{(ii)}$$

and since the velocity of the sphere perpendicular to the line of centres is unaltered,

$$v_2 = u \sin \alpha \qquad . \qquad . \qquad . \qquad . \qquad \text{(iii)}$$

These three equations are sufficient to determine V, v_1 and v_2.

If $\alpha = 45°$,

from (i),　　　　　　$MV + \dfrac{mv_1}{\sqrt{2}} - \dfrac{mv_2}{\sqrt{2}} = 0,$

from (ii),　　　　　　$\dfrac{mv_1}{\sqrt{2}} - \dfrac{mV}{2} = - \dfrac{meu}{2},$

and from (iii)　　　　　$\dfrac{mv_2}{\sqrt{2}} = \dfrac{mu}{2};$

$$\therefore \left(M + \frac{m}{2}\right) V = \frac{mu}{2}(1 + e),$$

and　　　　　　　　$V = u,$

if　　　　　　　　$2M + m = m (1 + e),$

or　　　　　　　　$2M = em.$

EXAMPLE (ii).

Two equal balls are lying in contact on a smooth table, and a third equal ball, moving along their common tangent, strikes them simultaneously. Prove that $\frac{3}{5}(1 - e^2)$ of its kinetic energy is lost by the impact, e being the coefficient of restitution for each pair of balls. (C.S.)

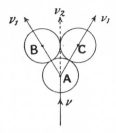

FIG. 76.

Let A (Fig. 76) be the centre of the moving ball, B and C the centres of the others.

Since the balls are equal, ABC is an equilateral triangle.

Let v be the velocity of A before impact, v_2 its velocity after impact, v_1 the common velocity of B and C after impact.

v_2 will be in the same line as v, B and C will move off along AB and AC.

We must apply the principle of momentum along the direction of A's motion for *all three balls*.

Newton's Law is applied along the line of centres for A and *one* of the others.

By the principle of momentum,

$$2v_1 \cos 30° + v_2 = v,$$

and by Newton's Law for A and C,

$$v_2 \cos 30° - v_1 = - ev \cos 30°;$$

these equations give

$$\sqrt{3}v_1 + v_2 = v \qquad . \qquad . \qquad . \qquad . \qquad \text{(i)}$$

$$\sqrt{3}v_2 - 2v_1 = - \sqrt{3}\,ev \qquad . \qquad . \qquad . \qquad \text{(ii)}$$

$$\therefore 3v_1 + \sqrt{3}v_2 = \sqrt{3}v, \text{ from (i),}$$

$$\therefore 5v_1 = \sqrt{3}v(1 + e),$$

$$\therefore v_1 = \frac{\sqrt{3}}{5}(1 + e)v.$$

Multiplying (i) by 2, and (ii) by $\sqrt{3}$ and adding,

$$5v_2 = (2 - 3e)v,$$

$$\therefore v_2 = \tfrac{1}{5}(2 - 3e)\,v.$$

The loss of kinetic energy is

$$\tfrac{1}{2}mv^2 - \tfrac{1}{2}m\frac{(2-3e)^2}{25}v^2 - m\frac{3}{25}(1+e)^2v^2,$$

$$= \tfrac{1}{2}mv^2\left[1 - \frac{4-12e+9e^2}{25} - \frac{6+12e+6e^2}{25}\right],$$

$$= \tfrac{1}{2}mv^2\left[\frac{15-15e^2}{25}\right] = \tfrac{1}{2}mv^2 \cdot \tfrac{3}{5}(1-e^2).$$

Hence the loss of kinetic energy is $\tfrac{3}{5}(1-e^2)$ of the original kinetic energy.

EXAMPLE (iii).

A particle of mass m is placed in a smooth straight tube, of mass M, which is closed at both ends and lies on a smooth horizontal table. The particle is projected from one end of the tube with velocity u and proceeds to rebound from each end alternately, the coefficient of resilience being e. Prove that the velocity of the tube is

$$\frac{mu(1+e^{2n-1})}{m+M}$$

after 2n — 1 impacts, and

$$\frac{mu(1-e^{2n})}{m+M}$$

after 2n impacts.   (Ex.)

Let u_1, v_1, u_2, v_2, etc., be the velocities of the particle and tube after the first, second, etc., impact.

The total momentum is unaltered so that

$$mu_n + Mv_n = mu, \text{ for all values of } n.$$

Also the relative velocity after each impact is $-e$ times that before the impact,

$$\therefore u_1 - v_1 = -eu,$$

$$u_2 - v_2 = +e^2u,$$

$$\bullet \qquad = \qquad \bullet$$

$$\therefore u_{2n-1} - v_{2n-1} = -e^{2n-1}u \quad . \quad . \quad . \quad \text{(i)}$$

$$u_{2n} - v_{2n} = +e^{2n}u \quad . \quad . \quad . \quad \text{(ii)}$$

Also $\qquad mu_{2n-1} + Mv_{2n-1} = mu \quad . \quad . \quad . \quad \text{(iii)}$

$$mu_{2n} + Mv_{2n} = mu \quad . \quad . \quad . \quad \text{(iv)}$$

Hence from (i) and (iii),

$$(M+m)\,v_{2n-1} = mu(1+e^{2n-1}),$$

$$\therefore v_{2n-1} = \frac{mu(1+e^{2n-1})}{m+M};$$

from (ii) and (iv),

$$(M+m)v_{2n} = mu(1-e^{2n}),$$

$$\therefore v_{2n} = \frac{mu(1-e^{2n})}{m+M}.$$

EXAMPLES XXIII.

1. An inelastic sphere of mass m is dropped with velocity V on the face of a smooth inclined plane of mass M and slope α which is free to move on a smooth horizontal plane in a direction perpendicular to the edge. Show that the loss of kinetic energy due to the impact is

$$\frac{1}{2}\frac{mMV^2\cos^2\alpha}{(M+m\sin^2\alpha)}.$$ (C.S.)

2. Three equal smooth balls A, B, C are placed in order on a smooth floor with their centres in a line perpendicular to a smooth wall which is perfectly elastic, the centre of the ball A being at a distance from the wall which is small in comparison with the distance of B. If the ball C is projected towards the wall, prove that A comes to rest temporarily after two collisions with B, independently of the coefficient of elasticity between a pair of balls.

Prove further that, if the coefficient of restitution is nearly unity, A comes permanently to rest after its fourth collision with B.   (C.S.)

3. A ball is projected on a pocketless billiard table. Show that if the effect of friction and rotation be neglected, it will travel always parallel to one of two fixed directions so long as it strikes the four cushions in order ; and that the velocity is decreased in the ratio $e^2 : 1$ after each complete circuit, e being the coefficient of restitution.   (C.S.)

4. Two equal smooth spheres A, B lie in contact on a smooth horizontal plane ; a third equal sphere C is projected with a given velocity along the table so as to strike A and B simultaneously. Find the velocities of each sphere after impact and show that the sphere C passes through and beyond the two spheres A and B if the coefficient of restitution between the spheres is less than $\frac{1}{9}$.   (C.S.)

5. A smooth inclined plane of slope α and mass M is free to move on a smooth horizontal plane in a direction perpendicular to its edge. A sphere of mass m is dropped on it. Prove that the sphere will rebound in a direction inclined to the horizontal at an angle θ,

where $$\tan\theta = \frac{(M+m)\sin^2\alpha - Me\cos^2\alpha}{M(1+e)\sin\alpha\cos\alpha},$$

where e is the coefficient of restitution.   (C.S.)

6. Two equal scale pans are suspended by inextensible string passing over a smooth pulley so that each remains horizontal. An elastic sphere falls vertically, and when its velocity is u it strikes one of the scale pans and rebounds vertically. Show that the sphere takes the same time to come to rest on the scale pan as it would if the scale pan were fixed.   (C.S.)

7. A spherical ball of mass m suspended by a string from a fixed point is at rest, and another spherical ball of mass m' which is falling vertically with velocity u impinges on it so that the line joining the centres of the balls makes an angle α with the vertical. Prove that the loss of kinetic energy is

$$\frac{1}{2}\frac{(1-e^2)mm'u^2\cos^2\alpha}{m+m'\sin^2\alpha},$$

where e is the coefficient of restitution.   (C.S.)

8. Four particles, each of mass m, are connected by equal inextensible strings of length a and lie on a smooth table at the corners of a rhombus the sides of which are formed by the strings. One of the particles receives a blow P along the diagonal outwards. Prove that the angular velocities of the strings after the blow are equal to $\dfrac{P \sin \alpha}{2ma}$, where 2α $\left(\alpha < \dfrac{\pi}{4}\right)$ is the angle of the rhombus at the particle which is struck.

(C.S.)

9. Two equal smooth spheres of mass m, perfectly elastic, collide obliquely. Initially one is at rest. Prove that the velocities of the two spheres after impact are at right angles, and express the final velocities in terms of the initial velocity V and the angle ϕ between the line of centres at impact and the direction of motion of the moving sphere before impact.

(C.S.)

10. A small smooth sphere of mass m impinges on a small smooth sphere of mass m' at rest, and m' starts moving with velocity V. If e is the coefficient of restitution, prove that, whether the impact is direct or oblique, the kinetic energy dissipated is

$$\frac{m'(m + m')(1 - e)V^2}{2m(1 + e)}.$$

(C.S.)

11. A particle falls vertically on a fixed rough elastic plane inclined at an angle α to the horizon. Show that if the direction of motion of the particle immediately after impact is horizontal,

$$\tan^2 \alpha - \mu(1 + e)\tan \alpha - e = 0,$$

where e is the coefficient of resilience, and μ that of friction.

(H.S.C.)

12. A smooth wedge ABC of mass M and with angle ABC $= \alpha$, is placed with the face AB on a smooth horizontal plane. A particle of mass m, moving with velocity u inclined at $(\alpha - \beta)$ to the horizontal strikes the face BC at an angle β. If e is the coefficient of elasticity, show that the horizontal velocity of the particle after the impact will exceed that of the wedge if

$(M + m) (\cos \alpha \cos \beta - e \sin \alpha \sin \beta) > m \cos^2 \alpha \cos (\alpha - \beta)$.

(Ex.)

13. If a ball is projected from a point on a smooth billiard table so as to strike in succession a side cushion, the top cushion, the other side cushion, and bottom cushion, show that the rectilinear portions of its path are parallel in pairs, assuming the cushions smooth and equally resilient.

Within what area on the table must the point of projection be in order that at the fourth impact as described above the ball when projected in the right direction may fall into a bottom pocket, a, b, being the lengths of the sides of the table measured along the inside edges of the cushions, c the radius of the ball, and e the coefficient of resilience between each cushion and the ball.   (Ex.)

14. A smooth inelastic sphere of mass M lies on a smooth horizontal plane ; a second smooth inelastic sphere of mass m falls on it. At the moment of impact the line of centres makes an angle α with the vertical, and the velocity of the falling sphere is U. Prove that the subsequent velocity of the lower sphere is

$$\frac{m \sin \alpha \cos \alpha U}{M + m \sin^2 \alpha}.$$

(H.C.)

15. What is meant by the impulsive tension of a string and in what units can it be measured ?

    Two particles of equal mass, 2 gm., are connected by a smooth light straight string which passes through a hole in a block of mass 8 gm. The system is placed on a smooth horizontal table with the block at rest, while the two particles are given the same velocity 10 cm./sec. in the direction of the string. If the coefficient of restitution between particle and block is $\frac{1}{2}$, find the velocity of the block after impact by one of the particles. Find also the impulsive tension of the string at the impact.   (N.U.3)

16. A body is placed at rest on an inclined inelastic plane of inclination 10° and coefficient of friction $\frac{1}{3}$. A second body of equal mass falls vertically on to it with a speed of 16 ft./sec. and coalesces with the first body.

    Find the initial velocity of the two bodies together down the plane, and the distance travelled before they come to rest.
                                                                    (N.U.3)

CHAPTER IV.

PROJECTILES.

§ **130.** We have now to consider the motion of a particle when projected under gravity in any direction. In doing this we shall assume, as before, that the acceleration due to gravity is constant. We shall also neglect the resistance of the air to the motion. The following terms are used in connection with projectiles :—

The Angle of Projection, is the angle that the direction in which the particle is projected makes with a horizontal plane through the point of projection. This angle is also called the *angle of elevation.*

The Trajectory is the path described by the particle.

The Range is the distance between the point of projection and the point where the trajectory meets any plane through the point of projection.

The downward acceleration due to the earth's attraction causes the path to be curved, and we shall show later that this curve is always a parabola.

Many important results, however, can be obtained without assuming any knowledge of the nature of the path.

§ **131.** The principle of the method employed is to consider the vertical and horizontal components of the motion separately. Since gravity acts vertically, it has no effect on the velocity of the particle in a horizontal direction.

The horizontal velocity therefore remains constant throughout the motion.

If the particle is projected with velocity u at an elevation α, the horizontal and vertical components of the initial velocity are $u \cos \alpha$ and $u \sin \alpha$ respectively.

The horizontal velocity throughout the motion is therefore $u \cos \alpha$. The vertical motion is dealt with in the same way as in paragraphs 54-58 taking $u \sin \alpha$ for the initial velocity of projection.

§ **132.** Suppose the particle projected from P (Fig. 77) with velocity u at an angle α to the horizontal PX through P.

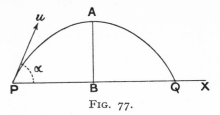

FIG. 77.

Let A be the highest point of the path, and Q the point where it again meets the horizontal plane through P.

1. To Find the Greatest Height Attained.

When the particle has reached the highest point A of its path it will have lost all its vertical velocity, hence using the formula

$$v^2 = u^2 - 2gs,$$

since u is now replaced by $u \sin \alpha$, we have, if h is the greatest height,

$$0 = u^2 \sin^2 \alpha - 2gh,$$
$$\therefore h = \frac{u^2 \sin^2 \alpha}{2g}.$$

2. To Find the Time taken to reach the Greatest Height.

Using the formula
we have

$$v = u - gt,$$
$$0 = u \sin \alpha - gt,$$
$$\therefore t = \frac{u \sin \alpha}{g}.$$

3. To Find the Time of Flight, i.e. the Time taken to return to the same Horizontal Level as P.

Using

$$s = ut - \tfrac{1}{2}gt^2, \text{ and putting } s = 0,$$
$$0 = u \sin \alpha \, T - \tfrac{1}{2}gT^2,$$
$$\therefore T = \frac{2u \sin \alpha}{g}.$$

This is twice the time taken to reach the highest point.

4. To Find the Range on the Horizontal Plane through P.

During the time T the particle has been moving horizontally with uniform velocity $u \cos \alpha$,

∴ horizontal distance described

$$= u \cos \alpha \,.\, T = \frac{2u^2 \sin \alpha \cos \alpha}{g},$$

∴ the range

$$R = \frac{2u^2 \sin \alpha \cos \alpha}{g} = \frac{u^2 \sin 2\alpha}{g}.$$

PROJECTILES

For a given velocity of projection u, this expression for the range is a maximum when $2\alpha = 90°$, or $\alpha = 45°$.

Hence for a given velocity of projection, *the horizontal range is greatest when the angle of projection is 45°.*

5. To Find the Velocity and Direction of Motion after a Given Time.

We know that the horizontal component of the velocity is constant and equal to $u \cos \alpha$.

The vertical component v after a time t is given by

$$v = u \sin \alpha - gt,$$

∴ if V is the resultant velocity,

$$V^2 = u^2 \cos^2\alpha + (u \sin \alpha - gt)^2,$$
$$= u^2 - 2ugt \sin \alpha + g^2t^2.$$

If θ be the angle which the direction of motion makes with the horizontal,

$$\tan \theta = \frac{\text{vertical component of velocity}}{\text{horizontal component of velocity}} = \frac{u \sin \alpha - gt}{u \cos \alpha}.$$

§ **133.** *For a given velocity of projection there are, in general, two possible angles of projection to obtain a given horizontal range.*

We have seen that the range

$$R = \frac{u^2}{g} \sin 2\alpha.$$

If R and u are given

$$\sin 2\alpha = \frac{gR}{u^2}.$$

Now for a given value of the sine of the angle 2α, there are two values of the angle less than $180°$. If 2θ is one value the other is $180° - 2\theta$. ∴ θ and $90° - \theta$ are two possible angles of projection unless $\frac{gR}{u^2} = 1$, when only one value is possible, viz. $90°$ for 2α, or $45°$ for α.

This is the case when the range is a maximum for the given velocity u.

The directions θ and $90° - \theta$ are equally inclined to the horizontal and vertical respectively, so that the direction for maximum range bisects the angle between them.

§ **134.** EXAMPLE (i).

A particle is projected with a velocity of 960 ft./sec., at an elevation of 30° : find (i) the greatest height attained, (ii) the time of flight and the range on a horizontal plane through the point of projection, (iii) the velocity and direction of motion at a height of 528 feet.

The initial horizontal velocity $= 960 \cos 30 = 960 \times \dfrac{\sqrt{3}}{2}$,

$$= 480 \sqrt{3} \text{ ft./sec.}$$

The initial vertical velocity $= 960 \sin 30° = 480$ ft./sec.

(i) If h be the greatest height, then at this height the particle has lost all vertical velocity,

$$\therefore 0 = 480^2 - 2gh$$
$$\therefore h = \frac{480 \times 480}{2 \times 32} = 3600 \text{ ft.}$$

(ii) If t be the time of flight, the vertical height at that time is zero,

$$\therefore 0 = 480t - \tfrac{1}{2}gt^2,$$
$$\therefore t = \frac{960}{32} = 30 \text{ seconds.}$$

The horizontal range is the distance travelled horizontally in 30 seconds with uniform velocity $480\sqrt{3}$ ft./sec.

$$= 480\sqrt{3} \times 30 = 14{,}400\sqrt{3} \text{ feet,}$$
$$= 24{,}941 \text{ feet approximately.}$$

(iii) If v is the vertical velocity at a height of 528 ft.

$$v^2 = 480^2 - 2g \cdot 528,$$
$$= 480^2 - 64 \times 528 = 64 \times 3072$$
$$\therefore v = 8 \times 32\sqrt{3} \text{ ft./sec.}$$
$$= 256\sqrt{3} \text{ ft./sec.}$$

The horizontal velocity is $480\sqrt{3}$, and if θ is the inclination of the direction of motion to the horizontal,

$$\tan \theta = \frac{256\sqrt{3}}{480\sqrt{3}} = \frac{32}{60} = \frac{8}{15}.$$

The resultant velocity V is given by

$$V^2 = 8^2 \times 32^2 \times 3 + 480^2 \times 3 = 8^2 \times 4^2 \times 867,$$
$$\therefore V = 32 \times 17\sqrt{3},$$
$$= 544\sqrt{3} \text{ ft./sec.}$$

EXAMPLE (ii).

A particle is projected with a velocity of 48 ft./sec. : find the maximum range on a horizontal plane through the point of projection and the two directions of projection to give a range of 36 ft.

If the angle of projection is α, the horizontal and vertical components of the initial velocity are $48 \cos \alpha$ and $48 \sin \alpha$.

The time of flight t, is given by

$$0 = 48 \sin \alpha \cdot t - \tfrac{1}{2}gt^2,$$
$$\therefore t = \frac{96 \sin \alpha}{32} = 3 \sin \alpha.$$

In this time the horizontal range is

$$3 \times 48 \sin \alpha \cos \alpha,$$
$$= 72 \sin 2\alpha.$$

This is a maximum when $2\alpha = 90°$, or $\alpha = 45°$, and then the value is 72 feet.

When the range is 36 feet we have

$$72 \sin 2\alpha = 36,$$
$$\therefore \sin 2\alpha = \tfrac{1}{2},$$
$$\therefore 2\alpha = 30°, \text{ or } 150°,$$
$$\therefore \alpha = 15° \text{ or } 75°.$$

EXAMPLE (iii).

A particle is projected out to sea with a velocity of 192 ft./sec. from the top of a cliff 256 feet high at an angle of 30° with the horizontal : find how far from the bottom of the cliff the particle hits the water.

The initial vertical velocity is 192 cos 60° = 96 ft./sec.
The initial horizontal velocity is 192 cos 30° = $96\sqrt{3}$ ft./sec.

The time t to reach a point 256 feet below the point of projection is given by

$$-256 = 96t - 16t^2,$$
$$\therefore t^2 - 6t - 16 = 0,$$
$$\therefore (t - 8)(t + 2) = 0,$$
$$\therefore t = 8 \text{ seconds.}$$

In this time the horizontal distance travelled is

$$8 \times 96\sqrt{3} = 768\sqrt{3} \text{ feet,}$$
$$= 1330 \text{ feet approximately.}$$

EXAMPLE (iv).

A bullet is fired with a velocity whose horizontal and vertical components are u, v : find its position at time t. If the horizontal velocity is 2000 ft./sec., find the elevation at which it must be fired if it is to hit a mark 6 feet above the muzzle at a distance of 500 yards.

If x, y are the horizontal and vertical distances from the muzzle after time t,

$$x = ut, \quad \quad \quad \quad \text{(i)}$$
$$y = vt - \tfrac{1}{2}gt^2 \quad \quad \quad \text{(ii)}$$

When $u = 2000$ ft./sec. and $x = 1500$ feet,

$$t = \frac{x}{u} = \frac{1500}{2000} = \frac{3}{4} \text{ second.}$$

The height at this time has to be 6 feet, and substituting $y = 6$, $t = \tfrac{3}{4}$ in equation (ii),

$$6 = \tfrac{3}{4}v - 16 \times \tfrac{9}{16},$$
$$\therefore \tfrac{3}{4}v = 6 + 9 = 15,$$
$$\therefore v = 20 \text{ ft./sec.}$$

If θ is the angle of elevation initially

$$\tan \theta = \frac{v}{u} = \frac{20}{2000} = \frac{1}{100}.$$
$$\therefore \theta = \text{about } 3\tfrac{1}{2} \text{ minutes.}$$

EXAMPLE (v).

If r be the horizontal range of a projectile, and h its greatest height, prove that the initial speed is

$$\left[2g\left(h + \frac{r^2}{16h}\right)\right]^{\frac{1}{2}}.$$

Let u be the initial speed, and α the angle of projection.
The horizontal range

$$r = \frac{2u^2 \sin \alpha \cos \alpha}{g} \qquad . \qquad . \qquad . \qquad . \qquad \text{(i)}$$

The greatest height

$$h = \frac{u^2 \sin{}^2\alpha}{2g} . \qquad . \qquad . \qquad . \qquad . \qquad \text{(ii)}$$

Now the value of u given in the question does not contain α, so that it must be obtained by eliminating α between equations (i) and (ii).

From (ii) we have $\operatorname{cosec}^2 \alpha = \dfrac{u^2}{2gh}.$

Dividing (i) by (ii), $4 \cot \alpha = \dfrac{r}{h}$, or $\cot \alpha = \dfrac{r}{4h}.$

Now

$$\operatorname{cosec}^2 \alpha = 1 + \cot^2 \alpha,$$

$$\therefore \frac{u^2}{2gh} = 1 + \frac{r^2}{16h^2},$$

$$\therefore u^2 = 2g\left(h + \frac{r^2}{16h}\right),$$

$$\therefore u = \left[2g\left(h + \frac{r^2}{16h}\right)\right]^{\frac{1}{2}}.$$

EXAMPLE (vi).

A projectile is fired from a point on a cliff to hit a mark 200 feet horizontally from the point and 200 feet vertically below it. The velocity of projection is that due to falling freely under gravity through 100 feet from rest. Show that the two possible directions of projection are at right angles, and that the times of flight are approximately 2·7 and 6·5 seconds.

The velocity v acquired in falling 100 feet is given by

$$v^2 = 2g \cdot 100 = 64 \times 100,$$
$$\therefore v = 80 \text{ ft./sec.}$$

If α is the angle of elevation at which the projectile is fired,

$$- 200 = 80 \sin \alpha \cdot t - 16t^2, \qquad . \qquad . \qquad . \qquad \text{(i)}$$

also

$$200 = 80 \cos \alpha \cdot t \qquad . \qquad . \qquad . \qquad . \qquad \text{(ii)}$$

From (ii) we get

$$t = \tfrac{5}{2} \sec. \alpha.$$

Substituting in (i),

$$- 200 = 200 \tan \alpha - 100 \sec^2 \alpha,$$
$$= 200 \tan \alpha - 100 - 100 \tan^2 \alpha,$$
$$\therefore \tan \alpha = \frac{2 \pm \sqrt{4 + 4}}{2} = 1 \pm \sqrt{2}.$$

One of these values is negative, and this means that one of the directions is below the horizontal.

The product of the two tangents is

$$(1 + \sqrt{2})(1 - \sqrt{2}) = -1,$$

and this, by a well-known result in geometry, shows that the directions are at right angles.

If

$$\tan \alpha_1 = 1 + \sqrt{2},$$

and

$$\tan \alpha_2 = 1 - \sqrt{2},$$

$$\sec^2 \alpha_1 = 1 + 3 + 2\sqrt{2},$$

$$= 6 \cdot 828,$$

$$\sec^2 \alpha_2 = 1 + 3 - 2\sqrt{2},$$

$$= 1 \cdot 172,$$

$$\therefore \sec \alpha_1 = 2 \cdot 6,$$

and

$$\sec \alpha_2 = 1 \cdot 08,$$

$$\therefore \text{the times are } \tfrac{5}{2} \times 2 \cdot 6 = 6 \cdot 5 \text{ seconds,}$$

and

$$\tfrac{5}{2} \times 1 \cdot 08 = 2 \cdot 7 \text{ seconds, approx.}$$

EXAMPLE (vii).

A vertical post subtends an angle α at a point A in the same horizontal plane as the foot of the post. Two particles are projected at the same instant from A, in directions making angles θ_1 and θ_2 with the horizontal, so that the former strikes the top of the post at the same moment that the latter strikes the bottom of the post. Prove that

$$\tan \theta_1 - \tan \theta_2 = \tan \alpha.$$

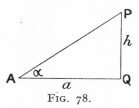

FIG. 78.

Let u_1, u_2 be the velocities of projection, h the height of the post PQ (Fig. 78) and a its horizontal distance from A.

Since the particles describe the same horizontal distance in the same time, their horizontal velocities are equal,

$$\therefore u_1 \cos \theta_1 = u_2 \cos \theta_2.$$

If t be the time taken to reach the post,

$$t = \frac{a}{u_1 \cos \theta_1} = \frac{a}{u_2 \cos \theta_2},$$

also

$$h = u_1 \sin \theta_1 . t - \tfrac{1}{2} gt^2,$$
$$o = u_2 \sin \theta_2 . t - \tfrac{1}{2} gt^2,$$
$$\therefore h = t(u_1 \sin \theta_1 - u_2 \sin \theta_2),$$
$$\therefore \frac{h}{u_1 \cos \theta_1} = t (\tan \theta_1 - \tan \theta_2),$$
$$\therefore \frac{h}{u_1 \cos \theta_1} = \frac{a}{u_1 \cos \theta_1}(\tan \theta_1 - \tan \theta_2),$$
$$\therefore a \tan \alpha = a(\tan \theta_1 - \tan \theta_2), \text{ since } h = a \tan \alpha,$$
$$\therefore \tan \alpha = \tan \theta_1 - \tan \theta_2.$$

EXAMPLES XXIV.

1. A particle is projected with a velocity of 96 ft./sec. at an elevation of 30°: find (i) the greatest height reached, (ii) the time of flight and the horizontal range, (iii) the velocity and direction of motion at a height of 11 feet.

2. Find the greatest range on a horizontal plane when the velocity of projection is (i) 64, (ii) 60, (iii) 96 feet per second.

3. A man can just throw a stone 200 feet : with what velocity does he throw it and how long is it in the air ?

4. A projectile is fired horizontally from a point 200 feet above a horizontal plane with a velocity of 2000 ft./sec.
   How far will it be horizontally from the point of projection when it reaches the plane ?

5. A shot is fired from a gun on the top of a vertical cliff, 400 feet high, with a velocity of 768 ft./sec., at an elevation of 30°. Find the horizontal distance from the foot of the cliff of the point where the shot strikes the water.

6. Find the velocity and direction of projection of a particle which passes in a horizontal direction just over the top of a wall which is 32 yards distant and 12 yards high.

7. Find, to the nearest yard, the range on a horizontal plane of a rifle bullet fired at an elevation of 3° with a muzzle velocity of 1000 ft./sec. (I.S.)

8. What is the least velocity of projection required to obtain a horizontal range of 100 yards, and what will be the time of flight ? (I.A.)

9. Show that a particle starting with a velocity of 100 ft./sec. at an angle $\tan^{-1} \tfrac{3}{4}$ to the horizon will just clear a wall 36 feet high at a horizontal distance of 80 yards from the point of projection. (I.A.)

10. A body is thrown from the top of a tower 96 feet high with a velocity of 80 ft./sec. at an elevation of 30° above the horizontal : find the horizontal distance from the foot of the tower of the point where it hits the ground. (I.A.)

11. A bullet is fired out to sea in a horizontal direction from a gun situated on the top of a cliff 280 feet high.
    Calculate the distance out to sea at which the bullet will strike the water, given that the initial velocity of the bullet is 800 ft./sec.
    Calculate also the inclination to the horizontal at which the bullet will strike the surface of the water. (H.S.D.)

12. A bullet is fired with an initial velocity of 2000 ft./sec. in a direction making 25° with the horizontal.
    Calculate how far from the starting-point the bullet will strike the ground again.   (H.S.D.)

13. If a particle is projected inside a horizontal tunnel which is 16 feet high with a velocity of 200 ft./sec., find the greatest possible range.
    (I.S.)

14. A ball is thrown from a height of 3 feet above the ground to clear a wall, 35 feet away horizontally, and 15 feet high.
    Show that the velocity of projection must not be less than that acquired by falling under gravity through $24\frac{1}{2}$ feet, and, when this is the velocity of projection, find how far beyond the wall it will reach the ground.   (I.S.)

15. A body is projected at such an angle that the horizontal range is three times the greatest height. Find the angle of projection, and if, with this angle the range is 400 yards, find the necessary velocity of projection and the time of flight.   (I.A.)

16. A ball is thrown with a velocity whose horizontal component is 40 ft./sec. from a point 4 feet 3 inches above the ground and 20 feet away from a vertical wall 16 feet 3 inches high in such a way as just to clear the wall. At what time will it reach the ground ?   (I.E.)

17. A ball is thrown from a point A in a horizontal plane so as just to pass over a wall standing on the same plane, the horizontal component of the ball's velocity being equal to the velocity it would acquire in falling from rest through a distance equal to the horizontal distance of A from the wall. Prove that the ball pitches behind the wall at a distance from it equal to 4 times the height of the wall.   (I.E.)

18. Find the least initial velocity which a projectile may have, so that it may clear a wall, 10 feet high and 13 feet distant, and strike the horizontal plane through the foot of the wall at a distance 7 feet beyond the wall, the point of projection being at the same level as the foot of the wall.   (H.S.D.)

19. The greatest range of a gun is 16 miles : find the muzzle velocity of the shot, and prove that, when the shot has travelled 4 miles horizontally it has risen 3 miles.   (H.C.)

20. A bullet is fired from a point O with a velocity whose horizontal and vertical components are u and v respectively : find the direction in which it is moving after a time t. If $u = 96$ ft./sec., $v = 288$ ft./sec., prove that at two points the direction of the bullet's motion is at right angles to the line joining the bullet to O, and find the positions of these points.   (H.C.)

21. A shell is observed to explode at the level of the gun from which it is fired after an interval of 10 secs. : and the sound of the explosion reaches the gun after a further interval of 3 secs. Find the elevation of the gun and the speed with which the shell is fired. (Assume the velocity of sound to be 1100 ft./sec.)   (H.C.)

22. Show that, if R be the maximum horizontal range for a given velocity of projection, a particle can be projected to pass through the point whose horizontal and vertical distances from the point of projection are $\frac{1}{2}R$ and $\frac{1}{4}R$ respectively, provided that the tangent of the angle of projection is either 1 or 3, and that in the second case the range on the horizontal plane is $\frac{3}{5}R$.   (I.S.)

23. A shot projected with velocity v can just reach a certain point on the horizontal plane through the point of projection. Show that, in order to hit a mark h feet above the ground at the same point, if the shot is projected at the same elevation, the velocity of projection must be increased to

$$\frac{v^2}{(v^2 - gh)^{\frac{1}{2}}}$$ (I.S.)

24. Prove that the time of flight T, and the horizontal range X of a projectile are connected by the equation

$$gT^2 = 2X \tan \alpha,$$

where α is the angle of elevation.

Show that when the maximum horizontal range is 100 miles, the time of flight is about 3 minutes, and determine the muzzle velocity and the height of the trajectory. (I.E.)

25. A body is projected so that on its upward path it passes through a point x feet horizontally and y feet vertically from the point of projection. Show that, if R feet is the range on a horizontal plane through the point of projection, the angle of elevation of projection is

$$\tan^{-1}\left(\frac{y}{x} \cdot \frac{R}{R - x}\right)$$ (I.S.)

26. A particle projected from a point meets the horizontal plane through the point of projection after describing a horizontal distance a, and in the course of its trajectory attains a greatest height b above the point of projection. Find the horizontal and vertical components of the velocity of projection in terms of a and b.

Show that when it has described a horizontal distance x, it has attained a height of $4bx(a - x)/a^2$. (H.C.)

27. If the horizontal range of a particle projected with velocity V is a, show that the greatest height x attained is given by the equation

$$16gx^2 - 8V^2x + ga^2 = 0.$$

Explain why two values of x are to be expected. (I.S.)

28. Show that the relative velocity of two bodies moving in any direction under the acceleration of gravity remains constant. A stone is projected horizontally from the top of a tower 180 feet high with a velocity of 50 ft./sec., and at the same instant another stone is projected in the same vertical plane from the foot of the tower with a velocity of 100 ft./sec. at an elevation of 60°. Show that the stones will meet, and find the height above the ground, and the distance from the tower at the instant of meeting. (I.E.)

29. A ball is projected from a point on the ground distant a from the foot of a vertical wall of height b, the velocity of projection being V at an angle α to the horizontal. Find how high above the wall the ball passes it.

If the ball just clears the wall prove that the greatest height reached is

$$\frac{1}{4} \frac{a^2 \tan^2 \alpha}{(a \tan \alpha - b)}.$$ (N.U.3)

30. A body of weight W falls through a height h from rest under gravity. Find the momentum added to the body during the fall.

From an aeroplane flying horizontally at 120 m.p.h. at a height
of 2 miles above the ground, a bullet is fired horizontally backwards
at 960 ft./sec. Find the direction in which the bullet is moving
when it reaches the ground, ignoring air resistance.   (N.U.3)

31. Two projectiles P, Q are fired with the same speed V, and at the same
inclination, α, to the horizontal from the same point, one being fired
one second after the other. Prove that their horizontal separation
remains constant while their vertical separation t seconds after the
second is fired is

$$V \sin \alpha - gt - \tfrac{1}{2}g. \qquad \text{(N.U.3)}$$

32. A particle is projected from a point O with elevation α and speed V.
Prove that the horizontal range is given by the formula

$$R = \frac{V^2}{g} \sin 2\alpha.$$

If $\alpha = 30°$, find in terms of R the height of the projectile when it
has moved a horizontal distance equal to $\tfrac{3}{4}R$.   (N.U.3)

33. An aeroplane is flying at a height of 3000 feet in a straight horizontal
course at a speed of 150 m.p.h., the direction of the course being such
as to carry it vertically over a fort, on which the pilot has to drop a
bomb. Find the angle between the vertical and the straight line
joining the aeroplane to the fort at the moment when the bomb
should be released.   (N.U.3)

34. A particle is projected with a velocity of 50 ft./sec. up a smooth
inclined plane of angle $\tan^{-1}\tfrac{3}{4}$ and length 50 feet ; on leaving the
plane at its upper edge it describes a parabola under gravity. Find
the greatest height attained, and the time taken to attain it after
leaving the plane.   (N.U.3)

35. If two particles move freely under the action of gravity, show that
their relative velocity remains constant.

A particle is projected from a point A with a velocity v along AB,
and simultaneously a particle is projected from B with a velocity
V along BA, the line AB having any direction. Show that the
particles will collide at a point vertically below the point which
divides AB in the ratio $v : V$.

§ 135. Range on an Inclined Plane through the Point of Projection.

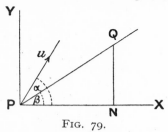

FIG. 79.

Let a particle be projected from a point P (Fig. 79) on a plane
of inclination β with velocity u, at an elevation α to the horizontal,
the direction of projection being in the vertical plane through the
line of greatest slope PQ of the inclined plane. Let PQ be the range,
and QN the perpendicular on the horizontal plane through P.

To obtain the time of flight we consider the motion perpendicular to the plane.

The initial velocity perpendicular to the plane is $u \sin (\alpha - \beta)$ and the acceleration in this direction is $- g \cos \beta$.

The time of flight T is therefore given by

$$o = u \sin (\alpha - \beta)T - \tfrac{1}{2}g \cos \beta \cdot T^2,$$

$$\therefore T = \frac{2u \sin (\alpha - \beta)}{g \cos \beta}.$$

The horizontal velocity during this time is constant and equal to $u \cos \alpha$, and the horizontal distance PN described is

$$\frac{2u^2 \sin (\alpha - \beta) \cos \alpha}{g \cos \beta},$$

and $PQ = PN \sec \beta$,

$$\therefore \text{range} = \frac{2u^2 \sin (\alpha - \beta) \cos \alpha}{g \cos^2 \beta}. \qquad . \qquad . \quad \text{(i)}$$

§ **136.** The maximum value of the range for given values of u and β is obtained as follows :—

$$R = \frac{2u^2 \sin (\alpha - \beta) \cos \alpha}{g \cos^2 \beta} = \frac{u^2}{g \cos^2 \beta}[\sin (2\alpha - \beta) - \sin \beta] \quad \text{(ii)}$$

Now since β and u are given, the quantity outside the bracket

$$\left(\frac{u^2}{g \cos^2 \beta} \right)$$

is constant, and the value of the expression in the bracket is a maximum when $\sin(2\alpha - \beta)$ is a maximum, i.e. when $2\alpha - \beta = \dfrac{\pi}{2}$,

$\therefore$ for maximum range,

$$\alpha = \frac{\pi}{4} + \frac{\beta}{2}.$$

We see also that

$$\alpha - \beta = \frac{\pi}{2} - \alpha,$$

or the direction of projection bisects the angle between the plane and the vertical.

The value of the maximum range is

$$\frac{u^2}{g \cos^2 \beta}(1 - \sin \beta) = \frac{u^2}{g(1 + \sin \beta)} \qquad . \qquad . \quad \text{(iii)}$$

§ **137.** For a given value of the range (other than the maximum value) with a given velocity of projection, we obtain from (ii) a value for $\sin(2\alpha - \beta)$.

Now for a given sine there are two angles less than 180°, so that we get two values for $2\alpha - \beta$, if θ is one value the other is $\pi - \theta$, so that
$$2\alpha - \beta = \theta,$$

and
$$\alpha = \frac{\theta}{2} + \frac{\beta}{2},$$

or
$$2\alpha - \beta = \pi - \theta,$$

and
$$\alpha = \frac{\pi}{2} + \frac{\beta}{2} - \frac{\theta}{2}.$$

There are thus two angles of projection for a given range. The angle of projection for a maximum is $\frac{\pi}{4} + \frac{\beta}{2}$,

also
$$\frac{1}{2}\left(\frac{\theta}{2} + \frac{\beta}{2} + \frac{\pi}{2} + \frac{\beta}{2} - \frac{\theta}{2}\right) = \frac{\pi}{4} + \frac{\beta}{2},$$

∴ the two directions of projection for a given range are equally inclined to the direction for maximum range.

§ **138.** In the preceding paragraphs the direction of projection was expressed as an elevation to the horizontal.

We can also take the elevation *relative to the inclined plane*.

In working problems care must be taken in reading the question to see which of these angles is given.

If θ is the inclination of the direction of projection to the line of greatest slope of the plane, the initial velocities perpendicular and parallel to the plane are $u \sin \theta$ and $u \cos \theta$.

The time of flight T is given by
$$0 = u \sin \theta . T - \tfrac{1}{2}g \cos \beta . T^2,$$

$$\therefore T = \frac{2u \sin \theta}{g \cos \beta} \qquad . \qquad . \qquad . \qquad \text{(iv)}$$

The range can be found as before, remembering that the horizontal velocity is now $u \cos (\beta + \theta)$, or by considering the motion *parallel to the plane*.

In time T the distance (R) travelled parallel to the plane is
$$R = u \cos \theta . T - \tfrac{1}{2}g \sin \beta . T^2 \qquad . \qquad . \qquad \text{(v)}$$

The relations (iv) and (v) are useful in problems where the times of flight for a given range are required. It is easy to eliminate θ from these two equations.

§ **139.** EXAMPLE (i).

A particle is projected with a velocity of 900 ft./sec. at an elevation of 60° to the horizontal from the foot of a plane of inclination 30°. Find the range on the inclined plane and the time of flight.

Let PQ (Fig. 80) represent the inclined plane.

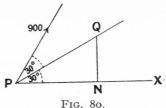

FIG. 80.

The component of velocity perpendicular to the plane is

$$900 \sin 30° = 450 \text{ ft./sec.}$$

The acceleration perpendicular to the plane is

$$g \cos 30° = \frac{\sqrt{3}}{2} g = 16\sqrt{3} \text{ ft./sec.}^2$$

The time of flight t is given by

$$0 = 450t - \tfrac{1}{2} . 16\sqrt{3} \, t^2,$$

$$\therefore t = \frac{450}{8\sqrt{3}} = \frac{75\sqrt{3}}{4} = 32\cdot5 \text{ sec. nearly.}$$

In $\dfrac{75\sqrt{3}}{4}$ sec. the particle travels a horizontal distance

$$\frac{75\sqrt{3}}{4} \times 450 \text{ feet.}$$

The distance up the plane is obtained by multiplying this by

$$\sec 30°, \text{ or } \frac{2}{\sqrt{3}},$$

$\therefore$ range on the plane

$$= \frac{75\sqrt{3}}{4} \times \frac{450}{1} \times \frac{2}{\sqrt{3}} = 16,875 \text{ ft.}$$

EXAMPLE (ii).

A particle is projected with a velocity of 64 ft./sec. at an angle of 45° to the horizontal. Find its range on a plane inclined at 30° to the horizontal when projected (i) up, (ii) down the plane.

(i) The component of velocity perpendicular to the plane is

$$64 \sin 15° \text{ ft./sec.}$$

The acceleration perpendicular to the plane is

$$32 \cos 30° = 16\sqrt{3} \text{ ft./sec.}^2$$

The time of flight is given by

$$0 = 64 \sin 15° . t - 8\sqrt{3} \, t^2,$$

$$\therefore t = \frac{64 \sin 15°}{8\sqrt{3}} = 1\cdot2 \text{ sec.}$$

The horizontal velocity is $\dfrac{64}{\sqrt{2}}$ ft./sec. and the horizontal distance in time $\dfrac{8 \sin 15°}{\sqrt{3}}$ sec. is

$$\frac{64 \times 8 \sin 15°}{\sqrt{6}} \text{ ft.}$$

The range up the plane is obtained by multiplying this by sec 30°, or $\dfrac{2}{\sqrt{3}}$,

∴ range up the plane

$$= \frac{64 \times 8 \sin 15°}{\sqrt{6}} \times \frac{2}{\sqrt{3}} = 62 \cdot 5 \text{ ft. nearly.}$$

(ii) The component of velocity perpendicular to the plane is 64 sin 75°. The time of flight is given by

$$0 = 64 \sin 75° - 8 \sqrt{3}\, t,$$

$$\therefore t = \frac{8 \sin 75°}{\sqrt{3}} = 4 \cdot 5 \text{ sec. nearly.}$$

The horizontal velocity is $\dfrac{64}{\sqrt{2}}$ ft./sec. and the horizontal distance in time $\dfrac{8 \sin 75°}{\sqrt{3}}$ sec. is

$$\frac{64 \times 8 \sin 75°}{\sqrt{6}} \text{ ft.,}$$

the range down the plane is

$$\frac{64 \times 8 \sin 75°}{\sqrt{6}} \times \frac{2}{\sqrt{3}},$$

$$= 233 \text{ ft. nearly.}$$

EXAMPLE (iii).

Show that for a given velocity of projection, the maximum range down an inclined plane of inclination α *is greater than that up the plane in the ratio*

$$\frac{1 + \sin \alpha}{1 - \sin \alpha}.$$

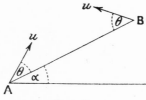

FIG. 81.

Let u be the given velocity of projection and θ the angle the direction of projection makes with the plane.

VOL. I.—13

When projected up the plane from A (Fig. 81) the time of flight is given by

$$0 = u \sin \theta . t - \tfrac{1}{2} g \cos \alpha . t^2,$$
$$\therefore t = \frac{2u \sin \theta}{g \cos \alpha}.$$

The range up the plane is

$$\frac{2u \sin \theta}{g \cos \alpha} . u \cos (\theta + \alpha) . \sec \alpha = \frac{2u^2}{g} . \frac{\sin \theta \cos (\theta + \alpha)}{\cos^2 \alpha}$$

$$= \frac{u^2}{g \cos^2 \alpha} [\sin (2\theta + \alpha) - \sin \alpha].$$

This is a maximum when $\sin (2\theta + \alpha) = 1$, and then

$$\text{range} = \frac{u^2}{g \cos^2 \alpha}(1 - \sin \alpha).$$

When projected down the plane from B at the same angle to the plane the time of flight has the same value

$$\frac{2u \sin \theta}{g \cos \alpha}.$$

The horizontal velocity is now, however, $u \cos (\theta - \alpha)$, the horizontal distance in time $\dfrac{2u \sin \theta}{g \cos \alpha}$ is $\dfrac{2u^2 \sin \theta \cos (\theta - \alpha)}{g \cos \alpha}$, and the range down the plane is

$$\frac{2u^2 \sin \theta \cos (\theta - \alpha)}{g \cos^2 \alpha} = \frac{u^2}{g \cos^2 \alpha}[\sin (2\theta - \alpha) + \sin \alpha].$$

This is a maximum when $\sin (2\theta - \alpha) = 1$, and then

$$\text{range} = \frac{u^2}{g \cos^2 \alpha}(1 + \sin \alpha).$$

Hence the ratio of the maximum ranges down and up the plane is

$$\frac{1 + \sin \alpha}{1 - \sin \alpha}.$$

EXAMPLE (iv).

If t_1 and t_2 be the two times of flight on an inclined plane through the point of projection corresponding to any given range short of the greatest, and α the inclination of the plane, prove that

$$t_1^2 + t_2^2 + 2t_1 t_2 \sin \alpha$$

is independent of α, the velocity of projection being given. 🖝

Let V be the velocity of projection, and θ the inclination of the initial direction to the plane.

The velocity perpendicular to the plane is $V \sin \theta$, and the time of flight t, is given by

$$0 = V \sin \theta . t - \tfrac{1}{2} g \cos \alpha . t^2 \qquad . \qquad . \qquad . \quad \text{(i)}$$

The velocity parallel to the plane is $V \cos \theta$, the acceleration down the plane is $g \sin \alpha$, and the range in time t is

$$R = V \cos \theta . t - \tfrac{1}{2} g \sin \alpha . t^2 \qquad . \qquad . \qquad . \quad \text{(ii)}$$

From (i) and (ii), $V \sin \theta . t = \frac{1}{2}g \cos \alpha . t^2$,

$\qquad\qquad V \cos \theta . t = R + \frac{1}{2}g \sin \alpha . t^2$.

Squaring and adding,

$$V^2t^2 = R^2 + gR \sin \alpha . t^2 + \frac{g^2}{4} t^4,$$

or $\quad \dfrac{g^2}{4} t^4 + t^2(gR \sin \alpha - V^2) + R^2 = 0$.

This is a quadratic in t^2, and if $t_1{}^2$, $t_2{}^2$ are its roots,

$$t_1{}^2 + t_2{}^2 = -\frac{4R}{g} \sin \alpha + \frac{4V^2}{g^2},$$

$$t_1{}^2 t_2{}^2 = \frac{4R^2}{g^2},$$

$$\therefore t_1 t_2 = \frac{2R}{g} ;$$

$$\therefore t_1{}^2 + t_2{}^2 + 2t_1 t_2 \sin \alpha = -\frac{4R}{g} \sin \alpha + \frac{4V^2}{g^2} + \frac{4R}{g} \sin \alpha,$$

$$= \frac{4V^2}{g^2}, \text{ and is independent of } \alpha.$$

EXAMPLES XXV.

1. A particle is projected with a velocity of 300 ft./sec. at an elevation of 60° from the foot of a plane of inclination 30°. The motion being in the vertical plane through a line of greatest slope of the plane, find the range on the plane and the time of flight.

2. A particle is projected with a velocity of 1280 ft./sec. at an elevation of 75°. Find the range on a plane of inclination 45° when the particle is projected (i) up, (ii) down, the plane.

3. A particle is projected from a point on a plane of inclination 30° with a velocity of 4000 cm./sec. at right angles to the plane. Find its range on the plane.

4. The greatest range, with a given velocity of projection, on a horizontal plane is 3000 metres. Find the greatest ranges up and down a plane inclined at 30° to the horizon.

5. A bullet is fired from the foot of an inclined plane with velocity 2000 ft./sec. at an elevation of 60°. Find the range if the inclination of the plane is (i) 30°, (ii) 45°. Find also the maximum ranges which can be obtained on these planes with the given initial velocity.

6. Show that the range up a plane of inclination β through the point of projection of a projectile fired at an elevation α *relative to the plane* is $R \sec \beta(1 - \tan \alpha \tan \beta)$ where R is the range on a horizontal plane, the *relative* elevation α, and the velocity of projection being the same. (I.S.)

7. A heavy particle is projected from a point on an inclined plane, inclined at 2β to the *vertical*, and moves towards the upper part of the plane in the vertical plane through a line of greatest slope of the inclined plane : the initial velocity of the particle is $u \cos \beta$ and its initial direction of motion is inclined at β to the *vertical*. Prove that

13 *

the time of flight of the particle is $\dfrac{u}{g}$, its range on the plane is $\dfrac{u^2}{2g}$, the velocity with which it strikes the plane is $u \sin \beta$, and its direction of motion has then turned through a right angle. (H.C.)

8. A particle is projected with speed u so as to strike at right angles a plane through the point of projection inclined at $30°$ to the horizon. Show that the range on this inclined plane is

$$\frac{4u^2}{7g}.$$ (I.S.)

9. A particle is projected with velocity V at an elevation α on a line through the point of projection making an angle β with the horizon. Prove that during the flight the direction of motion of the particle turns through an angle whose cotangent is

$$\tfrac{1}{2} \cos \beta \sec \alpha \operatorname{cosec} (\alpha - \beta) - \tan \alpha$$ (I.A.)

10. A projectile is to pass through a point whose angular elevation from the point of projection is θ, and at that point to impinge perpendicularly on an inclined plane of slope β to the horizontal. Show that the angle of elevation α at which it must be projected is given by

$$\tan \alpha = \cot \beta + 2 \tan \theta.$$ (H.C.)

11. If R is the maximum range on an inclined plane through the point of projection of a particle, and T the corresponding time of flight, show that

$$R = \tfrac{1}{2} g \, T^2.$$ (H.C.)

12. A shot is fired from a gun in a horizontal direction with a velocity of 1000 ft./sec. The gun is on the side of a hill of inclination $\tan^{-1} \tfrac{4}{5}$ to the horizontal. Find how far along the hill the shot will strike, and determine its velocity then in magnitude and direction. (I.C.)

13. A particle is projected with a velocity of 1600 feet per sec., at an elevation of $30°$, from a point on the side of a hill inclined at $30°$ below the horizontal. Find the range measured along the side of the hill, and the time of flight. (I.C.)

14. Find the range on an incline α of a shot fired with velocity V from a point on it at an elevation $\alpha + \theta$ so as to move in a vertical plane through a line of greatest slope.
If the shot hits the slope horizontally, show that

$$\tan \theta = \frac{\sin \alpha \cos \alpha}{1 + \sin^2 \alpha}.$$ (C.W.B.)

§ **140.** EXAMPLE (i).

A particle is projected with a velocity whose horizontal and vertical components are u, v, so as to pass through a point whose horizontal and vertical distances from the point of projection are h, k. Prove that $2u^2k + gh^2 = 2uvh$.

A particle is projected so as to pass through two points whose horizontal and vertical distances from the point of projection are $(36, 11)$ and $(72, 14)$ feet.

Find the velocity and direction of projection. (I.S.)

The time taken to describe a horizontal distance h is $\dfrac{h}{u}$.

In time $\dfrac{h}{u}$ the vertical height is k,

$$\therefore k = v\,\frac{h}{u} - \tfrac{1}{2}g\,\frac{h^2}{u^2},$$

$$\therefore 2u^2k + gh^2 = 2uvh.$$

If $h = 36$, $k = 11$,	$2u^2 \cdot 11 + 32 \cdot 36^2 = 2uv \cdot 36$	.	(i)
If $h = 72$, $k = 14$,	$2u^2 \cdot 14 + 32 \cdot 72^2 = 2uv \cdot 72$	.	(ii)

Multiplying (i) by 2, $2u^2 \cdot 22 + 64 \cdot 36^2 = 2uv \cdot 72$,

$$\therefore 2u^2(22 - 14) + 32 \times 36^2(2 - 4) = 0,$$

$$\therefore 16u^2 = 64 \times 36^2,$$

$$\therefore u = 72 \text{ ft./sec.}$$

Substituting for u in (i) we get

$$v = 30 \text{ ft./sec.}$$

The velocity of projection is

$$\sqrt{u^2 + v^2} = \sqrt{72^2 + 30^2} = 78 \text{ ft./sec.}$$

The inclination to the horizontal is

$$\tan^{-1}\frac{v}{u} = \tan^{-1}\frac{30}{72} = \tan^{-1}\frac{5}{12}.$$

Example (ii).

A ball thrown from a point P with velocity V, at an inclination α to the horizontal, reaches a point Q after t seconds. Find the horizontal and vertical distances of Q from P, and show that if PQ is inclined at θ to the horizontal the direction of motion of the ball when at Q is inclined to the horizontal at an angle $\tan^{-1}(2\tan\theta - \tan\alpha)$.   (I.E.)

If x, y be the horizontal and vertical distances of Q from P

$$x = V\cos\alpha \cdot t,$$
$$y = V\sin\alpha \cdot t - \tfrac{1}{2}gt^2.$$

If u, v be the horizontal and vertical components of velocity when at Q

$$u = V\cos\alpha,$$
$$v = V\sin\alpha - gt.$$

Now $$\tan\theta = \frac{y}{x} = \tan\alpha - \frac{gt}{2V\cos\alpha}.$$

The direction of motion at Q is inclined to the horizontal at

$$\tan^{-1}\frac{v}{u} = \tan^{-1}\!\left(\tan\alpha - \frac{gt}{V\cos\alpha}\right),$$

but $$\frac{gt}{V\cos\alpha} = 2\tan\alpha - 2\tan\theta,$$

$$\therefore \tan^{-1}\frac{v}{u} = \tan^{-1}(\tan\alpha - 2\tan\alpha + 2\tan\theta),$$

$$= \tan^{-1}(2\tan\theta - \tan\alpha).$$

EXAMPLES XXVI.

1. Show that if two particles are simultaneously projected from the same point, the direction of the line joining them is unaltered throughout the motion.   (I.A.)

2. A gun is fired from the top of a cliff of height h, and the shot attains a maximum height of $(h + b)$ above sea-level and strikes the sea at a distance a from the foot of the cliff. Prove that the angle of elevation of the gun is given by the equation

$$a^2 \tan^2 \alpha - 4ab \tan \alpha - 4bh = 0 \qquad \text{(I.E.)}$$

3. A projectile, starting from A, passes through B and C. If the horizontal and vertical distances of B from A are a, b respectively, and AC is horizontal and equal to c, find the angle of elevation and the greatest height reached by the projectile.   (Ex.)

4. A rifle is sighted to hit a mark on a level with the muzzle at an estimated distance of 1200 yards. If the muzzle velocity of the bullet is 1800 ft./sec., find the direction in which the rifle must be pointed.

If the true distance of the mark is 1150 yards, find how high above the mark the bullet will pass.   (H.S.D.)

5. If, with the same velocity of projection, the range of a projectile is half the greatest range, show that there are two possible angles of projection and find them. Compare the greatest height reached in these two possible paths.   (H.S.D.)

6. A particle is projected from a point at a height $3h$ above a horizontal plane, the direction of projection making an angle α with the horizon. Show that, if the greatest height above the point of projection is h, the horizontal distance travelled before striking the plane is

$$6\,h \cot \alpha. \qquad \text{(I.S.)}$$

7. Two shells are projected simultaneously from the same point with the same initial velocity so as to move in the same vertical plane, their initial directions of motion making angles α and α' respectively with the horizontal. Prove that the shells move so that the line joining them makes the same constant angle

$$\frac{\alpha + \alpha'}{2}$$

with the vertical.   (I.E.)

8. A projectile is thrown over a double inclined plane from one end of the horizontal base to the other, and just grazes the summit in its flight. Taking the motion to be in a vertical plane through the line of greatest slope, prove that the angle of projection is

$$\tan^{-1} (\tan \alpha + \tan \beta),$$

where α, β are the slopes of the faces.   (I.S.)

9. A particle is projected from a point A, and is viewed from a point B of its path, against the vertical through A : show that the particle appears to rise along this vertical at a uniform rate $\frac{1}{2} gt_0$, where t_0 is the time taken by the particle to reach B.   (H.C.)

10. A ball is projected so as just to clear two walls, the first of height a at distance b from the point of projection, and the second of height

b at a distance a from the point of projection.   Show that the range on a horizontal plane is

$$\frac{a^2 + ab + b^2}{a + b}$$

and that the angle of projection exceeds $\tan^{-1} 3$.   (Ex.)

11. Two particles A and B are projected simultaneously in the same vertical plane from the same point with the same speed but in perpendicular directions.   Prove that, as long as they are both in motion, the line joining them moves parallel to itself and the distance between them increases at a constant rate.   Prove also that, if A reaches the ground first, B has then travelled a horizontal distance equal to 4 times the greatest height of A.   (H.S.D.)

12. Two particles are projected simultaneously from the two points A and B (which are not in the same horizontal line) with the same initial velocity V and at the same inclination α to the horizon, so as to move towards each other.   Prove that their distance from each other will be a minimum after a time

$$\frac{h}{2V \cos \alpha}$$

where h is the horizontal distance between their points of projection. Prove also that this minimum distance will be k, where k is the initial difference of their vertical heights.   (H.S.D.)

13. Two particles are projected simultaneously with the same speed V in the same vertical plane, but at different inclinations θ_1, θ_2. Prove that their velocities are parallel after a time

$$\frac{V}{g} \cdot \frac{\cos \dfrac{\theta_1 - \theta_2}{2}}{\sin \dfrac{\theta_1 + \theta_2}{2}}.$$

(H.S.D.)

14. A projectile is aimed at a mark on a horizontal plane through the point of projection and falls 20 feet short when its elevation is $30°$ but overshoots the mark by 30 feet when its elevation is $45°$.   Show that the correct elevation is about $33° 26'$.   (I.E.)

15. If a man were projected from the earth with velocity V and elevation α and if at the same instant a stone were projected with the same velocity but elevation β, show that the stone would appear to the man to be travelling with constant velocity in a certain fixed direction.

Show further that if $\beta - \alpha = 60°$ the apparent velocity of the stone would be V.   (I.E.)

16. If the minimum kinetic energy of a projectile during its flight is $\frac{1}{n}$ of its initial value, prove that the direction of projection makes an angle $\sec^{-1} n^{\frac{1}{2}}$ with the horizontal.

Prove that the curve obtained by plotting the kinetic energy against the time is a parabola.   (N.U.3)

17. Show that it is not possible for a body to be projected from a point A so as to pass through another point B unless the speed of projection is such that if the particle were projected vertically it would rise to a height at least $\frac{1}{2}(AB + BN)$, where BN is the perpendicular from B on the horizontal plane through A.   (N.U.4)

§ 141. The Path of a Projectile (neglecting air resistance) is a Parabola.

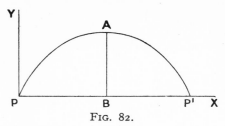

FIG. 82.

Let u, α be the velocity and angle of projection from P (Fig. 82). Taking PX horizontal and PY vertical as co-ordinate axes, we have, after time t,

$$x = u \cos \alpha . t \qquad . \qquad . \qquad . \qquad . \qquad \text{(i)}$$

$$y = u \sin \alpha . t - \tfrac{1}{2}gt^2 . \qquad . \qquad . \qquad . \qquad \text{(ii)}$$

Substituting for t in (ii),

$$y = x \tan \alpha - \frac{gx^2}{2u^2 \cos^2 \alpha} \qquad . \qquad . \qquad . \qquad \text{(iii)}$$

This equation represents a parabola with its axis vertical. When $y = 0$, equation (iii) gives

$$x = 0, \text{ or } x = \frac{2u^2 \sin \alpha \cos \alpha}{g}.$$

The first of these values corresponds to P, and the second to P' where PP' is the horizontal range.

§ 142.

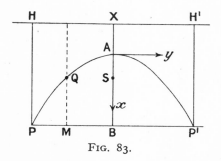

FIG. 83.

We can obtain the equation of the path in a simpler form by taking the horizontal and vertical through the highest point A (Fig. 83) as axes. We know that the horizontal and vertical velocities at A are $u \cos \alpha$, and zero.

Hence in time t, if x is measured vertically downwards, and y horizontally,

$$y = u \cos \alpha . t,$$

$$x = \tfrac{1}{2}gt^2 = \frac{gy^2}{2u^2 \cos^2 \alpha};$$

$$\therefore y^2 = \frac{2u^2 \cos^2 \alpha}{g} . x.$$

This represents a parabola with vertex at A and axis AB vertical. Its latus rectum is $\dfrac{2u^2 \cos^2 \alpha}{g}$.

If S is the focus,

$$AS = \frac{u^2 \cos^2 \alpha}{2g}.$$

The directrix HXH′ is horizontal and at a height $\dfrac{u^2 \cos^2 \alpha}{2g}$ above A.

The height of A above P is $\dfrac{u^2 \sin^2 \alpha}{2g}$,

$\therefore$ the height of the directrix above P is

$$\frac{u^2 \cos^2 \alpha}{2g} + \frac{u^2 \sin^2 \alpha}{2g} = \frac{u^2}{2g}.$$

This shows that the height of the directrix above the point of projection *depends only on the initial velocity, it is the same for all possible paths with this particular velocity.*

We see also that the height of the directrix above the point of projection is the height to which the particle would rise if projected *vertically* upwards.

The vertical velocity at a point Q is given by

$$v^2 = u^2 \sin^2 \alpha - 2g . QM,$$

the horizontal velocity is $u \cos \alpha$,

$\therefore$ the resultant velocity at Q is $\sqrt{u^2 - 2g . QM}$.

The velocity acquired by falling to Q from the directrix, a height of $\dfrac{u^2}{2g} - QM$

is

$$\sqrt{2g\left(\frac{u^2}{2g} - QM\right)} = \sqrt{u^2 - 2g . QM}.$$

The velocity at any point is therefore equal to the velocity acquired by falling freely from the directrix to that point. It should be noticed that the latus rectum $\dfrac{2u^2 \cos^2 \alpha}{g}$ depends only on the *horizontal velocity*.

§ 143. *To show how to project a particle with given velocity u from one given point P to pass through another given point Q.*

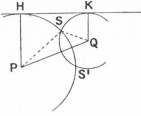

Fig. 84.

Let HK (Fig. 84) be the common directrix for paths from P with the given velocity u, and let PH, QK be perpendicular to HK.

HK is at a height $\dfrac{u^2}{2g}$ above P.

With centres P, Q and radii PH, QK describe circles.

If these circles cut at S and S′, these points are the foci of the two possible paths from P to Q.

For, SP = PH, and SQ = QK.

Similarly for S′.

Now the tangent to the path at P is the required direction of projection, and we know that the tangent to a parabola at any point P bisects the angle between the line joining P to the focus and the perpendicular from P on the directrix.

Hence the required directions of projection bisect the angles SPH and S′PH.

We also see that there are, in general, two possible directions of projection.

If the circles touch (instead of cutting), their point of contact will be a point S in PQ (Fig. 85), and in this case there is only one

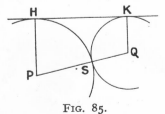

Fig. 85.

possible path from P to Q with the given velocity of projection, and its focus is at S. In this case the particle can just reach Q.

The range on the line PQ is thus a maximum for the given velocity of projection, and we see that the direction of projection bisects SPH, i.e. it bisects the angle between PQ and the vertical.

This is the result already obtained in determining the maximum range on an inclined plane.

If the circles do not meet it is impossible to project a particle from P to Q with the given initial velocity.

144. The Bounding Parabola.

We can easily find the locus of all points Q which can just be reached by projecting a particle from P with given velocity u.

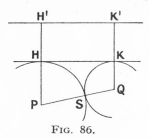

FIG. 86.

Let HK (Fig. 86) be the common directrix for all paths from P with velocity u.

If Q is one of the points which can just be reached, we have seen that the focus of the path is at S, where PS = PH and QS = QK.

Draw H'K' horizontal, and at a height above HK equal to PH. Then QK' = QK + KK' = QS + HH' = QS + PH = QS + SP = PQ.

∴ Q lies on a parabola having P as focus and H'K' as directrix. The vertex of this parabola is obviously at H, and its latus rectum is 4PH or $\dfrac{2u^2}{g}$.

If referred to HP and HK as axes of x and y, its equation is

$$y^2 = \frac{2u^2}{g} \cdot x.$$

A particle projected from P with velocity u can reach any point within or on this curve, which is therefore called the *bounding parabola*.

We may use this curve to find the maximum range on any plane. For, suppose we want the maximum range on a horizontal plane at a depth h below P. The depth below H is

$$h + \frac{u^2}{2g},$$

and the equation of the horizontal line at this depth is

$$x = h + \frac{u^2}{2g}.$$

This cuts the parabola $y^2 = \dfrac{2u^2}{g}\, x,$

where $y^2 = \dfrac{2u^2}{g}\left(h + \dfrac{u^2}{2g}\right).$

145. Motion on the Surface of a Smooth Inclined Plane.

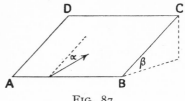

FIG. 87.

Suppose a particle projected with velocity u on the surface of a smooth inclined plane ABCD (Fig. 87) of slope β, in a direction inclined at an angle α to the line of greatest slope of the plane.

The acceleration due to gravity has components $g \sin \beta$ in the direction of the line of greatest slope of the plane, and $g \cos \beta$ perpendicular to the plane.

The latter is destroyed by the reaction of the plane, so that the particle moves with an acceleration $g \sin \beta$ parallel to the line of greatest slope.

The motion relative to the plane is therefore the same as in paragraph 132 if we use $g \sin \beta$ for the acceleration instead of g.

EXAMPLE.

A particle is projected up an inclined plane (of slope 30°) at an angle of 30° with the line of greatest slope, with initial velocity V. Write down the equations of motion and find the equation of the path on the plane, and its distance from the starting-point when it again reaches that level.

Taking the horizontal line and the line of greatest slope through the starting-point as axes of x and y, then at time t,

$$x = V \sin 30° \cdot t, \qquad \qquad \qquad \text{(i)}$$
$$y = V \cos 30° \cdot t - \tfrac{1}{2}g \sin 30° \cdot t^2 . \qquad \qquad \text{(ii)}$$

These are the equations of motion, and substituting the value of t obtained from (i) in (ii),

$$y = x \cot 30° - \frac{g}{4} \cdot \frac{x^2}{V^2 \sin^2 30°},$$

or $$y = \sqrt{3}\, x - \frac{gx^2}{V^2},$$

and this is the equation of the path.

When $\dot{y} = 0$, $$\frac{gx^2}{V^2} = \sqrt{3} \cdot x,$$

$$\therefore x = 0 \text{ or } \frac{\sqrt{3}\, V^2}{g}.$$

The latter is the distance from the starting-point when it again reaches that level.

§ **146.** The following examples are of a rather more difficult nature :—

EXAMPLE (i).

Show that the magnitude of the velocity of a projected particle at any point of its path is that which would result from falling freely under gravity from a certain fixed line. A projectile is fired from a point A on a horizontal plane. If t is the time from A to any point P of its path, and $t + t'$ the whole time of flight, show that the height of P is $\frac{1}{2}gtt'$. (H.S.C.)

Let u and α be the velocity and angle of projection. At a height h the horizontal and vertical components of velocity v_1 and v_2 are given by

$$v_1^2 = u^2 \cos^2 \alpha,$$
$$v_2^2 = u^2 \sin^2 \alpha - 2gh.$$

If V is the resultant velocity at this height

$$V = \sqrt{u^2 - 2gh}.$$

Now the velocity acquired by falling from height x to height h is

$$\sqrt{2g(x - h)} = \sqrt{2gx - 2gh},$$

and this is the same as V if

$$2gx = u^2,$$

or
$$x = \frac{u^2}{2g}.$$

Hence the velocity at any height is equal to that acquired by falling to that height from a fixed line at height

$$\frac{u^2}{2g}$$

above the point of projection.

The whole time of flight T is given by

$$0 = u \sin \alpha . T - \tfrac{1}{2}gT^2,$$
$$\therefore T = \frac{2u \sin \alpha}{g},$$
$$\therefore t + t' = \frac{2u \sin \alpha}{g}.$$

If h is the height of P,

$$h = u \sin \alpha . t - \tfrac{1}{2}gt^2,$$

but
$$u \sin \alpha = \frac{g}{2}(t + t')$$
$$\therefore h = \tfrac{1}{2}gt^2 + \tfrac{1}{2}gtt' - \tfrac{1}{2}gt^2$$
$$= \tfrac{1}{2}gtt'.$$

EXAMPLE (ii).

A tennis ball is projected from a point whose height above the ground is h feet, and which is a horizontal distance a from the net which is also of height h. The direction of projection makes an angle α with the horizontal, and is in a vertical plane perpendicular to the net. If the ball strikes the ground within a distance b on the other side of the net, show that for a given value of α the velocity of projection must lie between two limits, and that in order that this may be possible tan α must exceed the value

$$\frac{ah}{b(a + b)}.$$

(H.S.C.)

If u is the velocity of projection, the time taken to reach the net is

$$\frac{a}{u \cos \alpha}.$$

Now at this time the ball must be at least h feet from the ground, or on a level with its point of projection in order to get over the net.

$$\therefore u \sin \alpha \cdot \frac{a}{u \cos \alpha} - \frac{g}{2} \cdot \frac{a^2}{u^2 \cos^2 \alpha} \not< 0,$$

$$\therefore a \tan \alpha - \frac{ga^2}{2u^2 \cos^2 \alpha} \not< 0,$$

or

$$u^2 \not< \frac{ga}{2 \sin \alpha \cos \alpha} \qquad \cdot \qquad \cdot \qquad \cdot \qquad \cdot \quad \text{(i)}$$

If t is the time taken to reach the ground

$$- h = u \sin \alpha \cdot t - \tfrac{1}{2}gt^2,$$
$$\therefore gt^2 - 2u \sin \alpha \cdot t - 2h = 0,$$
$$\therefore t = \frac{u \sin \alpha + \sqrt{u^2 \sin^2 \alpha + 2gh}}{g}.$$

The horizontal distance described in this time must not be greater than $a + b$,

$$\therefore u^2 \sin \alpha \cos \alpha + u \cos \alpha \sqrt{u^2 \sin^2 \alpha + 2gh} \not> g(a + b),$$
$$\therefore u^4 \sin^2 \alpha \cos^2 \alpha + 2u^2 \cos^2 \alpha \cdot gh \not> g^2(a + b)^2 + u^4 \sin^2 \alpha \cos^2 \alpha$$
$$- 2gu^2 \sin \alpha \cos \alpha \cdot (a + b),$$
$$\therefore 2u^2 g \cos \alpha[h \cos \alpha + (a + b) \sin \alpha] \not> g^2(a + b)^2,$$
$$\therefore u^2 \not> \frac{g(a + b)^2}{2 \cos \alpha[h \cos \alpha + (a + b) \sin \alpha]} \qquad \cdot \qquad \cdot \quad \text{(ii)}$$

Now α will be a minimum when u has the maximum value given by (ii), also, as above,

$$a \tan \alpha \not< \frac{ga^2}{2u^2 \cos^2 \alpha},$$
$$\therefore a \tan \alpha \not< \frac{a^2 \cos \alpha[h \cos \alpha + (a + b) \sin \alpha]}{\cos^2 \alpha (a + b)^2},$$
$$\therefore (a + b)^2 \sin \alpha \not< ah \cos \alpha + a(a + b) \sin \alpha,$$
$$\therefore (ab + b^2) \tan \alpha \not< ah,$$
$$\therefore \tan \alpha \not< \frac{ah}{b(a + b)}.$$

EXAMPLE (iii).

A particle on a smooth plane, of inclination α, *is distant a from a small hole in the plane, on a higher level than the hole, in a direction inclined at* β *to the line of greatest slope. If the particle is projected along the plane with velocity v so as to fall into the hole, show that the time t is given by the equation*

$$g^2 \sin^2 \alpha . t^4 - 4(v^2 + ag \sin \alpha \cos \beta)t^2 + 4a^2 = 0.$$

But if the particle is projected into the air with the same velocity v so as to fall into the hole, the time t is given by

$$g^2 t^4 - 4(v^2 + ag \sin \alpha \cos \beta)t^2 + 4a^2 = 0. \qquad \text{(Ex.)}$$

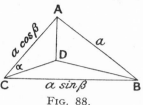

FIG. 88.

Let A (Fig. 88) represent the point of projection, B the hole, AC the line of greatest slope, CB being horizontal and D the projection of A on the horizontal plane through CB.

The co-ordinates of B referred to the horizontal line through A and the line of greatest slope are $a \sin \beta$, and $- a \cos \beta$.

If θ is the angle to the horizontal line through A at which the particle is projected, then since the acceleration down AC is $g \sin \alpha$,

$$a \sin \beta = v \cos \theta . t,$$
$$- a \cos \beta = v \sin \theta . t - \tfrac{1}{2}g \sin \alpha . t^2,$$
$$\therefore v \cos \theta . t = a \sin \beta,$$
$$v \sin \theta . t = - a \cos \beta + \tfrac{1}{2}g \sin \alpha . t^2.$$

Squaring and adding,

$$v^2 t^2 = a^2 \sin^2 \beta + a^2 \cos^2 \beta + \frac{g^2}{4} \sin^2 \alpha . t^4 - ag \sin \alpha \cos \beta . t^2,$$
$$\therefore g^2 \sin^2 \alpha . t^4 - 4(v^2 + ag \sin \alpha \cos \beta)t^2 + 4a^2 = 0.$$

The horizontal and vertical distances of B from A are DB and AD, also $AD = AC \sin \alpha = a \cos \beta \sin \alpha$,

$$DB^2 = AB^2 - AD^2 = a^2 - a^2 \cos^2 \beta \sin^2 \alpha.$$

If θ is now the angle of projection to the horizontal plane

$$DB = v \cos \theta . t,$$
$$- a \cos \beta \sin \alpha = v \sin \theta . t - \tfrac{1}{2}gt^2,$$
$$\therefore v \cos \theta . t = DB,$$
$$v \sin \theta . t = - a \cos \beta \sin \alpha + \frac{g}{2} t^2,$$
$$\therefore v^2 t^2 = a^2 - a^2 \cos^2 \beta \sin^2 \alpha + a^2 \cos^2 \beta \sin^2 \alpha + \frac{g^2}{4} t^4 - ag \sin \alpha \cos \beta . t^2.$$
$$\therefore 4v^2 t^2 = 4a^2 + g^2 t^4 - 4ag \sin \alpha \cos \beta . t^2,$$
$$\therefore g^2 t^4 - 4(v^2 + ag \sin \alpha \cos \beta)t^2 + 4a^2 = 0.$$

EXAMPLE (iv).

A particle is projected with velocity V from a point whose perpendicular distance from an inclined plane of slope α is h, in a direction making an angle θ with the line of greatest slope and in the same vertical plane with it. If the particle strikes the plane perpendicularly, prove that

$$tan^2\,\theta + \frac{V^2}{gh\,\sin\,\alpha}\,tan\,\theta + \left(1 - \frac{V^2\cos\,\alpha}{2gh\,\sin^2\,\alpha}\right) = 0,$$

it being assumed that the whole motion takes place in the vertical plane containing the point from which the particle is projected. Prove also that in order that it may be possible for the particle to strike the plane perpendicularly, V^2 must be greater than

$$gh\,(\sqrt{4 - 3\cos^2\,\alpha} - \cos\,\alpha).$$

The velocity perpendicular to the plane is $V\sin\,\theta$.

The time of flight t is given by

$$- h = V\sin\,\theta \cdot t - \tfrac{1}{2}g\cos\,\alpha \cdot t^2 \qquad . \qquad . \qquad . \quad \text{(i)}$$

Since the particle strikes the plane perpendicularly, it must have lost all velocity parallel to the plane.

Now the initial velocity parallel to the plane is $V\cos\,\theta$, and the acceleration *down* the plane is $g\sin\,\alpha$,

$$\therefore 0 = V\cos\,\theta - g\sin\,\alpha \cdot t,$$

$$\therefore t = \frac{V\cos\,\theta}{g\sin\,\alpha}.$$

Substituting this value for t in equation (i),

$$- h = \frac{V^2\sin\,\theta\cos\,\theta}{g\sin\,\alpha} - \frac{g}{2}\cdot\frac{V^2\cos^2\,\theta\cos\,\alpha}{g^2\sin^2\,\alpha},$$

$$\therefore h\sec^2\,\theta + \frac{V^2}{g\sin\,\alpha}\,tan\,\theta - \frac{V^2}{2g}\cdot\frac{\cos\,\alpha}{\sin^2\,\alpha} = 0,$$

$$\therefore tan^2\,\theta + 1 + \frac{V^2}{gh\sin\,\alpha}\,tan\,\theta - \frac{V^2\cos\,\alpha}{2gh\sin^2\,\alpha} = 0,$$

$$\therefore tan^2\,\theta + \frac{V^2}{gh\sin\,\alpha}\,tan\,\theta + \left(1 - \frac{V^2\cos\,\alpha}{2gh\sin^2\,\alpha}\right) = 0.$$

If this relation is possible the value of tan θ must be real,

$$\therefore \frac{V^4}{g^2h^2\sin^2\,\alpha} > 4 - \frac{4V^2\cos\,\alpha}{2gh\sin^2\,\alpha},$$

$$\therefore \frac{V^4}{g^2h^2\sin^2\,\alpha} + \frac{2V^2\cos\,\alpha}{gh\sin^2\,\alpha} > 4,$$

$$\therefore \left(\frac{V^2}{gh\sin\,\alpha} + \frac{\cos\,\alpha}{\sin\,\alpha}\right)^2 > 4 + \frac{\cos^2\,\alpha}{\sin^2\,\alpha},$$

$$> \frac{4 - 3\cos^2\,\alpha}{\sin^2\,\alpha},$$

$$\therefore \frac{V^2}{gh\sin\,\alpha} + \frac{\cos\,\alpha}{\sin\,\alpha} > \frac{\sqrt{4 - 3\cos^2\,\alpha}}{\sin\,\alpha},$$

$$\therefore V^2 > gh[\sqrt{4 - 3\cos^2\,\alpha} - \cos\,\alpha].$$

EXAMPLES XXVII.

1. A and B are two points, such that the co-ordinates of B referred to A as origin, the axis of x being horizontal in the vertical plane through AB and the axis of y being the upward-drawn vertical, are a and b.

It is required to project a particle from A to pass through B, the magnitude of the velocity of projection being V. Show that this is impossible if V^2 is less than

$$g(b + \sqrt{a^2 + b^2}),$$

but that, if

$$V^2 > g(b + \sqrt{a^2 + b^2})$$

there are two possible directions of projection.   (H.C.)

2. A projectile is aimed with velocity u at a vertical wall whose distance from the point of projection is a, Prove that the greatest height above the level of the point of projection at which the projectile can hit the wall is

$$\frac{u^4 - g^2 a^2}{2gu^2}.$$
                                                            (H.C.)

3. A shot fired at an object a feet distance from the gun and on the same level, goes b feet beyond the object when the elevation of the gun is α. Find an expression for the change in elevation required to hit the object. The resistance of the air is to be neglected. If α is small, find the simplest approximate expression for the required change of angle, and calculate the change when $\alpha = 2°5'$, $a = 5280$, $b = 720$.   (Ex.)

4. A particle is projected along a smooth straight tube of length l and inclination α from the lower end with velocity u, more than sufficient to carry it right through the tube. Find the length of the latus rectum of the parabolic path described by the particle after leaving the tube, and the equation of the path referred to the upper end of the tube as origin.

Compare the greatest height to which the particle rises with that to which it would have risen if the tube had been of infinitesimally small length.   (Ex.)

5. A particle is projected under gravity along the face of a smooth inclined plane from a given point at its foot, with varying velocity and direction so as just to reach the top of the plane. If l is the length of the face along the line of greatest slope, and α its inclination to the horizon, show that the time taken to reach the top is the same for all paths and equal to

$$\left(\frac{2l}{g \sin \alpha}\right)^{\frac{1}{2}}.$$

Show also that the locus of the focus of the path is a parabola of latus rectum $4l$.   (H.S.C.)

6. A particle is projected with velocity $\sqrt{2ga}$ from a point at a height h above a level plain. Show that the tangent of the angle of elevation for maximum range on the plain is

$$\sqrt{\frac{a}{a + h}}$$

and that the maximum range is $2\sqrt{a(a + h)}$.   (C.S.)

7. A particle is projected with a velocity whose horizontal and vertical components are u and v. Show that if it rises higher than h above the plane of projection it will be at a height h at two points of its path, the distance between which is

$$\frac{2u}{g}(v^2 - 2gh)^{\frac{1}{2}}.$$

If two particles are projected from a point at the same instant with velocities whose horizontal and vertical components are u_1, v_1 and u_2, v_2 respectively, show that the interval between their passing through the other common point of their paths is

$$\frac{2(v_1 u_2 - u_1 v_2)}{g(u_1 + u_2)}. \qquad \text{(C.S.)}$$

8. Two vertical posts of heights a, b stand on level ground at a distance c apart ; a stone is projected from the ground level with the least possible velocity consistent with its just clearing the two posts.

Prove the latus rectum of this parabolic trajectory is $\dfrac{c^2}{d}$ where $d^2 = (a - b)^2 + c^2$ and that the range on the ground level is

$$\frac{c[d^2 + 2(a + b)d + (a - b)^2]^{\frac{1}{2}}}{2d}. \qquad \text{(C.S.)}$$

9. A shot is fired with initial velocity V at a mark in the same horizontal plane ; show that if a small error $\epsilon°$ is made in the angle of elevation and an error of $2\epsilon°$ in azimuth, the shot will strike the ground at a distance from the mark

$$\frac{\epsilon V^2}{90g} \pi$$

Show also that if the angle of elevation is less than about $31\frac{1}{2}°$, an error in elevation will cause the shot to miss the mark by a greater amount than an equal error in azimuth. (C.S.)

10. A particle is projected with a given velocity v from the foot of an inclined plane of slope α. The direction of projection lies in a plane containing the line of greatest slope and makes an angle θ with the face of the plane. Prove that if the particle strikes the plane perpendicularly cot $\theta = 2$ tan α.

Show that, for different values of α, the range on the plane when the particle strikes it perpendicularly cannot be greater than

$$\frac{v^2}{g\sqrt{3}}. \qquad \text{(C.S.)}$$

11. A particle is projected with velocity u at an elevation α. Show that after a time $\dfrac{u}{g}$ cosec α its direction will be at right angles to its direction of projection, and that its distance from the point of projection will be equal to that below a horizontal line at a height $\dfrac{u^2}{g}$ above the point of projection. (C.S.)

12. A stone is projected from a point P on the ground over a house so as just to clear the top of the walls and the ridge of the roof : the breadth of the house is $2a$, the height of each wall is l, and the height of the ridge is $h + l$. Find the position of P and the velocity of projection. (C.S.)

13. Prove that if the difference in level between two points A and B is L, the velocity of projection from A in order that B may be just within range of A is

$$\sqrt{g(\mathrm{AB} \pm \mathrm{L})}$$

according as B is above or below A. (C.S.)

14. Show that all points in a vertical plane, which can be reached by shots fired with velocity v from a fixed point at a distance c from the plane, lie within a parabola of latus rectum $\dfrac{2v^2}{g}$ whose focus is at a distance $\dfrac{c^2 g}{2v^2}$ vertically below the foot of the perpendicular on the plane from the point of projection. (C.S.)

15. A fort is on the edge of a cliff of height h. Show that there is an annular region in which the fort is out of range of a ship, but the ship is not out of range of the fort, of area $8\pi k h$, where $\sqrt{2gk}$ is the velocity of the shells used by both. (C.S.)

16. A gun fires a shell with a muzzle velocity of 1040 feet per second. Neglecting the resistance of the air, what is the furthest horizontal distance at which an aeroplane at a height of 2500 feet can be hit and what gun elevation is required ? Show that the shell would then take approximately 44·2 seconds to reach the aeroplane. (C.S.)

17. A ball is dropped from the top of a tower 100 feet high. At the same instant a ball of equal mass is thrown from a point on the ground 50 feet from the foot of the tower so as to strike the first ball when just half-way down. Find the initial velocity and the direction of projection of the second ball. If the two balls coalesce, how long will they take to reach the ground ? (C.S.)

18. Particles are projected simultaneously from a point under gravity in various directions with velocity V. Prove that at any subsequent time t they will all lie on a sphere of radius Vt, and determine the motion of the centre of this sphere. (C.S.)

19. Show that all the points in a vertical plane which can be reached by a projectile thrown from a given origin in the plane with given velocity lie within or on a parabola, and show that this parabola touches all the trajectories.

Prove that the time to reach a point on the enveloping parabola at a distance r from the origin is

$$\sqrt{\frac{2r}{g}}.$$

(C.S.)

§ 147. The following examples involve impacts of projected particles :—

Example (i).

A ball is thrown from a point distant a from a smooth vertical wall against the wall, and returns to the point of projection. Prove that the velocity u of projection and the elevation α of projection are connected by the equation

$$u^2 \sin 2\alpha = ag\left(1 + \frac{1}{e}\right),$$

where e is the coefficient of restitution between the ball and the wall.

14 *

Since the wall is smooth the vertical motion is unaffected by the impact, i.e. the time of flight is still

$$\frac{2u \sin \alpha}{g}.$$

The ball approaches the wall with horizontal velocity $u \cos \alpha$, and rebounds with horizontal velocity $eu \cos \alpha$.

Hence the times taken to reach the wall and rebound a horizontal distance a are $\dfrac{a}{u \cos \alpha}$ and $\dfrac{a}{eu \cos \alpha}$ respectively,

$$\therefore \frac{2u \sin \alpha}{g} = \frac{a}{u \cos \alpha} + \frac{a}{eu \cos \alpha},$$

$$\therefore \frac{2u \sin \alpha}{g} = \frac{a(1 + e)}{eu \cos \alpha},$$

$$\therefore u^2 \sin 2\alpha = ag(1 + \frac{1}{e}).$$

EXAMPLE (ii).

A particle projected from a point on a smooth inclined plane at the rth impact strikes the plane normally, and at the nth impact is at the point of projection. If e is the coefficient of restitution, prove that

$$e^n - 2e^r + 1 = 0. \hspace{2cm} \text{(C.S.)}$$

Let α be the inclination of the plane, θ the angle between the direction of projection and the plane, v the velocity of projection.

Consider the motion perpendicular to the plane.

The time to the first impact is

$$\frac{2v \sin \theta}{g \cos \alpha}.$$

The particle reaches the plane again with the same normal velocity $v \sin \theta$, and rebounds with velocity $ev \sin \theta$. At the second impact it rebounds with normal velocity $e^2 v \sin \theta$, and so on.

Hence the time T to the *rth* impact is given by

$$T = \frac{2v \sin \theta}{g \cos \alpha}(1 + e + e^2 + \ldots + e^{r-1}) = \frac{2v \sin \theta}{g \cos \alpha} \cdot \frac{1 - e^r}{1 - e}.$$

The time T' to the *nth* impact is given by

$$T' = \frac{2v \sin \theta}{g \cos \alpha} \cdot \frac{1 - e^n}{1 - e}.$$

Now consider the motion parallel to the plane.

After time T the particle has lost all the velocity parallel to the plane.

$$\therefore 0 = v \cos \theta - g \sin \alpha \cdot T,$$

$$\therefore T = \frac{v \cos \theta}{g \sin \alpha}.$$

After time T' its distance up the plane from the point of projection is zero,

$$\therefore o = v \cos \theta . T' - \tfrac{1}{2}g \sin \alpha . T'^2,$$

$$\therefore T' = \frac{2v \cos \theta}{g \sin \alpha},$$

$$\therefore T' = 2T,$$

$$\therefore \frac{1 - e^n}{1 - e} = 2\frac{1 - e^r}{1 - e},$$

$$\therefore 1 - e^n = 2 - 2e^r,$$

$$\therefore e^n - 2e^r + 1 = 0.$$

EXAMPLES XXVIII.

1. A particle of mass m is projected with velocity v at an angle α to the horizontal, and at the same instant a particle of mass $3m$ is dropped from a height $\dfrac{v^2 \sin^2 \alpha}{g}$, at a horizontal distance of $\dfrac{v^2 \sin \alpha \cos \alpha}{g}$ from the point of projection of the first particle. Show that the particles will collide. If the particles now coalesce, find the position of the point at which the particles strike the ground; and the time which elapses before they reach it. (I.E.)

2. A particle is projected in a vertical plane perpendicular to a smooth wall so as to return to the point of projection after striking the wall. Show that the angle between the direction of projection and the horizontal is given by

$$\tan \theta = \frac{egt^2}{2a(1 + e)},$$

where t is the time of flight, a the distance from the wall of the point of projection, and e the coefficient of restitution. (H.S.C.)

3. A body slides from rest down a smooth plane of length l and inclination α, and at the bottom impinges on a smooth horizontal plane ; show that the range on the horizontal plane after the first rebound is $2el \sin \alpha \sin 2\alpha$, where e is the coefficient of restitution between the body and the horizontal plane. (I.A.)

4. A mass of 10 oz. moving horizontally at a point A, 56 feet above the ground with a velocity of 44 ft./sec., is struck at A by a mass of 1 oz. moving vertically upwards with a velocity of 550 ft./sec., and the two masses unite ; find the position of the point at which the combined mass strikes the ground. (I.A.)

5. From a point distant a from a smooth wall a particle, whose initial height above the ground is h, is projected with horizontal velocity u towards the wall. If $a < \sqrt{\dfrac{2h}{g}}u$, show that the particle strikes the ground at a point distant $e\left(\sqrt{\dfrac{2h}{g}}u - a\right)$ from the wall, e being the coefficient of restitution between the wall and the particle. (H.S.D.)

6. A ball is thrown with a speed of 64 ft./sec. at an angle of elevation of 45°. It strikes a vertical wall 32 feet away and returns to the point of projection. Find the coefficient of restitution between the ball and the wall. (H.S.D.)

7. An elastic particle is projected with velocity u, at an inclination to the horizontal, from a point on the ground distant a from a smooth vertical wall towards the wall. Prove that, after rebounding from the wall, it can strike the ground again at a point further from the wall than the point of projection if

$$u^2 > \frac{1+e}{e} ag,$$

where e is the coefficient of restitution.

8. A particle is dropped from a height h on to a smooth and perfectly elastic inclined plane and rebounds. Find how far down the plane is its next point of impact. (H.S.C.)

9. Find the maximum range on a plane, inclined at an angle α to the horizontal of a particle projected with velocity u from the lowest point of the plane in a vertical plane through a line of greatest slope of the plane. Find also the maximum range that can be obtained at the end of the second impact on the plane after rebounding, the coefficient of restitution between the plane and the particle being e. (H.S.C.)

10. A particle is dropped from a vertical height a upon the highest point of a plane, of length b and inclination α, and reaches the bottom at the fourth impact. Show that

$$b = 4ae(1 + e)(1 + e^2)(1 + e + e^2) \sin \alpha,$$

where e is the coefficient of restitution.

11. A particle is projected from the foot of a plane of inclination α in a direction making an angle θ with the plane, and at the nth impact rebounds vertically, show that

$$\cos (\alpha + \theta) = \sin \theta \sin \alpha \frac{1+e}{1-e}(1 - e^n),$$

where e is the coefficient of restitution.

12. A ball is projected from the ground at an angle α to the horizontal and rebounds from a smooth vertical wall to the point of projection. If the line joining the point of projection to the point of impact makes an angle θ with the horizontal, prove that.

$$(1 + e) \tan \theta = \tan \alpha,$$

where e is the coefficient of restitution.

13. In a certain game a ball is rolled along a horizontal plane until it strikes an inclined plane from which it rebounds. The object of the game is to make the ball after rebounding fall into a hole in the inclined plane. If θ be the inclination of the plane, e the coefficient of restitution between the ball and the plane, and if the hole be situated at a distance d from the junction of the planes, show that in order that the ball may enter the hole, its velocity of projection V must be given by

$$dg = 2eV^2 \sin \theta (1 - e \tan^2 \theta). \qquad \text{(H.S.D.)}$$

14. A particle is projected with a velocity of magnitude V from a point of a plane, inclined to the horizontal at an angle α, in the vertical plane through the line of greatest slope through the point of projection. The direction of projection is up the plane and makes an angle β with the plane. The coefficient of restitution between the plane and the particle is e. Prove that the range of the particle on the plane at the moment of its second impact with the plane is greatest when $\cot 2\beta = (1 + e) \tan \alpha$, and that this greatest range is

$$\frac{V^2(1 + e) \tan \beta}{g \cos \alpha},$$

where β has the value given by the first equation.   (H.C.)

15. An elastic particle is projected at an elevation α with velocity V from a point in a horizontal plane at a distance $a \left(< \dfrac{V^2 \sin 2\alpha}{g} \right)$ from a smooth vertical wall. If the coefficient of restitution is e, show that the particle reaches the horizontal plane at a distance

$$a(1 + e) - \frac{e V^2 \sin 2\alpha}{g}$$

from the point of projection.   (C.W.B.)

CHAPTER V.

MOTION IN A CIRCLE.

§ **148.** In the present chapter we shall consider the motion of a particle moving in a circle with uniform speed, and also certain points in connection with the motion of a particle in a vertical circle under gravity.

It is evident from Newton's First Law of Motion that, if a particle is describing a circle with uniform speed, there can be no force acting on it in the direction of the tangent to the circle, otherwise the speed would alter. It is also clear that there must be an inward force acting to cause the particle to describe a curved path. This means that there must be an inward acceleration along the normal to the path, and we shall now find what the magnitude of this acceleration must be.

§ **149.** *If a particle is moving in a circle of radius r with constant speed v, its acceleration is* $\dfrac{v^2}{r}$ *and is directed towards the centre of the circle.*

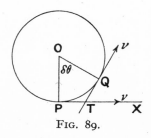

Fig. 89.

Let O (Fig. 89) be the centre of the circle, P the position of the particle at any instant, and Q its position after a short interval of time δt.

Let the small angle POQ be $\delta\theta$, and the small arc PQ be δs. The velocity at P is v along the tangent PT, and the velocity at Q is v along the tangent TQ, and $\angle QTX = \delta\theta$.

Resolving the velocity at Q along and perpendicular to PX, the components are

$v \cos \delta\theta$ along PX, and $v \sin \delta\theta$ perpendicular to PX.

The change in velocity along the tangent PX is $v \cos \delta\theta - v$. Hence the acceleration along the tangent PX is

$$Lt \ \frac{v(\cos \delta\theta - 1)}{\delta t} = Lt \ \frac{- 2v \sin^2 \dfrac{\delta\theta}{2}}{\delta t}$$

$$= Lt \ \frac{- 2v\left(\dfrac{\delta\theta}{2}\right)^2}{\delta t} = 0.$$

The change in velocity along the normal PO is $v \sin \delta\theta$. The rate of change of velocity is therefore

$$Lt \ \frac{v \sin \delta\theta}{\delta t} = Lt \ \frac{v \sin \delta\theta}{\delta\theta} \cdot \frac{\delta\theta}{\delta t} = v\frac{d\theta}{dt},$$

and is directed towards O.

Now $\frac{d\theta}{dt}$ is the angular velocity of P in the circle, so that, denoting this by ω, the acceleration is $v\omega$ towards the centre.

Since $v = r\omega$, we have the following values for the acceleration,

$$\frac{v^2}{r} \ \text{or} \ r\omega^2.$$

§ 150. If the mass of the particle is m, the force required to produce this acceleration is $\frac{mv^2}{r}$ or $mr\omega^2$, and it must act continuously towards the centre of the circle.

This force may be produced in various ways, e.g. the particle may be connected to O by an inextensible string, or it may be threaded on a smooth circular wire ; in the first case the tension of the string, and in the second case the reaction of the wire provides the necessary central force.

It must be noticed carefully that although (in the case of a particle swinging round in a circle at the end of a string) the string is in a state of tension, there is no tendency for the particle to move *outwards* along the radius of the circle. If the string breaks the particle continues to move straight on along the *tangent* to the circle.

In the case of a train going round a curve the necessary inward force is provided by the pressure of the outer rail against the flanges of the wheels. In the case of a motor car the force is provided by the friction between the wheels and the ground. In both cases it is possible to make the weight of the train or car provide this force by banking up the track so that the outer wheels are above the inner ones. This will be considered later.

EXAMPLE (i).

A mass of 5 lb. moves on a smooth horizontal plane with a speed of 8 ft./sec., being attached to a fixed point on the plane by a string of length 4 ft. ; find the tension of the string.

Here $v = 8$, $r = 4$.

The acceleration towards the fixed point is $\dfrac{64}{4} = 16$ ft./sec.^{2},

∴ the tension must be $5 \times 16 = 80$ pdls. $= 2\frac{1}{2}$ lb. wt.

Note.—The force given by $\dfrac{mv^2}{r}$ or $mr\omega^2$ is always in *absolute units,* i.e. in F.P.S. units the force is in poundals, in C.G.S. units it is in dynes.

EXAMPLE (ii).

A particle of mass 8 lb., resting on a smooth table and attached to a fixed point on the table by a string 4 feet long, is making 300 revolutions per minute ; find the tension in the string.

300 R.P.M. = 5 rev. per sec.,

∴ the angular velocity $= 10\pi$ radians per sec.

The tension is $mr\omega^2 = 8 \cdot 4 \cdot 10^2\pi^2$ pdls.

$= 100\pi^2$ lb. wt.

$= 1000$ lb. wt. nearly.

EXAMPLE (iii).

An engine, of mass 80 tons, is moving in an arc of a circle of radius 800 feet, with a speed of 30 m.p.h. ; what force must be exerted by the rails towards the centre of the circle ?

30 m.p.h. = 44 ft./sec.

80 tons = 80 . 2240 lb.,

∴ the force is

$$\frac{80 \cdot 2240 \cdot 44 \cdot 44}{800} \text{ pdls.,}$$

$$= 6\tfrac{1}{20} \text{ tons wt.}$$

EXAMPLE (iv).

A particle is tied by an elastic string of length 1 foot to a fixed point on a smooth horizontal table, upon which the particle is describing a circle round the point at a constant speed. If the modulus of elasticity of the string is equal to the weight of the particle and the number of revolutions per minute is 20, show that the extension of the string is nearly 2 inches. [*Take $g = 32$ ft./sec.^{2}, and $\pi^2 = 10$.*]   (I.S.)

Let m be the mass of the particle.

20 R.P.M. = $\frac{1}{3}$ rev. per sec.

∴ the angular velocity is $\dfrac{2\pi}{3}$ radians per sec.

If x feet is the length of the string, the tension ($mr\omega^2$) is

$$mx\,\frac{4\pi^2}{9} \text{ pdls.}$$

Now the extension of the string is $(x - 1)$ ft., and since the modulus $E = mg$, the tension T is given by

$$T = \frac{mg}{1}(x - 1) \text{ pdls.}$$

$$\therefore mg(x - 1) = mx\,\frac{4\pi^2}{9},$$

$$\therefore x = 1\tfrac{5}{31} \text{ ft.}$$

The extension is $\tfrac{5}{31}$ ft. or nearly 2 ins.

EXAMPLES XXIX.

1. A particle of mass 5 lb. rests on a smooth horizontal plane, and is attached by a string 4 feet long to a fixed point on the plane. If the particle describes a horizontal circle at 8 ft./sec., find the tension in the string.

2. A string 2 feet long can just sustain a weight of 40 lb. without breaking. A mass of 4 lb. is attached to one end of the string and revolves uniformly on a smooth table, the other end of the string being fixed to a point on the table ; find the greatest number of complete revolutions the mass can make in a minute without breaking the string.

3. An engine, of mass 60 tons, is moving in an arc of a circle of radius 800 feet at 60 m.p.h. What force must be exerted by the rails towards the centre of the circle ?

4. A motor car, weighing 2 tons, is rounding a curve of radius half a mile on a level track at 60 m.p.h. ; what force of friction is necessary between the wheels and the ground ?

5. One end of an elastic string, 2 feet long, is attached to a fixed point on a smooth table, and the other end to a mass of 4 lb. resting on the table. If the 4 lb. mass were suspended vertically by the string the extension would be 4 inches. The mass is made to describe a circle round the fixed point at 40 R.P.M. Calculate the extension of the string.

6. An elastic string of unstretched length l, fixed at one end, can just support a mass of m lb. when hanging vertically and extended by half its length. The mass and string are now placed on a smooth horizontal table with one end of the string fixed. The string is stretched to double its length and the mass is projected along the table with such velocity that it describes a horizontal circle about the fixed point as centre. Find the time of revolution of the mass.
(H.S.D.)

7. Two equal particles are connected by a string passing through a hole in a smooth table, one particle being on the table, the other underneath. How many revolutions per minute would the particle on the table have to perform in a circle of radius 6 inches, in order to keep the other particle at rest.
(I.S.)

8. A rough horizontal table can rotate about a vertical axis, and a weight is placed on the table at a distance of 2 feet from the axis. The table is made to rotate with gradually increasing velocity ; if the coefficient of friction between the weight and the table is $\tfrac{1}{4}$, show that the weight will not move as long as the number of revolutions per minute is less than 19.
(H.S.C.)

9. A plane horizontal circular disc is constrained to rotate uniformly about its centre, describing two complete revolutions per second. Show that the greatest distance from the centre of the disc at which a small object can be placed so as to stay on the disc is very nearly 2·43 μ inches, where μ is the coefficient of friction between the object and the disc. (H.C.)

10. The wheels of a bicycle are 30 inches in diameter, the gear-ratio between the crank axle and wheel axle is $2\frac{1}{2}$, and the length of the crank is 8 inches. Find the velocity of the end of the crank and the magnitude and direction of its acceleration, when at its highest point, the bicycle travelling at the rate of 30 ft./sec. (Q.E.)

§ 151. The Conical Pendulum.

If a particle be tied by a string to a fixed point O, and move in a horizontal circle, so that the string describes a cone whose axis is the vertical through O, the string and particle form what is called a conical pendulum.

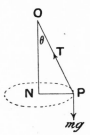

FIG. 90.

Let P (Fig. 90) represent the particle of mass m, and OP the string of length l, and let ON be the vertical through O. Then if PN is perpendicular to ON, N is the centre of the horizontal circle described by P.

Let T be the tension in the string, θ its inclination to the vertical, and ω the angular velocity of the particle about N.

The only forces acting on the particle are the tension of the string and its own weight mg.

It is obvious that P must be below O so that the tension has an upward vertical component to balance the weight mg.

The horizontal component of the tension must provide the central force necessary to keep the particle moving in its circle. The value of this central force is mPN . ω^2 or $ml \sin \theta . \omega^2$,

$$\therefore T \sin \theta = ml \sin \theta . \omega^2 \qquad . \qquad . \qquad . \quad (i)$$

Since there is no vertical acceleration, the vertical component of T must equal the weight mg.,

$$\therefore T \cos \theta = mg \qquad . \qquad . \qquad . \qquad . \quad (ii)$$

From (i) $\qquad T = ml\omega^2 = 4\pi^2 n^2 ml$ pdls.,

where n is the number of revolutions made by P per second.

Substituting for T in (ii),

$$\cos \theta = \frac{mg}{ml\omega^2} = \frac{g}{l\omega^2}.$$

Now $ON = l \cos \theta$,

$$\therefore ON = \frac{g}{\omega^2},$$

i.e. the vertical depth of P below O is independent of the length of the string, and varies inversely as the square of the angular velocity.

If we use the speed v of P instead of its angular velocity ω,

$$v = PN \cdot \omega = l \sin \theta \cdot \omega \; ;$$

equation (i) then becomes

$$T \sin \theta = ml \sin \theta \cdot \frac{v^2}{l^2 \sin^2 \theta} = \frac{mv^2}{l \sin \theta},$$

and, dividing by (ii),

$$\tan \theta = \frac{v^2}{gl \sin \theta},$$
$$\therefore v^2 = gl \sin \theta \tan \theta.$$

§ 152. Governors of Steam-engines.

The fact that, when a weight is swung round as a conical pendulum, the depth of the weight below the point of suspension depends only on the angular velocity, is made use of in governors for regulating the supply of steam to an engine which is required to rotate a shaft at a constant rate.

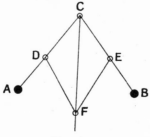

FIG. 91.

Two light rods are hinged at C (Fig. 91) to a vertical shaft which is rotated by the engine, and at the other ends of these rods are weights A and B. Two other rods DF, EF are hinged to AC and BC and also to a collar F which can slide up and down the shaft.

A lever is attached to F which can open or close a valve admitting steam to the engine. This is arranged so that when F rises it closes the valve.

When the speed of rotation of the shaft increases, the weights A and B rise and pull F up, thus shutting off some of the steam so that the engine is slowed down. If the speed decreases too much, F is lowered and lets in more steam.

§ 153. EXAMPLE (i).

A small body, attached by a string to a fixed point, describes a horizontal circle at the uniform angular speed of one revolution per second. Prove that its distance below the fixed point does not depend on the length of the string, and find the tension of the string when the mass of the body is 2 lb., and the length of the string is 14 inches. (H.S.D.)

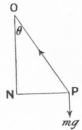

FIG. 92.

Let O (Fig. 92) be the fixed point, P the body, OP the string inclined at an angle θ to the vertical ON, and PN perpendicular to ON.

Then, if m is the mass, T the tension of the string, and ω the angular velocity of P,

$$T \sin \theta = m\mathrm{PN} . \omega^2 = ml \sin \theta . \omega^2 \quad . \qquad . \qquad . \quad \text{(i)}$$

$$T \cos \theta = mg \quad . \qquad . \qquad . \qquad . \qquad . \qquad . \quad \text{(ii)}$$

From (i) $\qquad\qquad T = ml\omega^2 \quad . \qquad . \qquad . \qquad . \qquad . \quad \text{(iii)}$

$$\therefore l \cos \theta = \frac{mg}{m\omega^2} = \frac{g}{\omega^2},$$

but $l \cos \theta$ is the depth of P below O, which is therefore equal to $\frac{g}{\omega^2}$, and is independent of the length of the string.

When P is making one revolution per second, $\omega = 2\pi$, and if $m = 2$ lb., $l = 1\frac{1}{6}$ feet, we have, from (iii),

$$T = 2 . \tfrac{7}{6} . 4\pi^2 = \tfrac{28}{3}\pi^2 \text{ pdls.}$$

Taking $\pi^2 = 10$,

$$T = \frac{280}{3} \text{ pdls. or } \frac{280}{3 \times 32} \text{ lb. wt.}$$

i.e. $93\frac{1}{3}$ pdls. or $2\frac{11}{12}$ lb. wt.

EXAMPLE (ii).

If the mass of the bob in a conical pendulum is 4 lb., and the length of the string is 2 feet, find the maximum number of revolutions per second of the pendulum when the greatest tension that can with safety be allowed in the string is 40 lb. wt. (I.S.)

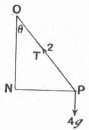

FIG. 93.

Let T be the tension in the string, ω the angular velocity, and θ the inclination of the string to the vertical.

In Fig. 93, O is the point of suspension, P the bob, PN the perpendicular on the vertical ON through O.

$$T \sin \theta = 4 \text{PN} \cdot \omega^2 = 4 \cdot 2 \sin \theta \cdot 4\pi^2 n^2,$$

where n is the number of revolutions per second,

$$\therefore T = 32\pi^2 n^2 \text{ pdls.,}$$
$$= \pi^2 n^2 \text{ lb. wt.}$$

The maximum value of T is 40 lb. wt.

$$\therefore \pi^2 n^2 = 40,$$

$$\therefore n^2 = \frac{40}{\pi^2} = 4, \text{ taking } \pi^2 = 10.$$

Hence the greatest number of revolutions per second is 2.

EXAMPLE (iii).

An elastic thread, whose unstretched length is 20 inches, has a mass of 5 lb. at one end and makes 60 R.P.M. as a conical pendulum. The string is then 24 inches long ; find the tension in the string and express in ft. lb. the kinetic energy of the mass and the potential energy due to stretching the thread.   (I.S.)

60 R.P.M. = 1 per sec., and the angular velocity is 2π.

If T is the tension, and θ the inclination of the string to the vertical,

$$T \sin \theta = 5 \times 2 \sin \theta \times 4\pi^2,$$

$$\therefore T = 40\pi^2 = 400 \text{ pdls. nearly, or } 12 \cdot 5 \text{ lb. wt.}$$

Also $T \cos \theta = 5g,$

$$\therefore \cos \theta = \frac{5g}{T} = \frac{5g}{400} = \frac{32}{80} = \frac{2}{5},$$

$$\therefore \sin \theta = \frac{\sqrt{21}}{5}.$$

If v is the speed of the mass,

$$v = 2 \sin \theta \cdot \omega = \frac{4\pi\sqrt{21}}{5} \text{ ft./sec.,}$$

$$\therefore \text{ its kinetic energy is } = \frac{5}{2} \cdot \frac{16\pi^2 \times 21}{25} = 16 \times 21 \text{ ft. pdls. nearly,}$$

$$= 10\tfrac{1}{2} \text{ ft. lb.}$$

The potential energy due to stretching the thread is equal to the work done in stretching it from its natural length, 20 inches, to 24 inches, i.e. by $\frac{1}{3}$ foot. The mean of the initial and final tensions is

$$\frac{T}{2} = \frac{400}{2} = 200 \text{ pdls.,}$$

∴ the work done in stretching is $\frac{200}{3}$ ft. pdls., or $\frac{200}{96}$ ft. lb.

The potential energy is therefore $2\frac{1}{12}$ ft. lb.

EXAMPLE (iv).

A mass m at C is freely jointed to two equal light rods CA and CB ; the end A of CA is pivoted to a fixed point A, and the end B is freely jointed to a heavy bead of mass m which slides on a smooth vertical bar AB. If the mass C rotates in a horizontal circle with uniform angular velocity ω, prove that the inclination of the rods CA and CB to the vertical is $\cos^{-1}\frac{3g}{l\omega^2}$, where l is the length of either rod. (I.E.)

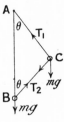

FIG. 94.

Let T_1, T_2 be the tensions in AC, BC (Fig. 94), and θ the angle BAC. Resolving vertically for the weight at B,

$$T_2 \cos \theta = mg \qquad (i)$$

Resolving vertically for the weight at C,

$$T_1 \cos \theta = mg + T_2 \cos \theta = 2mg \qquad (ii)$$

Now since the mass at C is describing a horizontal circle of radius $l \sin \theta$ about AB, the two tensions must exert a force of $ml \sin \theta \cdot \omega^2$, towards AB and in a direction bisecting the angle ACB.

$$\therefore T_1 \sin \theta + T_2 \sin \theta = ml \sin \theta \cdot \omega^2,$$
$$\therefore T_1 + T_2 = ml\omega^2.$$

Hence, from (i) and (ii),

$$\frac{2mg}{\cos \theta} + \frac{mg}{\cos \theta} = ml\omega^2,$$

$$\therefore \frac{3mg}{\cos \theta} = ml\omega^2,$$

$$\therefore \cos \theta = \frac{3g}{l\omega^2}.$$

EXAMPLE (v).

A horizontal rod of length 20 feet is pivoted about a vertical axis at its centre. Equal heavy bodies hang, one from each end of the rod, by chains 12 feet long, of negligible weight. Prove that if the whole system rotates steadily at n R.P.M., and if the angle of inclination of each chain to the vertical is small this angle is approximately equal to

$$\frac{\pi^2 n^2}{90g}.$$

(N.U.3.)

The chains will be inclined to the vertical so that the bodies are more than 10 feet from the axis.

Since the bodies are rotating steadily, i.e. with uniform speed, the chain will not be inclined forward so that there is a component of tension along the tangent to the path ; the vertical plane through the rod will contain both chains.

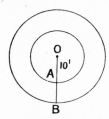

FIG. 94A.

Consider the plan shown in Fig. 94A, where O is the plan of the axis, A the plan of one end of the rod and B the body attached to that end. OA = 10 feet, AB = 12 sin θ feet, where θ is the inclination of the chain to the vertical. (AB is the horizontal projection of the chain.) The body is describing a circle of radius (10 + 12 sin θ) feet. Let T be the tension in the chain, ω the angular velocity, and m the mass of each body.

Resolving horizontally and vertically, we have

$$T \sin \theta = m(10 + 12 \sin \theta)\omega^2,$$
$$T \cos \theta = mg,$$
$$\therefore \tan \theta = \frac{(10 + 12 \sin \theta)\omega^2}{g} = \frac{(10 + 12 \sin \theta)}{g} \cdot \frac{4\pi^2 n^2}{60^2}.$$

Now since θ is small, n is small, and the term 12 sin θ (which is divided by $60^2 g$) can be neglected ; also tan $\theta = \theta$ approximately.

Hence
$$\theta = \frac{40\pi^2 n^2}{60^2 g} = \frac{\pi^2 n^2}{90g}.$$

EXAMPLES XXX.

1. A particle of mass m is describing a circle on a smooth plane at the end of a horizontal string of length a. If the particle make n complete revolutions a minute, compare the tension of the string with the weight of the particle. A man holds one end of a string,

10 inches long, to the other end of which a weight is attached, and swings the weight round so as to make it describe a horizontal circle at a uniform rate of 80 R.P.M. Show that the inclination of the string to the vertical is very nearly 57°. (I.S.)

2. A particle moves as a conical pendulum at the end of a string of length 16 inches. If the string is inclined at 60° to the vertical, show that the particle is making approximately eleven revolutions in 10 seconds. (I.A.)

3. A small heavy body is attached by a string 4 feet long to a fixed point A, and is caused to move with uniform speed in a horizontal circle. If the tension in the string is twice the weight of the body, show that the angular velocity is 4 radians per second. (H.S.D.)

4. An elastic string, of unstretched length 3 feet, has one end attached to a fixed point and the other to a mass of 8 lb. which revolves as a conical pendulum, making 40 R.P.M. If the length of the string is then $3\frac{1}{2}$ feet, find what the extension will be when the weight hangs at rest. (I.S.)

5. A mass of 1 lb., suspended by a cord 5 feet long, is revolving as a conical pendulum at 80 R.P.M. ; find the radius of the circle it describes, and the tension of the cord. (I.A.)

6. Show that in the conical pendulum, the inclination of the string to the vertical being θ, $\sec\theta = \dfrac{r\omega^2}{g}$, where r is the length of the string, and ω the angular velocity. If the string is extensible, so that its tension is equal to $\dfrac{\lambda(r-a)}{a}$, where r is the stretched and a the natural length, find the cosine of the angle which the string makes with the vertical and show that $\dfrac{ma\omega^2}{\lambda}$ must be less than unity. (H.S.D.)

7. A particle of mass 4 lb. is whirled round at the end of a string 20 inches long, so as to describe a horizontal circle, making 60 R.P.M. ; calculate the tension in the string (in lb. wt.) and prove that the fixed end of the string is a little less than 10 inches above the centre of the circle. (H.C.)

8. A particle suspended by a fine string from a fixed point describes a circle uniformly in a horizontal plane. If it makes 3 complete revolutions every 2 seconds, show that its vertical depth below the fixed point is 4·3 inches approximately. [Take $\pi = \frac{22}{7}$.] (H.C.)

9. A particle, attached to a fixed point by a string one yard long, describes a horizontal circle. The string can only support a tension equal to 15 times the weight of the particle. Show that the greatest possible number of revolutions per second is just over two. [$\pi = \frac{22}{7}$.] (H.C.)

10. Two small weights, of 2 oz. and 1 oz. respectively, are connected by a light inextensible string, a foot long, which passes through a smooth fixed ring. The 2 oz. weight hangs at a distance of 9 inches below the ring, while the 1 oz. weight describes a horizontal circle. Show that the plane of this circle is $1\frac{1}{2}$ inches below the ring, and show also that the 1 oz. weight makes very nearly 153 R.P.M. (H.C.)

11. Two unequal masses are connected by a string of length l which passes through a fixed smooth ring. The smaller mass moves as

a conical pendulum while the other mass hangs vertically. Find the semi-angle of the cone, and the number of revolutions per second when a length a of the string is hanging vertically. (C.S.)

12. A heavy particle is attached to the middle point of a string of length $2l$, one end of which is fastened to a fixed point O, and the other end is tied to a ring of the same weight as the particle, which slides on a vertical rod through O. Show that if the particle moves in a horizontal plane with uniform angular velocity ω about the rod, the inclination of both portions of the string to the vertical is

$$\cos^{-1}\left(\frac{3g}{l\omega^2}\right).$$ (C.S.)

13. A particle is attached by means of two equal strings to two points A and B in the same vertical line, and describes a horizontal circle with uniform angular speed. Prove that, in order that both strings may remain stretched, the angular speed must exceed $\sqrt{\frac{2g}{h}}$, where $h = AB$, and that, if the speed is $2\sqrt{\frac{2g}{h}}$, the ratio of the tensions of the strings is 5 : 3. (H.S.D.)

14. A light arm CB, of length a, is freely pivoted at its end C which is fixed, and carries at B a mass m ; the arm is maintained in a horizontal position by a string attached to B and to a point A fixed vertically above C at a distance b from it. Find the magnitude and direction of the stress in CB when CB is revolving about the vertical at the uniform rate of n revolutions per second. (N.U.3)

15. A particle of mass m moving in a horizontal circle is kept in its path by a string tied to a point at a height h above the centre of the circle. Find the period of rotation.
  If $m = 4$ oz., $h = \frac{1}{2}$ inch, and the length of the string is 2 feet, find the tension of the string in lb. wt. (N.U.3)

16. A smooth hemispherical bowl of internal radius a is held with its rim horizontal, and a particle describes in it a horizontal circle of radius c, less than a. Find the period of rotation.
  A particle of mass m describes a horizontal circle of radius 24 cm. inside a smooth hemispherical bowl of internal radius 25 cm. which is held with its rim horizontal. A fine weightless thread tied to the particle passes through a small smooth hole at the bottom of the bowl and supports another particle of mass m which hangs at rest. Show that the speed of the first particle is a little less than 4 metres per second. (N.U.4)

§ 154. Motion of a Railway Carriage or Motor Car round a Curved Track.

Let ABCD (Fig. 95) represent a section of a railway carriage or car in the vertical plane passing through its centre of mass G and the centre of the circle which it is describing, A and B being the points where the wheels meet the ground and A on the inside of the curve.

15 *

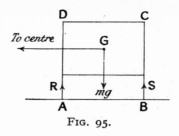

FIG. 95.

Let v be the speed, r the radius of the circle, and m the mass. The central force $\frac{mv^2}{r}$ necessary to cause the circular motion should really be applied at G, the centre of mass, but it can, of course, only be applied in practice at the points of contact with the rails or ground.

In the case of a railway carriage the flanges of the wheels are on the insides of the rails so that, unless a second (or check) rail is placed on the inside of the curve with the inner flanges between the two rails, all the inward thrust is supplied by the outer rail.

In either case, if the curve is at all sharp, there is a considerable side thrust on the rails, and this is usually eliminated by banking the track as explained below.

A level track has another disadvantage, due to the fact that the central force is applied at the ground instead of at the centre of gravity. It is well known that a car rounding a curve at high speed tends to tilt up on its outer wheels.

The force $\frac{mv^2}{r}$, applied horizontally at B or A, is equivalent to an equal horizontal force at G together with a couple which tends to make the carriage rotate in the direction ADCB, i.e. to lift the inner wheel off the ground. The only force present to prevent this rotation is the weight mg, acting vertically through G.

If h is the height of the centre of gravity, and $2a$ the lateral distance between the rails, i.e. the gauge, the moment of the couple tending to tilt the carriage about B is $\frac{mv^2h}{r}$, while the moment of the weight about B (assuming that the centre of gravity is midway between A and B), is mga.

If $$\frac{mv^2h}{r} > mga, \text{ or } v > \sqrt{\frac{gar}{h}},$$

the carriage will upset.

§ **155.** We can obtain this result in another way by considering the vertical pressures at A and B.

Let R, S be the vertical pressures at A and B. The total horizontal force along BA is $\dfrac{mv^2}{r}$, hence, taking moments about G,

$$Sa - Ra = \frac{mv^2}{r}h,$$

$$\therefore S - R = \frac{mv^2h}{ra},$$

but
$$S + R = mg,$$

$$\therefore S = \tfrac{1}{2}m\left(g + \frac{v^2h}{ra}\right),$$

and
$$R = \tfrac{1}{2}m\left(g - \frac{v^2h}{ra}\right).$$

It is evident that the vertical pressure S on the outer rail is always greater than that on the inner rail, and also that, when $\dfrac{v^2h}{ra} = g$, $R = 0$, or the vertical pressure on the inner rail vanishes. At this point the carriage begins to tilt about B.

§ 156. Suppose a car or carriage is placed on an inclined track, sloping downwards towards the centre of the curve which is being described at an angle θ, as shown in Fig. 96.

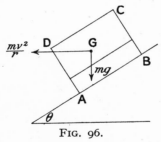

FIG. 96.

We now have the component of the weight, $mg \sin \theta$, acting at G down the slope.

The component of the central force $\dfrac{mv^2}{r}$ down the slope is $\dfrac{mv^2}{r} \cos \theta$, so that if

$$mg \sin \theta = \frac{mv^2}{r} \cos \theta,$$

or
$$\tan \theta = \frac{v^2}{gr},$$

the component of the weight is sufficient to supply the necessary central force down the slope, the component perpendicular to the slope being supplied by the reaction of the track.

In this case there will be no side thrust on the track, and as the weight component acts through G there will be no tendency to upset. The normal thrusts of the wheels on the track will also be equal. The value of θ for a given value of r depends on v.

In the case of a railway track the angle is chosen for the average speed at which trains take the curve. At higher speeds than this there is a side thrust on the outer rail outwards, at lower speeds there will be an inward thrust on the inner rail, the weight component being greater than is necessary.

In the case of a motor track the banking is graduated, getting steeper towards the outside of the track. As the speed of the car increases it skids or is steered on to the steeper part.

§ 157. Motion of a Bicyclist riding in a Curve.

In this case the centre of gravity, if the cycle and rider are upright, is vertically above the line of contact of the wheels with the ground. The weight has therefore no moment about this point and cannot, therefore, counteract the upsetting couple. For this reason the rider has to lean inwards on rounding a corner.

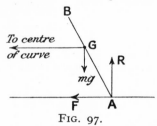

FIG. 97.

Let AB (Fig. 97) represent the bicycle and rider, and G their centre of mass. The friction of the ground F acts inwards at A, and the other forces acting are the weight mg, vertically through G, and the normal reaction of the ground (R) at A.

Since there is no vertical motion

$$R = mg.$$

Also R and F have to produce a force through G which has a horizontal component of $\dfrac{mv^2}{r}$, so that the resultant of R and F must pass through G.

If θ is the angle made by AB with the vertical,

$$\tan \theta = \frac{F}{R},$$

but

$$F = \frac{mv^2}{r},$$

$$\therefore \tan \theta = \frac{mv^2}{mgr} = \frac{v^2}{gr}.$$

This is the same as the angle of banking necessary to prevent any tendency to skid.

§ 158. EXAMPLE (i).

A train is running at 45 m.p.h. on a curve of mean radius 1200 feet, and the distance between the rails is 4 feet 8½ inches. Find how much the outer rail must be raised in order that there may be no side thrust on the rail. (I.S.)

45 m.p.h. = 66 ft./sec.

Let m lb. be the mass of the train, and θ the angle the plane of the rails makes with the horizontal.

The horizontal inward force required is $\dfrac{m \times 66^2}{1200}$ pdls., and the component of this parallel to the plane of the rails is

$$\frac{m \times 66^2}{1200} \cos \theta,$$

the component of the weight in this direction is $mg \sin \theta$;

∴ the required value of θ is given by

$$mg \sin \theta = \frac{m \times 66^2}{1200} \cos \theta,$$

$$\therefore \tan \theta = \frac{66 \times 66}{32 \times 1200} = \frac{363}{3200}.$$

The height to which the outer rail should be raised is $56\tfrac{1}{2} \sin \theta$ ins. Now as θ is small we may take $\sin \theta = \tan \theta$,
∴ the height required

$$= \frac{113}{2} \times \frac{363}{3200} = 6\cdot4 \text{ ins.}$$

EXAMPLE (ii).

A railway truck weighing 10 tons travels round a curve, of ½ mile radius, at 15 m.p.h. The distance between the rails is 5 feet, and the centre of gravity of the truck is 6 feet above the rails. If the rails are at the same level, find the vertical pressure upon each, and the horizontal pressure between the flange and the rail. How much should the outer rail be raised to avoid pressure on the flange ? (I.E.)

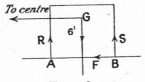

FIG. 98.

Let A (Fig. 98) represent the inner and B the outer point of contact with the rails, and let R and S be the vertical pressures at A and B, F the horizontal thrust at B.

$$F = \frac{mv^2}{r} = \frac{22400 \times 22^2}{2640} \text{ pdls.}$$

$$= \frac{11}{192} \text{ tons wt.}$$

and $R + S = 10 \text{ tons wt.}$

Taking moments about G,

$$2\tfrac{1}{2}S - 2\tfrac{1}{2}R = 6F,$$

$$\therefore S - R = \frac{12}{5}F,$$

$$\therefore 2S = 10 + \frac{12}{5}F = \frac{811}{80},$$

$$\therefore S = \frac{811}{160} \text{ tons wt.},$$

$$\therefore R = 10 - \frac{811}{160} = \frac{789}{160} \text{ tons wt.}$$

If θ is the slope of the track necessary to prevent side thrust,

$$mg \sin \theta = \frac{mv^2}{r} \cos \theta,$$

$$\therefore \tan \theta = \frac{v^2}{gr} = \frac{22 \times 22}{32 \times 2640} = \frac{11}{1920}.$$

The height to which the outer rail must be raised is

$$5 \sin \theta \doteqdot 5 \tan \theta = \frac{55}{1920} \text{ ft.}$$

$$= \tfrac{1}{3} \text{ inch nearly.}$$

EXAMPLE (iii).

An aeroplane weighing 1 ton flies at 90 m.p.h. Find the angle at which it must bank in order to turn without side-slipping in a horizontal circle of 200 yards radius, assuming that its design enables it to do this, and that the line of the resultant air pressure lies in the plane of symmetry of the machine. (Q.E.)

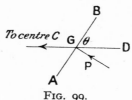

FIG. 99.

Let AB (Fig. 99) represent the section of the wings, G the centre of gravity, and CGD the horizontal line through G, the centre of the circle described being in the direction of C.

The air pressure may be taken as a force P acting through G perpendicular to AB. Let $\angle$BGD = θ.

Now P has to support the weight of the plane mg, and also provide the central force $\dfrac{mv^2}{r}$ along GC.

Here
$$v = 90 \text{ m.p.h.} = \frac{90 \cdot 88}{60} = 132 \text{ ft./sec.,}$$

$$r = 200 \text{ yards} = 600 \text{ ft.,}$$

$$\therefore P \cos \theta = mg,$$

and
$$P \sin \theta = \frac{m \cdot 132^2}{600},$$

$$\therefore \tan \theta = \frac{132 \cdot 132}{32 \cdot 600} = \frac{363}{400},$$

$$\therefore \theta = 42° \ 13' \text{ approximately.}$$

EXAMPLES XXXI.

1. The gauge of a railway is 4 feet $8\frac{1}{2}$ inches, and the line runs along an arc of a circle of radius half a mile. The average speed of the trains on the line is 45 m.p.h. What should be the height of the outer above the inner rail ? (I.S.)

2. A motor track describes a curve of 250 feet radius, and is sloping downwards towards the inside of the curve at an angle $\tan^{-1}\frac{1}{5}$. At what speed must a car run along it so that there should be no tendency to side-slip ? (I.S.)

3. Explain clearly the advantage of raising the outer rail above the inner on a curved railway track. Calculate by how much the outer rail should be raised on a circular track of radius r, if b is the breadth between the rails and v is the speed of a train on the track. (I.A.)

4. If the radius of a curved railway track is 1000 yards, and a train has to travel round the track at 30 m.p.h., by how much should the outer rail be raised above the inner if the distance between the rails is 57 inches ? (I.A.)

5. A motor car is rounding a curve of 50 yards radius on a level road. Find the maximum speed at which this is possible, if the distance between the wheels is $4\frac{1}{2}$ feet, and the centre of gravity is 2 feet from the ground and midway between the line of the wheels. Find also the least coefficient of friction between the road and tyres which will prevent side-slip at the maximum speed. (H.S.C.)

6. A motor car is moving round the curve of a track at 75 m.p.h., the radius of the curve being 110 yards. Calculate the angle which the track makes with the horizon, if the total pressure exerted by the car on the track is normal to the plane of the track. If the weight of the car is $1\frac{1}{2}$ tons, calculate the total pressure on the track. (H.S.D.)

7. Assuming that the height of the centre of gravity of a locomotive above the rails is 6 feet, and the width of the rails is $4\frac{2}{3}$ feet, find the greatest speed at which it could travel on a curve of radius 150 yards without toppling over. (I.E.)

8. A train is travelling at 35 m.p.h. round a curve of radius 200 yards. If the width of the rails is 5 feet, calculate how much the outer rail must be raised above the inner, if lateral pressure on the rails is to be avoided. (H.S.D.)

9. A bicyclist is describing a curve of 50 feet radius at a speed of 10 m.p.h. ; find the inclination to the vertical of the plane of the bicycle. What is the least coefficient of friction between the bicycle and the road that the bicycle may not side-slip ?   [Assume the rider and his machine to be in one plane.]   (H.C.)

10. The shape of a cycle track at a corner is that of a circle whose radius is 100 yards. Find the angle at which the track should be inclined to the horizontal in order that a rider can take the corner at 30 m.p.h. without any lateral reaction between his bicycle and the track. If a motor-cyclist can take the corner safely at 60 m.p.h., find the least possible value of the coefficient of friction between the track and his tyres.   (H.C.)

11. A motor car is rounding a curve of radius 150 feet on a level road. What is the maximum speed at which this is possible without over-turning when the distance between the wheels is 4 feet, and the centre of gravity of the car and its load is midway between the wheels and 3 feet from the ground ?   (Q.E.)

12. An aeroplane is describing a horizontal circle of 100 yards radius at 75 m.p.h. Assuming that the air pressure on it acts through its centre of gravity at right angles to the planes, determine the angle at which they must be inclined to the vertical.   (H.S.D.)

13. The sleepers of a railway line at a point where the curve of the track has a radius of 60 yards have such a slope that a train moving at 30 m.p.h. exerts no lateral force on the rails. What lateral force would an engine of weight 100 tons exert on the rails at this point if it were at rest ?   (I.E.)

14. A car takes a banked corner of a racing track at a speed V, the lateral gradient α being designed to reduce the tendency to side-slip to zero for a lower speed U. Show that the coefficient of friction necessary to prevent side-slip for the greater speed V must be at least

$$\frac{(V^2 - U^2) \sin \alpha \cos \alpha}{V^2 \sin^2 \alpha + U^2 \cos^2 \alpha}.$$ (C.S.)

15. A railway track round a curve of 440 yards radius is laid so that there is no lateral pressure on the rails when a train travels round at 40 m.p.h.   Determine the lateral pressure, in terms of the weight of the train, when the speed is 20 m.p.h.   (Neglect the length of the train.)   (I.C.)

16. A railway truck is loaded so that the pressure on each wheel is 5 tons, and the centre of gravity of the loaded truck is 6 feet above the rails, and the distance from centre to centre of the wheels on an axle is 5 feet.   Find the alteration due to centrifugal action in the vertical pressure on the rails when the truck is going on the level round a track of 1200 feet radius at a speed of 15 m.p.h.   (I.C.)

17. A curve on a railway line is banked up so that the lateral thrust on the inner rail due to a truck moving with speed v_1 is equal to the thrust on the outer rail when the truck is moving with speed v_2 ($v_2 > v_1$). Show that there will be no lateral thrust on either rail when the truck is moving with speed,

$$[\tfrac{1}{2}(v_1^2 + v_2^2)]^{\frac{1}{2}}.$$ (H.C.)

18. A car travels round a curve on a track of 50 yards radius at a speed of 30 m.p.h.   Show that if there is no side pressure between the car and the track, the track must be banked at an angle of approximately

22°. What would be the component of force on the car across the track, if a car weighing 1 ton went round this curve at 45 m.p.h. ?
(Q.E.)

19. A motor car makes a quick turn on the level round a circle of 30 feet radius. If the centre of gravity of the car be midway between the wheels and at a height of 3 feet 2 inches, and if the wheel gauge is 4 feet 8 inches, find the speed at which the car will overturn, assuming that no side-slipping occurs. (Q.E.)

20. In a conical pendulum the speed of the bob is v, and the radius of the circle in which it moves is r, while the string makes an angle α with the vertical. Prove that $v^2 = r\,g\,\tan\alpha$.

A cyclist travels on a level track of radius 220 feet, and the coefficient of friction between the tyres and the ground is 0·32. Find the greatest speed at which he may travel. (N.U.3)

21. A car travels at v ft./sec. along a curved track of radius R feet. Find the inclination of the track to the horizontal if there is to be no tendency for the car to slip sideways.

Prove that if $v = 30\ R$, $= 1000$ and the inclination of the track is 1 in 100, the total sideways frictional force on the wheels must be about 1·8 per cent. of the weight of the car. (N.U.3.)

§ 159. Equilibrium of a Smooth Ring on a Rotating Wire.

If a smooth ring is threaded on a wire in the form of a plane curve which is caused to rotate, with uniform angular velocity, about a vertical axis in its plane, the ring can usually remain at rest relatively to the wire at points other than the lowest point of the wire.

We will consider the case where the curve is a circle rotating about a vertical diameter.

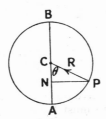

FIG. 100.

Let the diameter AB (Fig. 100) be the axis of rotation, C the centre, r the radius, and ω the angular velocity.

Let P be the position of a smooth ring threaded on the circle, PN the perpendicular on AB, and let $\angle PCN = \theta$.

If the ring is to remain at P it must be acted on by a force $m \cdot PN \cdot \omega^2$ along PN since it is moving in a horizontal circle about N as centre. This force must be provided by the horizontal component of the reaction of the wire on the ring, and the vertical component of this reaction must balance the weight mg.

Now since the wire and ring are smooth the reaction of the wire must be along the radius PC, and if its value is R, then for P to remain stationary relative to the wire, we must have

$$R \sin \theta = m\text{PN} \cdot \omega^2 = mr \sin \theta \cdot \omega^2 . \qquad . \qquad . \quad \text{(i)}$$

$$\text{and } R \cos \theta = mg \quad . \qquad . \qquad . \qquad . \qquad . \qquad . \quad \text{(ii)}$$

The first equation gives

$$R = mr\omega^2, \text{ unless } \sin \theta = 0,$$

and this value of R will satisfy the second equation if

$$\cos \theta = \frac{g}{r\omega^2}.$$

The value $\sin \theta = 0$, gives the positions A and B, the lowest and highest points of the circle.

The value $\cos \theta = \frac{g}{r\omega^2}$, gives a possible inclined position *provided that*

$$\frac{g}{r\omega^2} < 1, \quad \text{or} \quad \omega > \sqrt{\frac{g}{r}}.$$

If ω is less than this value no inclined position such as P is possible. In this case the lowest and highest points are the only possible positions of equilibrium, and of these the highest one is unstable.

When an inclined position is possible, it is the only stable one.

§ 160. Effect of the Earth's Rotation on Gravity.

The weight of a body is due to the earth's attraction on it. The force of attraction varies inversely as the square of the distance from the centre of the earth (for bodies outside the surface of the earth), and hence is greater at the poles, where it is nearer the centre, than at the equator.

When a body is at relative rest on the earth's surface the pressure of the earth on the body must balance what we call its weight.

At the poles, where there is no rotation, this pressure is an actual measure of the earth's attraction.

But consider a body of mass m at the equator. It is carried round in a circle of radius r (about 3960 miles) in a day.

[Strictly this day is not the mean solar day of 24 hours, but the sidereal day of 23 hours 56 minutes 4 seconds, or 86,164 seconds.]

Taking the number of seconds in the day as 86,400, the angular velocity ω is therefore $\frac{2\pi}{86400}$.

Now owing to this circular motion there must be a force $mr\omega^2$ towards the centre of the earth, and this must equal the resultant of the earth's attraction and the pressure of the earth's surface on the body. The latter is equal to the apparent weight mg, where g is the actual acceleration due to gravity at the equator. The earth's attraction is mg' where g' is the value the acceleration would have if there were no rotation.

$$\therefore mg' - mg = mr\omega^2,$$
$$\therefore g' - g = r\omega^2 = \tfrac{1}{9} \text{ nearly.}$$

This means that the acceleration due to gravity is reduced by about $\frac{1}{289}$ of itself at the equator.

§ 161. When the body is not at the equator the effect is more complicated.

For a body at P (Fig. 101) in latitude λ the radius of the circle

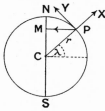

FIG. 101.

described by the body is $r \cos \lambda$.

The central force necessary to produce this circular motion is no longer directed towards the centre of the earth, but along PM. This actually alters the apparent direction of the weight as well as the magnitude, the diminution becoming smaller as λ increases until it is zero at the poles.

The forces acting on the body at P are (1) the attraction of the earth along PC, and (2) the pressure of the earth on it. The resultant of these two forces must be in the direction of PM.

Let X, Y be the components of the pressure of the earth on the body at P along and perpendicular to CP.

The acceleration of P is ω^2PM along PM.

Hence, resolving X, Y and mg along and perpendicular to PM, we have

$$Y \sin \lambda + (mg - X) \cos \lambda = m\omega^2\text{PM} = m\omega^2 r \cos \lambda \quad \text{(i)}$$
$$Y \cos \lambda - (mg - X) \sin \lambda = 0 \quad . \quad . \quad . \quad \text{(ii)}$$

Solving these equations, we have

$$X = m(g - \omega^2 r \cos^2 \lambda) = mg\left(1 - \frac{\omega^2 r}{g} \cos^2 \lambda\right),$$
$$Y = m\omega^2 r \sin \lambda \cos \lambda = mg \frac{\omega^2 r}{g} \sin \lambda \cos \lambda.$$

Now $\dfrac{\omega^2 r}{g}$ is approximately $\dfrac{1}{288}$, so that its square may be neglected.

If the resultant of X and Y is W inclined at an angle θ to CP,

$$W = \sqrt{X^2 + Y^2},$$
$$= mg\left[\left(1 - \frac{\omega^2 r}{g}\cos^2 \lambda\right)^2 + \left(\frac{\omega^2 r}{g}\sin \lambda \cos \lambda\right)^2\right]^{\frac{1}{2}},$$
$$= mg\left[1 - \frac{\omega^2 r}{g}\cos^2 \lambda\right], \text{ neglecting the square of } \frac{\omega^2 r}{g},$$
$$= mg - m\omega^2 r \cos^2 \lambda.$$

The apparent weight is therefore diminished by $m\omega^2 r \cos^2 \lambda$, and the direction of the weight is turned through an angle θ, where

$$\tan \theta = \frac{\omega^2 r \sin \lambda \cos \lambda}{g - \omega^2 r \cos^2 \lambda},$$
$$= \frac{\omega^2 r}{g}\sin \lambda \cos \lambda \text{ approximately.}$$

§ 162. Tension in a Rotating Ring.

Suppose a circular wire or belt is rotating in its own plane about an axis through its centre perpendicular to its plane.

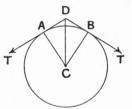

FIG. 102.

Let C (Fig. 102) be the centre.

Consider an elementary portion of the wire AB of length δs, subtending a small angle $\delta \theta$ at the centre.

Let m be the mass per unit length and r the radius of the circle. The mass of AB is $m\delta s$ or $mr\delta \theta$.

If ω is the angular velocity, the force towards the centre necessary for the circular motion is

$$mr\delta \theta \cdot r\omega^2 = mr^2\omega^2\delta \theta.$$

This force is provided by the tensions T, in the adjoining portions of the wire, and these tensions are perpendicular to the radii CA and CB, and meet in D.

The angle between these tensions is $180 - \delta \theta$, and the sum of their components in the direction DC is

$$= 2T \sin \frac{\delta \theta}{2} = T\delta \theta, \text{ since } \delta \theta \text{ is small.}$$

$$\therefore T\delta\theta = mr^2\omega^2\delta\theta,$$
$$\therefore T = mr^2\omega^2 = mv^2,$$

where v is the linear velocity of a point on the ring.

If m is in lb. and r in feet, T is in poundals.

If T_M is the maximum tension the wire can bear, the maximum value of ω is $\sqrt{\dfrac{T_M}{mr^2}}$.

The maximum tension which a wire or belt can bear is usually stated as a force per unit cross-section.

If the cross-section of the wire is A, T_0 the maximum tension it can bear per unit area, and ρ the density, then

$$m = \rho A,$$
$$\text{and } T_M = T_0 A.$$

The maximum angular velocity ω is then given by

$$\omega = \sqrt{\frac{T_0 A}{\rho A r^2}} = \sqrt{\frac{T_0}{\rho r^2}},$$

and is independent of A.

EXAMPLES XXXII.

1. A uniform circular wire of small cross-section is rotating in its own plane about its centre with uniform speed v. If the wire weighs 490 lb. per cu. ft., and can just stand a strain of 90,000 lb. wt. per sq. in., show that the greatest value of v is about 920 ft./sec.   (I.E.)

2. Prove that if we take the radius of the earth as 3960 miles, gravity at the equator is diminished by the earth's rotation by ·00343 of itself.
(I.A.)

3. A circular hoop rotates with uniform angular velocity ω about a vertical diameter AOB, O being the centre. A smooth ring P of weight W can slide on the hoop. If α be the angle of inclination of the radius OP to the vertical when the ring is in equilibrium with respect to the hoop, prove that $\cos\alpha = \dfrac{g}{\omega^2 a}$, where a is the radius of the hoop.
Obtain also the reaction between the ring and the hoop.   (H.S.D.)

4. A uniform circular wire, of radius 10 feet and mass 1 lb., rotates uniformly about its centre 10 times per second ; show that the wire will break unless it will stand a tension of 196 lb. wt.

5. A smooth parabolic tube, of latus rectum $4a$ and vertex downwards, revolves uniformly about its axis, which is vertical. Show that if the angular velocity be $\sqrt{\dfrac{g}{2a}}$ a particle will rest anywhere in the tube.

6. Assuming the earth to be a sphere rotating uniformly about the polar axis, whose attraction per unit mass is the same at all points of the surface, prove that a pendulum, which beats seconds at the poles, will lose approximately $30\,k\cos^2\lambda$ beats per minute in latitude λ, the ratio of the weight of the body at the poles to its weight at the equator being $1 + k : 1$.
(H.S.C.)

MOTION IN A VERTICAL CIRCLE.

§ 163. The complete investigation of the motion of a particle constrained to move on a curve in a vertical plane is beyond the scope of this book. When the curve is smooth we can, however, find the velocity of the particle at any point by means of the principle of energy. The time taken to describe a given length of arc or to acquire a certain velocity cannot be found easily, and in the case of the circle it is impossible to obtain an exact value for it. We shall deal more fully with the motion of a particle on a cycloid in a later chapter, but for the present shall consider certain results which can be obtained from a knowledge of the velocity in any position.

When a particle is sliding down a smooth curve, we know from the principle of energy that the kinetic energy gained is equal to the potential energy lost, since the reaction of the curve is perpendicular to the direction of motion and therefore does no work. The same applies to a particle suspended by a string and swinging in a vertical plane about a fixed point.

If m is the mass of the particle, u the initial and v the final velocity, and h the vertical height descended,

$$\tfrac{1}{2}mv^2 - \tfrac{1}{2}mu^2 = mgh,$$
$$\therefore v^2 - u^2 = 2gh, \quad \text{or} \quad v^2 = u^2 + 2gh.$$

If the particle is moving *up* the curve

$$v^2 = u^2 - 2gh.$$

§ 164. In dealing with motion in a vertical circle there are differences in the nature of the problem according to whether the particle is, or is not, able to leave the circle. If a ring is threaded on the circle it cannot leave the curve, but if a particle is suspended by a string, this may go slack when it gets above the horizontal position. Similarly a particle moving down the outside of a vertical circle, or projected up the inside can come away from the curve. In these cases the usual problem is to find where it will leave the curve.

We shall consider first the case of a ring or bead threaded on the circle.

§ 165. Motion of a Ring threaded on a Smooth Vertical Circle.

Let C (Fig. 103) be the centre of the circle, A the lowest point, B the highest point, and a the radius.

Let the mass of the ring be m, and V its velocity of projection from the lowest point.

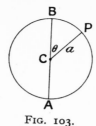

FIG. 103.

When it reaches a position P, such that $\angle BCP = \theta$, it has risen a vertical distance $a + a \cos \theta$, and its velocity v is given by

$$v^2 = V^2 - 2ga \,(1 + \cos \theta).$$

If V is just large enough to take the particle up to B, we must have

$$0 = V^2 - 4ag,$$
$$\therefore V = \sqrt{4ag},$$

and with this value of V the ring will just come to rest at B.

In the position P, the force along PC required for the circular motion is $\dfrac{mv^2}{a}$, and the component of the weight in this direction is $mg \cos \theta$.

If $mg \cos \theta > \dfrac{mv^2}{a},$ or $v^2 < ag \cos \theta,$

the weight is more than sufficient to provide the central force, and there is an *inward* pressure on the circle equal to

$$mg \cos \theta - \frac{mv^2}{a}.$$

If
$$v^2 > ag \cos \theta,$$

the weight component is not sufficient to provide the central force, and there is an *outward* pressure on the circle equal to

$$\frac{mv^2}{a} - mg \cos \theta.$$

When P is below the centre, the weight component along the radius always acts away from the centre, and there is always an outward pressure on the curve.

§ 166. Motion of a Suspended Particle in a Vertical Circle.

Let a particle of mass m be suspended at A (Fig. 104) from a point C by a light string of length a.

Let the particle be projected at right angles to the string with

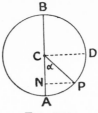

FIG. 104.

velocity V. Let v be the velocity at any point P of its path below the level of the centre, and draw PN perpendicular to CA.

Then the particle has risen a vertical distance AN, and

$$AN = a - a\cos\alpha = a\,(1 - \cos\alpha),$$
$$\therefore v^2 = V^2 - 2g\,.\,AN$$
$$= V^2 - 2ag\,(1 - \cos\alpha) \qquad . \qquad . \qquad . \qquad \text{(i)}$$

Now the component of the weight along CP is $mg\cos\alpha$ and acts outwards; also, since the velocity in the circular path is v, a force towards C equal to $\dfrac{mv^2}{a}$ is required. The tension (T) in the string must therefore balance the weight component and also provide this central force,

$$\therefore T = mg\cos\alpha + \frac{mv^2}{a},$$

$$= mg\cos\alpha + \frac{mV^2}{a} - 2mg(1 - \cos\alpha),$$

$$= \frac{mV^2}{a} + mg(3\cos\alpha - 2) \qquad . \qquad . \qquad . \qquad \text{(ii)}$$

when the particle is at A, $\cos\alpha = 1$, and

$$T = \frac{mV^2}{a} + mg.$$

It is clear that as long as P is below the horizontal radius CD, the weight component acts outwards and the string can never go slack.

If V is just large enough to take the particle to the level of the centre at D, then from (i)

$$0 = V^2 - 2ag$$
$$\therefore V = \sqrt{2ag}.$$

If V is greater than this value, the particle will go above the level of the centre, and in this case it is better to consider the angle made by the string with CB (Fig. 105). Let this angle be θ.

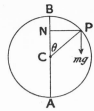

FIG. 105.

The height of P above A is $a + a \cos \theta = a(1 + \cos \theta)$.
Hence, if v is the velocity at P,

$$v^2 = V^2 - 2ag(1 + \cos \theta).$$

Now the weight component along the string is $mg \cos \theta$, and acts towards C. The central force necessary owing to the motion in a circle with velocity v is $\dfrac{mv^2}{a}$.

If

$$mg \cos \theta > \frac{mv^2}{a},$$

or

$$v^2 < ag \cos \theta,$$

the weight component is greater than the force required owing to the motion, and the string will become slack, the particle leaving the circular path and moving as a free projectile.

It will leave the circle when

$$v^2 = ag \cos \theta,$$

but

$$v^2 = V^2 - 2ag(1 + \cos \theta),$$
$$\therefore V^2 = ag \cos \theta + 2ag(1 + \cos \theta),$$
$$= ag(2 + 3 \cos \theta).$$

This equation gives the value of θ at which the string becomes slack with a given initial velocity V.

If the string is to remain tight up to the highest point, i.e. where $\theta = 0$, we must have

$$V^2 = 5ag,$$
$$\text{or } V = \sqrt{5ag}.$$

This is the minimum velocity required for the particle to describe a complete circle.

The tension T in the string when the particle is at P is given by

$$T = \frac{mv^2}{a} - mg \cos \theta,$$
$$= \frac{mV^2}{a} - mg \cos \theta - 2mg(1 + \cos \theta)$$
$$= \frac{mV^2}{a} - mg(2 + 3 \cos \theta).$$

The whole of the above argument applies to the case of a particle projected up the inside of a smooth vertical circular hoop. In this case the tension of the string is replaced by the pressure of the hoop.

§ 167. Motion on the Outside of a Smooth Vertical Circle.

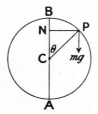

Fig. 106.

Let C (Fig. 106) be the centre, B the highest and A the lowest point of the circle, and a its radius.

Let a particle of mass m at B be slightly displaced so that it slides down the circle. Let v be its velocity when at a point P such that $\angle$ BCP $= \theta$. Draw PN perpendicular to CB.

The particle has descended a vertical distance

$$BN = a - a \cos \theta = a(1 - \cos \theta),$$
$$\therefore v^2 = 2ag(1 - \cos \theta).$$

Let R be the pressure of the curve on the particle, then, since the component of the weight along the radius is $mg \cos \theta$, the resultant force acting on the particle in the direction PC is

$$mg \cos \theta - R.$$

But since the particle is moving in a circle about C with velocity v, the central force towards C must be $\dfrac{mv^2}{a}$,

$$\therefore \frac{mv^2}{a} = mg \cos \theta - R,$$

$$\therefore \quad R = mg \cos \theta - \frac{mv^2}{a},$$
$$= mg \cos \theta - 2mg(1 - \cos \theta),$$
$$= mg(3 \cos \theta - 2).$$

If $3 \cos \theta > 2$, there is a pressure between the curve and the particle.

If $3 \cos \theta < 2$, the pressure R becomes negative, which means that the particle has left the curve.

The pressure R becomes zero, and the particle leaves the curve when

$$3 \cos \theta = 2,$$
or
$$\cos \theta = \tfrac{2}{3}.$$

The particle then moves as a free projectile, its initial velocity v being given by

$$v^2 = 2ag(1 - \tfrac{2}{3}) = \tfrac{2}{3}ag,$$

or
$$v = \sqrt{\frac{2ag}{3}}.$$

Its initial direction of motion is inclined downwards at an angle $\cos^{-1} \tfrac{2}{3}$ to the horizontal.

§ **168.** EXAMPLE (i).

A particle of mass m lb. is suspended from a fixed point by a string a ft. long. It is projected horizontally with a velocity of $2\sqrt{ag}$ ft./sec. Find the height of the particle above the point of suspension when the string becomes slack. Find also the tension in the string when the particle is at a depth $\dfrac{a}{2}$ below the point of suspension.

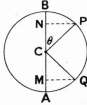

FIG. 107.

Let C (Fig. 107) be the point of suspension, and A the lowest point from which the particle is projected.

If CP is the position of the string when it becomes slack, and $\angle BCP = \theta$, then if v is the velocity of the particle at P,

$$v^2 = 4ag - 2ag(1 + \cos\theta),$$
$$= 2\,ag(1 - \cos\theta).$$

Now since the string becomes slack in this position,

$$\frac{mv^2}{a} = mg\cos\theta,$$
$$\text{or } v^2 = ag\cos\theta,$$
$$\therefore ag\cos\theta = 2ag(1 - \cos\theta),$$
$$\therefore \cos\theta = \tfrac{2}{3},$$

∴ the height above C is $a\cos\theta$ or $\tfrac{2}{3}a$.

In the position Q where $CM = AM = \dfrac{a}{2}$, $\angle ACQ = 60°$, and the velocity v is given by

$$v^2 = 4ag - 2g \cdot \frac{a}{2} = 3ag.$$

The tension in the string is

$$mg\cos 60° + \frac{mv^2}{a},$$
$$= \tfrac{1}{2}mg + 3mg = \tfrac{7}{2}mg \text{ pdls.}$$

Example (ii).

Show that the velocity with which a particle hanging from a fixed point by a string of length a must be started so as to describe a complete vertical circle must not be less than $\sqrt{5ag}$. The particle is started with a velocity $2\sqrt{ag}$, and when the string is horizontal is held at such a point that the particle just completes the circle. Where must the point be situated on the string ?   (I.E.)

The result in the first part of the question was obtained in the general discussion in § 166. We can, however, obtain it without considering the intermediate inclined positions of the string.

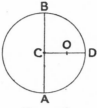

Fig. 108.

Let A (Fig. 108) be the lowest and B the highest points of the circle whose centre is C the point of suspension.

Let V be the velocity at A, and v that at B, then

$$v^2 = V^2 - 4ag.$$

Now if the particle is to describe the complete circle, the string must be just taut when the particle reaches B,

$$\therefore \frac{mv^2}{a} \text{ must not be less than } mg,$$

or
$$v^2 \not< ag,$$
$$\therefore V^2 - 4ag \not< ag,$$
$$\therefore V^2 \not< 5ag.$$

If $V = 2\sqrt{ag}$, the velocity v when the particle is level with the centre at D is given by

$$v^2 = 4ag - 2ag = 2ag.$$

If the string is now held at a point O distant x from D, and the particle is just to complete the vertical circle about O as centre, the string must be just taut when the particle is vertically over O, i.e. at a height x above O. Now at this height its velocity u is given by

$$u^2 = v^2 - 2gx,$$
$$= 2ag - 2gx,$$

and as the string is just taut,

$$\frac{mu^2}{x} = mg,$$

or
$$u^2 = gx,$$
$$\therefore gx = 2ag - 2gx,$$
$$\therefore 3gx = 2ag,$$
$$\therefore x = \tfrac{2}{3}a.$$

EXAMPLE (iii).

A particle is hanging from a fixed point by a light cord 3 feet long, and is started moving with an initial horizontal speed such that the cord slackens when the particle is 5 feet above its lowest point. Find how much higher it will rise.

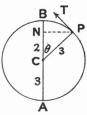

FIG. 109.

Let C (Fig. 109) be the point of suspension, A the lowest point of the vertical circle with C as centre.

The cord slackens in the position CP where $\cos \theta = \tfrac{2}{3}$.

Now if v is the velocity at P, then, since the cord slackens,

$$\frac{mv^2}{3} = mg \cos \theta,$$
$$\therefore v^2 = 3g \cos \theta = 2g,$$
$$\therefore v = \sqrt{2g} = 8 \text{ ft./sec.}$$

The particle now moves as a free projectile, its initial velocity being 8 ft./sec. along the tangent PT, and inclined to the horizontal at an angle $\cos^{-1}\tfrac{2}{3}$.

The vertical component of its velocity is

$$8 \sin \theta = \tfrac{8}{3}\sqrt{5} \text{ ft./sec.}$$

If h is the height it rises,

$$0 = \tfrac{64}{9} \cdot 5 - 2gh,$$
$$\therefore h = \tfrac{5}{9} \text{ ft.}$$

EXAMPLE (iv).

A particle attached to a fixed point O by an inelastic string of length r is let fall from a point in the horizontal through O at a distance $r \cos \theta$ from O. Show that the velocity of the particle, when it is vertically below O, is $\sqrt{2gr(1 - \sin^3\theta)}$.

(H.S.D.)

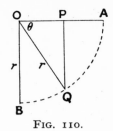

FIG. 110.

Let OA (Fig. 110) be horizontal and equal to r, OB vertical and equal to r, and let P be the point in OA from which the particle is let fall.

Then, since OP $= r \cos \theta$, the particle reaches the circle through A and B whose centre is O, at a point Q such that $\angle$POQ $= \theta$.

At this point the particle has fallen a vertical distance PQ, which is equal to $r \sin \theta$, hence its velocity u is given by

$$u^2 = 2gr \sin \theta.$$

Now when the string becomes taut, all velocity in the direction of the string is destroyed, and the particle begins to move along the arc QB with a velocity equal to the component of u perpendicular to OQ, i.e. $u \cos \theta$.

Hence, if v is the velocity in the circle at Q after the jerk,

$$v^2 = 2gr \sin \theta \cos^2 \theta.$$

When the particle reaches B it has descended a further vertical distance $r - r \sin \theta = r(1 - \sin \theta)$, and its velocity V is given by

$$V^2 = v^2 + 2gr(1 - \sin \theta),$$
$$= 2gr \sin \theta \cos^2 \theta + 2gr(1 - \sin \theta),$$
$$= 2gr(\sin \theta - \sin^3 \theta + 1 - \sin \theta),$$
$$= 2gr(1 - \sin^3 \theta).$$
$$\therefore V = \sqrt{2gr(1 - \sin^3 \theta)}.$$

EXAMPLES XXXIII.

1. A mass of 2 oz. is attached by a string 4 feet long to a fixed point, and is describing a circle in a vertical plane round that point. Find the least velocity at the lowest point in order that the mass may make complete revolutions. Find also the tension of the string in this case when the mass is 2 feet below the horizontal diameter of the circle. (I.S.)

2. A heavy particle is free to move in a vertical circle of radius l ; the particle is projected with velocity u from the lowest point A of the circle, and just reaches a point B ; show by applying the principle of energy that $u = \sqrt{\dfrac{g}{l}} \, . \, AB$. (I.S.)

3. A mass of 1 gm., hanging by a string 1 metre long, is swinging as a pendulum through an arc of total magnitude 1 radian. Find the

central acceleration and the tension of the string when the mass is passing through its lowest point.   (I.S.)

4. A weight, attached to an inextensible string, is whirled in a vertical circle of 2 feet radius. If the greatest and least tensions of the string are in the ratio of 11 : 1, calculate the least velocity of the weight (approximately).   (I.A.)

5. A mass of 0·5 lb. is attached by a light string 3 feet long to a fixed point. The string is held taut and horizontally, and the mass is allowed to fall. Find the speed of the mass when the string makes an angle θ with the horizontal. Find also the tension of the string when it is vertical, and when it makes an angle of 30° with the vertical.

On passing through the lowest point the mass catches up a ring of mass 0·25 lb. at rest and carries it on. How high will the two masses rise ?

6. A weight of 2 lb. is whirled round in a vertical plane with a constant speed of 20 ft./sec., at the end of an elastic cord. The natural length of the cord is 6 feet, and it extends 1 foot for every 7 lb. of tension. Find the length of the cord at the top and bottom of the path of the weight.   (I.E.)

7. A heavy particle at the end of a tight 4 foot string, the other end of which is fixed, is let fall from a horizontal position of the string ; when the string is vertical it encounters an obstruction at its middle point so that the particle continues in a circle of 2 feet radius. Find how high the particle will go before the string becomes slack.
                                                          (H.S.C.)

8. A motor car, weighing 1 ton, runs under a bridge at 30 m.p.h., the roadway being in the form of an arc of a circle of radius 63 feet. Find the reaction between the car and the road at the lowest point of the arc.   (H.S.C.)

9. The roadway of a bridge over a canal is in the form of a circular arc of radius 50 feet. What is the greatest speed (in m.p.h.) at which a motor cycle can cross the bridge without leaving the ground at the highest point ?   (I.S.)

10. A particle, of mass m, oscillates through 180° on the inside of a smooth circular hoop of radius a fixed in a vertical plane. If v is the speed at any point, prove that the pressure on the hoop at that point is $\dfrac{3mv^2}{2a}$.   (H.C.)

11. A ball of weight W hanging at the end of a cord of length a is given a horizontal velocity v. Find the tension in the cord immediately the ball starts moving.

If the cord is 8 feet long, what initial velocity would double the original tension ; how far would the ball rise in that case ; and what would be the tension in the cord at the moment when the ball reached its highest point ?   (H.S.C.)

12. A heavy particle hangs by a string of length a from a fixed point O and is given an initial horizontal velocity $\sqrt{2gh}$. Prove that, if the particle makes complete revolutions, h is at least equal to $\dfrac{5a}{2}$; that

if the string becomes slack h is between a and $\dfrac{5a}{2}$; and that in this latter case the greatest height reached above the lowest point is

$$\frac{(4a - h)(a + 2h)^2}{27a^2}.$$ (H.S.C.)

13. A stone of mass 1 lb. is whirled round in a horizontal circle at the end of a string 3 feet long, whose other end is fixed. If the string can only stand a tension of 8 lb. wt., what is the greatest velocity which the stone can have and how many revolutions does it make per second in this case ?

If the stone is whirled round in a vertical circle what is the greatest velocity that the stone can have at the highest point of its path in order that it may describe the complete circle without the string breaking ? (I.E.)

14. A rope 20 feet long has one end A attached to a fixed point and at the other end B carries a small mass of 100 lb. The rope is held taut and horizontally and the mass allowed to fall. Calculate the tension when the rope is vertical. In the vertical position the rope catches against a peg 12 feet below A, so that the mass begins a new path of radius 8 feet. Show that the tension in the rope is thereby doubled and find whether or no the mass will describe a complete circle about the peg as centre. (Q.E.)

15. A smooth circular tube is held fixed in a vertical plane. A particle of mass m, which can slide inside the tube, is slightly displaced from rest at the highest point of the tube. Find the pressure between the particle and the tube when it is at an angular distance θ from the highest point of the tube. Also find the vertical component of the acceleration of the particle when $\theta = 120°$. (C.S.)

16. A particle hanging by a light string of length l from a fixed point O is projected horizontally from its lowest position with velocity

$\sqrt{\dfrac{7gl}{2}}$. Prove that the string slackens after swinging through 120°.

(C.S.)

17. A heavy particle P is attached by two unequal light inextensible strings to fixed points A, B in the same horizontal line, and is projected so as *just* to describe a vertical circle. When P is in its lowest position the string PB breaks, and P then describes a horizontal circle. Prove that the angle PAB is $\frac{1}{2}\cos^{-1}\frac{2}{3}$. Prove also that, if the tension of the string PA is unchanged when the string PB breaks, the angle APB is a right angle. (C.S.)

18. A mass of 1 lb. is attached to the end of a string which is 20 inches long and is tied to a fixed point A. Initially the string is horizontal and the mass allowed to fall. Determine the tension in the string when the mass is vertically below A.

If the string catches against a peg B vertically below A so that the mass begins to describe a circle about B, find the least depth of B below A in order that the mass may describe a complete circle about B. (C.S.)

19. A particle slides, from rest at a depth $\dfrac{r}{2}$ below the highest point, down the outside of a smooth sphere of radius r; prove that it leaves the

sphere at a height $\frac{r}{3}$ above the centre. Show further that when the particle is at a distance $r\sqrt{2}$ from the vertical diameter of the sphere it is at a depth $4r$ below the centre of the sphere.   (C.S.)

20. A string with equal heavy particles at the ends lies over a smooth fixed pulley. In the position of equilibrium each particle is level with the centre of the pulley. One particle is slightly displaced downwards, so that the system moves under gravity. Find the pressure exerted by the second particle on the pulley as it passes the highest point, and prove that it leaves the pulley when it has traversed an arc of about $108\frac{1}{2}°$.   (H.S.C.)

21. A smooth wire circle of given radius is in a vertical plane and a particle is projected with velocity u upwards along the wire (1) inside at an angular distance α_1 with the vertical, (2) outside at an angular distance α_2 with the vertical. Show that, if the particle does not leave the wire at starting,

$$ga\cos\alpha_2 > u^2 > ga\cos\alpha_1.$$

If θ_1, θ_2 are the angular distances at which the particle leaves the wire in the two cases, show that

$$\cos\theta_1 - \cos\theta_2 = \tfrac{2}{3}(\cos\alpha_1 - \cos\alpha_2).$$ (H.S.C.)

22. Two particles m and m' begin simultaneously to slide down a smooth circular tube whose plane is vertical, starting from the extremities of a horizontal diameter, so that they collide at the lowest point. Show that the vertical heights to which they rise after impact are in the ratio $[(2e+1)m' - m]^2 : [(2e+1)m - m']^2$, where e is the coefficient of restitution between the masses.   (I.A.)

23. CA is a cord 10 feet long, fixed at C, having a weight of 10 lb. attached at A. When the cord is horizontal the weight is let go, and when the cord becomes vertical it strikes against a peg 6 feet below C. Show that the tension in the cord just after striking the peg is double what it was just before striking. Show also that the weight will complete the circle about the peg.   (C.S.)

24. A heavy particle is tied to one end of an inelastic string 6 feet long, the other end of which is attached to a fixed point O. The particle is held, with the string tight, at a point 3 feet above O and then let fall ; find the velocity of the particle immediately after the string again becomes tight, and the height above O to which it subsequently rises.

25. A heavy particle is suspended as a simple pendulum by a string of length a. When in its lowest position it is projected horizontally with a velocity equal to that which it would acquire by falling freely through a height h. Show that, if the string becomes slack during the subsequent motion, it does so when the particle is at a vertical height $\tfrac{2}{3}(h-a)$ above the fixed end of the string.

26. A particle is attached by a string 2 feet long to a point O, and it is projected horizontally with a velocity of 12 ft./sec. from a point 2 feet vertically above O. Prove that the string will remain tight while the particle describes complete vertical circles. But if the string will not stand a tension of more than 5 times the weight of the particle, prove that it will break and find the vertical distance below O of the particle when the string breaks.   (Ex.)

27. A particle, suspended from a fixed point by a string of length a, is projected horizontally so as to describe part of a circle in a vertical plane ; show that if the parabolic path of the particle after the string becomes slack passes through the original point of projection, the velocity of projection is $(\frac{7}{2}ga)^{\frac{1}{2}}$. Show that in the subsequent motion the particle oscillates between two points at vertical height $\frac{1}{16}a$ above its original position. (H.C.)

28. A smooth semi-circular rim is in a vertical plane with the diameter AB vertical. A particle is projected along the rim from the lowest point A with velocity u. Find the angle the radius to the particle makes with the vertical when the particle leaves the rim. Also, find the value of u in order that after leaving the rim the particle may describe a parabola with latus rectum equal to the diameter of the semi-circle. In that case, where is the focus ? (Ex.)

29. A particle describes a circle of radius a in a vertical plane, moving round at the end of a taut string fastened at the centre. If the velocity of the particle as it swings past the lowest point of the circle is v_0, prove that the tension in the string when it is inclined at an angle θ to the radius to the lowest point is

$$m\left(3g \cos \theta - 2g + \frac{v_0{}^2}{a}\right).$$

If $5ga > v_0{}^2 > 2ga$, prove that the string becomes slack before the particle reaches its highest point.
What happens (i) when $v_0{}^2 > 5ga$, and (ii) when $v_0{}^2 < 2ga$? (N.U.3)

30. A smooth circular cylinder is fixed with the axis horizontal, and a string placed over the cylinder at right angles to the axis has particles m, M tied to its ends. These particles rest against the cylinder ; the radius to the first is horizontal, that to the second makes an angle α with the vertical, and they are on opposite sides of the axis.
If $m < M \sin \alpha$, find the speed of the particles in any position after they have been released from rest and while they are both still in contact with the cylinder ; and prove that when M leaves the cylinder the radius to it has turned through an angle θ which satisfies the equation

$$\sin \theta \, [(3M + m) \sin \alpha - 2m] = \cos \alpha \, [(3M + m) \cos \theta - 2M].$$
(N.U.4)

CHAPTER VI.

SIMPLE HARMONIC MOTION.

§ 169. In the case of bodies such as a tight string, a weight hanging from a spiral spring, or the prong of a tuning-fork, it is found that, when the body is disturbed from its equilibrium position, it moves in such a manner that each part of the body has an acceleration which is always directed towards the equilibrium position and varies in magnitude as the distance of the particle from that position. The result is that the body oscillates to and fro about its equilibrium position.

§ 170. This kind of motion is very common in nature, and since it is the kind which produces all musical notes it is called *Simple Harmonic Motion* (abbreviated to S.H.M.), which may be defined as follows :—

When a particle moves so that its acceleration along its path is directed towards a fixed point in that path, and varies as its distance from this fixed point, the particle is said to move with simple harmonic motion.

Let x be the displacement from a fixed point O in the path, and $\omega^2 x$ the magnitude of the acceleration towards O at this distance, where ω is some constant, then, since the acceleration is in the opposite direction to that in which x increases, we have

$$\frac{d^2x}{dt^2} = -\omega^2 x \qquad . \qquad . \qquad . \qquad . \qquad \text{(i)}$$

This is the fundamental equation representing a simple harmonic motion.

§ 171. We shall consider first the case when the motion takes place in a straight line, but it may be pointed out at once that any motion which can be represented by an equation like (i), where x is a displacement from a fixed position, is simple harmonic. For example, x may be the distance of a point P on a curve measured from a fixed point on the curve along the curve, and then P will move along the curve with simple harmonic motion.

Again, x may be the angle made by a line fixed in a body, which is moving about a fixed point O as axis, with some line through O fixed in space. The body will then move about O with simple harmonic motion.

Mathematically, the solution of equation (i),.i.e. the value of x in terms of t, is always of the same form, and when x represents a displacement of any kind from a fixed position, the equation represents the same kind of motion whether x is a straight, curved, or angular displacement.

§ 172. Simple Harmonic Motion in a Straight Line.

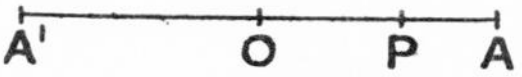

FIG. III.

Let O (Fig. III) be a fixed point in a straight line A'OA, and let a point P move along the line with S.H.M. about O.

Then, if $OP = x$, the acceleration of P is towards O and equal to $\omega^2 x$, where ω is some constant,

$$\therefore \frac{d^2x}{dt^2} = -\omega^2 x \qquad . \qquad . \qquad . \qquad \text{(i)}$$

or
$$v\frac{dv}{dx} = -\omega^2 x \qquad . \qquad . \qquad . \qquad \text{(ii)}$$

Integrating equation (ii) we get

$$\tfrac{1}{2}v^2 = -\tfrac{1}{2}\omega^2 x^2 + C \qquad . \qquad . \qquad . \qquad \text{(iii)}$$

Now, if $x = a$ when $v = 0$,
$$C = \tfrac{1}{2}\omega^2 a^2,$$
and
$$v^2 = \omega^2(a^2 - x^2),$$
or
$$v = \omega\sqrt{a^2 - x^2} \qquad : \qquad . \qquad . \qquad \text{(iv)}$$

This equation gives the value of the velocity v for any displacement x. The maximum value of x is. a, i.e. the maximum displacement from O is equal to a, and this is called the *amplitude* of the motion.

When $x = a$, v is zero. Also when $x = -a$, v is zero.

Hence, if $OA = a$, P moves between A and a point A' on the other side of O, such that $OA' = OA = a$; it then stops and returns to A. The maximum velocity is when $x = 0$, i.e. at O, and then

$$v = \omega a.$$

The maximum values of the acceleration are when $x = \pm a$, i.e. when P is in its extreme positions.

The values of the maximum accelerations are $\pm \omega^2 a$.

§ **173.** To find the connection between x and t we have to solve equation (i), or put $v = \dfrac{dx}{dt}$ in equation (iv) and solve the resulting equation.

The method of doing this is explained in the next paragraph, and it is found that the result depends on whether we measure t from the instant when P is in its extreme position A, or in its central position O. If t is measured from the instant when P is at A, the solution is

$$x = a \cos \omega t \quad . \quad . \quad . \quad . \quad \text{(v)}$$

If t is measured from the instant when P is at O, the solution is

$$x = a \sin \omega t \quad . \quad . \quad . \quad . \quad \text{(vi)}$$

It can easily be verified by differentiation that either of these values of x satisfies equation (i), and they also satisfy the initial conditions stated.

The first gives $x = a$ when $t = 0$; the second gives $x = 0$ when $t = 0$.

If t is increased by $\dfrac{2\pi}{\omega}$ in either (v) or (vi) we get the same value of x again, for $\cos(\omega t + 2\pi) = \cos \omega t$, and $\sin(\omega t + 2\pi) = \sin \omega t$.

This increment in t also gives the same values again for $\dfrac{dx}{dt}$.

Hence, after successive intervals of time $\dfrac{2\pi}{\omega}$, the point P is in the same position moving with the same velocity.

$\dfrac{2\pi}{\omega}$ is therefore called the *Period of a complete oscillation.*

It should be noticed that this is independent of a, the amplitude of the motion; it depends only on the value of the constant ω.

The time taken to move from the initial position to that given by the displacement x is

$$\frac{1}{\omega} \cos^{-1} \frac{x}{a} \quad \text{or} \quad \frac{1}{\omega} \sin^{-1} \frac{x}{a},$$

according as the initial position is the extreme or central one.

The point is, of course, in the same position after any further interval of time $\dfrac{2\pi n}{\omega}$, where n is a whole number.

§ 174. *Solution of the Equation* $\dfrac{d^2x}{dt^2} = -\omega^2 x.$

In § 172 we obtained the value of v or $\dfrac{dx}{dt}$ by using $v\dfrac{dv}{dx}$ for the acceleration instead of $\dfrac{d^2x}{dt^2}$,

$$\frac{dx}{dt} = \omega\sqrt{a^2 - x^2}.$$

To integrate this equation we write it

$$\frac{dx}{\sqrt{a^2 - x^2}} = \omega dt.$$

The integral of the left-hand side is $\sin^{-1}\dfrac{x}{a}$,

$$\therefore \sin^{-1}\frac{x}{a} = \omega t + A,$$

where A is a constant to be determined from the initial conditions.

If $x = a$ when $t = 0$,

$$A = \sin^{-1}\frac{a}{a} = \frac{\pi}{2},$$

$$\therefore \sin^{-1}\frac{x}{a} - \frac{\pi}{2} = \omega t,$$

but $\dfrac{\pi}{2}$ less than the angle whose sine is $\dfrac{x}{a}$ is the angle whose cosine is $\dfrac{x}{a}$.

$$\therefore \cos^{-1}\frac{x}{a} = \omega t,$$

$$\therefore x = a \cos \omega t.$$

If $x = 0$ when $t = 0$, $A = 0$, and then

$$\sin^{-1}\frac{x}{a} = \omega t,$$

$$\therefore x = a \sin \omega t.$$

§ 175. If the time is measured from an instant t' seconds after the particle is in its extreme position, we have $x = a$ when $t = -t'$, and the constant A of the last paragraph becomes $A = \dfrac{\pi}{2} + \omega t'$.

$$\therefore \sin^{-1}\frac{x}{a} - \frac{\pi}{2} = \omega t + \omega t',$$

$$\therefore \cos^{-1}\frac{x}{a} = \omega t + \epsilon, \text{ where } \epsilon = \omega t',$$

$$\therefore x = a \cos (\omega t + \epsilon).$$

Similarly, if $x = 0$ when $t = -t'$, $A = \omega t'$, and

$$\sin^{-1}\frac{x}{a} = \omega t + \omega t',$$

$$\therefore x = a \sin (\omega t + \epsilon).$$

The quantity ϵ is called the *Epoch*.

The *phase* of the motion is the time that has elapsed since the particle was at its maximum distance in the positive direction.

Taking $$x = a \cos (\omega t + \epsilon),$$

x is a maximum at time t_0 where

$$\omega t_0 + \epsilon = 0,$$

∴ the phase at time t is $t - t_0 = t + \dfrac{\epsilon}{\omega} = \dfrac{\omega t + \epsilon}{\omega}.$

For two harmonic motions of the same period given by

$$x = a_1 \cos (\omega t + \epsilon_1),$$
$$x = a_2 \cos (\omega t + \epsilon_2),$$

the difference in phase is $\dfrac{\epsilon_1 - \epsilon_2}{\omega}.$

If $\epsilon_1 = \epsilon_2$ the motions are in the same phase. If $\epsilon_1 - \epsilon_2 = \pi$, they are in opposite phases.

§ **176.** It should be noted that the equation

$$\frac{d^2x}{dt^2} = - \omega^2 x + h,$$

also represents S.H.M., although not about the origin from which x is measured.

If we move the origin to the point $x = \dfrac{h}{\omega^2}$, the new co-ordinate

x' becomes $x - \dfrac{h}{\omega^2},$

$$\therefore \frac{d^2x'}{dt^2} = \frac{d^2x}{dt^2},$$

and $\qquad - \omega^2 x + h = - \omega^2 x' - h + h = - \omega^2 x',$

$$\therefore \frac{d^2x'}{dt^2} = - \omega^2 x',$$

and the motion is harmonic about the new origin.

§ **177.** The results obtained in the preceding paragraphs are of great importance as, although we obtained them for motion in a straight line, they hold, as already explained, whatever kind of displacement x represents.

The results are collected below for reference.

If a is the amplitude of a simple harmonic motion, x the displacement from the central position at time t, v the velocity at this displacement,

$$v = \omega \sqrt{a^2 - x^2}$$
$$x = a \cos \omega t \text{ (if } t = 0 \text{ when } x = a)$$
$$x = a \sin \omega t \text{ (if } t = 0 \text{ when } x = 0).$$

The period $\qquad T = \dfrac{2\pi}{\omega}.$

ω is the square root of the constant which when multiplied by the displacement gives the magnitude of the acceleration.

§ **178.** EXAMPLE (i).

If the period of a simple harmonic motion is 8 seconds, and the particle oscillates through a distance of 4 feet on each side of the central position, find the maximum velocity, and also the velocity when the particle is 2 feet from the central position, giving each result to the nearest $\frac{1}{10}$th. (I.S.)

Since the period

$$T = \frac{2\pi}{\omega},$$

$$\omega = \frac{2\pi}{T} = \frac{2\pi}{8} = \frac{\pi}{4}.$$

The amplitude

$$a = 4 \text{ ft.}$$

The velocity at displacement x is

$$v = \omega\sqrt{a^2 - x^2}.$$

The maximum velocity is when $x = 0$, and then

$$v = \omega a = \frac{\pi}{4} \times 4 = 3\cdot1 \text{ ft./sec.}$$

When $x = 2$ ft.,

$$v = \frac{\pi}{4}\sqrt{16 - 4} = \frac{\pi}{4}\sqrt{12} = 2\cdot7 \text{ ft./sec.}$$

EXAMPLE (ii).

If the displacement of a moving point at any time be given by an equation of the form

$$x = a \cos \omega t + b \sin \omega t,$$

show that the motion is a simple harmonic motion.

If $a = 3$, $b = 4$, $\omega = 2$, determine the period, amplitude, maximum velocity and maximum acceleration of the motion. (I.S.)

We have to show that the acceleration varies as the displacement. Differentiating the value given for x with respect to t,

$$\frac{dx}{dt} = -a\omega \sin \omega t + b\omega \cos \omega t \qquad . \qquad . \qquad . \quad \text{(i)}$$

Differentiating again,

$$\frac{d^2x}{dt^2} = -a\omega^2 \cos \omega t - b\omega^2 \sin \omega t,$$
$$= -\omega^2(a \cos \omega t + b \sin \omega t)$$
$$= -\omega^2 x \qquad . \qquad . \qquad . \qquad . \qquad . \quad \text{(ii)}$$

Hence the motion is simple harmonic.

The period $= \frac{2\pi}{\omega}$,

and if $\omega = 2$, this is equal to $\pi = 3\cdot14$ seconds.

The amplitude is the value of x when $\frac{dx}{dt} = 0$, and then from (i),

$$- a\omega \sin \omega t + b\omega \cos \omega t = 0,$$
$$\therefore \tan \omega t = \frac{b}{a} = \tfrac{4}{3},$$
$$\therefore \sec^2 \omega t = 1 + \tfrac{16}{9} = \tfrac{25}{9},$$
$$\therefore \cos \omega t = \tfrac{3}{5} \text{ and } \sin \omega t = \tfrac{4}{5}.$$

Substituting in the expression for x,

$$x = a \cos \omega t + b \sin \omega t$$
$$= \tfrac{9}{5} + \tfrac{16}{5} = 5 \text{ ft.}$$

Also $\frac{dx}{dt}$ is a maximum when the differential coefficient of the right-hand side of (i) is zero, i.e. when

$$a \cos \omega t + b \sin \omega t = 0,$$

or $$\tan \omega t = -\frac{a}{b} = -\tfrac{3}{4}.$$

In this case
$$\sin \omega t = \pm \tfrac{3}{5}, \quad \cos \omega t = \mp \tfrac{4}{5},$$

and $$\frac{dx}{dt} = -6 \cdot \tfrac{3}{5} - 8 \cdot \tfrac{4}{5} = -10,$$

or $$= 6 \cdot \tfrac{3}{5} + 8 \cdot \tfrac{4}{5} = 10.$$

The maximum acceleration is when x is a maximum, i.e. when $x = 5$, and then

$$\frac{d^2x}{dt^2} = -\omega^2 x = -20.$$

EXAMPLE (iii).

At the ends of three successive seconds the distances of a point moving with S.H.M. from its mean position, measured in the same direction, are 1, 5 and 5. Show that the period of the complete oscillation is

$$\frac{2\pi}{\cos^{-1}\tfrac{3}{5}} \text{ seconds.}$$ (H.S.C.)

Using $x = a \sin \omega t$,
we have $1 = a \sin \omega t$,
$$5 = a \sin(\omega t + \omega) = a \sin \omega t \cos \omega + a \cos \omega t \sin \omega,$$
$$5 = a \sin(\omega t + 2\omega) = a \sin \omega t \cos 2\omega + a \cos \omega t \sin 2\omega.$$

Substituting for $a \sin \omega t$ in the last two equations,

$$\cos \omega + a \cos \omega t \sin \omega = 5 \qquad \qquad \text{(i)}$$
$$\cos 2\omega + a \cos \omega t \sin 2\omega = 5 \qquad \qquad \text{(ii)}$$
$$\therefore \sin 2\omega \cos \omega + a \cos \omega t \sin \omega \sin 2\omega = 5 \sin 2\omega$$
$$\sin \omega \cos 2\omega + a \cos \omega t \sin 2\omega \sin \omega = 5 \sin \omega,$$
$$\therefore \sin 2\omega \cos \omega - \cos 2\omega \sin \omega = 5 \sin 2\omega - 5 \sin \omega,$$
$$\therefore \sin \omega = 5 \sin 2\omega - 5 \sin \omega,$$
$$\therefore 6 \sin \omega = 10 \sin \omega \cos \omega.$$

This gives $\sin \omega = 0$, or $\cos \omega = \tfrac{3}{5}$.

If $\sin \omega = 0$, ω must be zero or a multiple of π, and these values do not satisfy equations (i) and (ii) so that they may be rejected.

The other value gives $\omega = \cos^{-1} \frac{3}{5}$,

and the period

$$= \frac{2\pi}{\omega} = \frac{2\pi}{\cos^{-1}\frac{3}{5}}.$$

EXAMPLE .(iv).

A point P moves in a circle with uniform angular velocity ω about the centre O. If Q be the orthogonal projection of P upon a fixed diameter, show that Q moves along the diameter with simple harmonic motion.

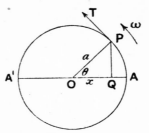

FIG. 112.

Let AOA′ (Fig. 112) be a diameter of the circle, a the radius, and suppose that P is moving in the direction APA′.

The velocity and acceleration of Q must be the same as the components, parallel to AA′, of the velocity and acceleration of P.

Now the acceleration of P is $a\omega^2$ in the direction of PO.

Hence, if $\angle POQ = \theta$, the component parallel to AA′ is $a\omega^2 \cos \theta$,

∴ the acceleration of Q $= a\omega^2 \cos \theta$ towards O.

If $OQ = x$, $\cos \theta = \dfrac{x}{a}$,

∴ the acceleration of Q $= \omega^2 x$ towards O.

Hence the motion of Q is a simple harmonic motion along AA′.

The various formulæ for S.H.M. obtained in the preceding paragraphs can be deduced from the motion of Q.

The velocity of P is $a\omega$ along the tangent PT, and the component parallel to AA′ is $a\omega \sin \theta$, hence, if v is the velocity of Q,

$$v = a\omega \sin \theta = a\omega \sqrt{1 - \frac{x^2}{a^2}} = \omega \sqrt{a^2 - x^2}.$$

It is evident that as P moves round the circle from A to A′ and back to A, Q moves from A through O to A′ and back to A.

The time taken from A to A′ and back to A is the same as that taken by P to describe the circle, i.e. $\dfrac{2\pi}{\omega}$; hence, if T is the period of a complete oscillation of Q,

$$T = \frac{2\pi}{\omega}.$$

The time, t, taken for Q to move from A to a point distant x from O is the time taken by OP to move through the angle θ, i.e. $\dfrac{\theta}{\omega}$,

$$\therefore t = \frac{\theta}{\omega} = \frac{1}{\omega}\cos^{-1}\frac{x}{a},$$

EXAMPLES XXXIV.

1. A particle moves in a straight line with simple harmonic motion ; find the time of a complete oscillation when (1) the acceleration at a distance of 4 feet is 8 ft./sec.², (2) the acceleration at a distance of 9 inches is 12 ft./sec.².

2. The amplitude of a particle moving with S.H.M. is 5 feet, the acceleration at a distance of 2 feet from the mean position is 4 ft./sec.², find the velocity when the particle is in its mean position, and also when it is 4 feet from this position.

3. A particle, moving with S.H.M., has a velocity of 6 ft./sec. when passing through its mean position, and the acceleration at 2 feet from the mean position is 8 ft./sec.². Find the amplitude and the period of the oscillation.

4. A point, moving with S.H.M., has velocities of 4 ft./sec. and 3 ft./sec. when at distances of 3 feet and 4 feet from its central position. Find the period, and the maximum acceleration.

5. A particle is moving with S.H.M. of period π seconds, and the maximum velocity is 8 ft./sec. Find the amplitude and the velocity at a distance of 3 feet from the central position.

6. If a particle is making simple harmonic oscillations, the period being 2 seconds, and the amplitude being 3 feet, find the maximum velocity and the maximum acceleration. (H.S.D.)

7. A particle starts from rest, and moves with S.H.M. with a period of $2T$. Show that it describes $\frac{1}{4}$ of the distance before it next comes to instantaneous rest in $\frac{1}{3}$ of the time T, and attains half of its maximum velocity in $\frac{1}{6}$ of the time T. (I.S.)

8. A particle moving with S.H.M. passes through two points A and B, 22 inches apart, with the same velocity, having occupied 2 seconds in passing from A to B ; after another 2 seconds it returns to B. Find the period and amplitude of the oscillation. (I.A.)

9. A particle performs 150 complete simple harmonic oscillations per minute, and its greatest acceleration is 10 ft./sec.² ; find its greatest velocity and the distance between the extreme positions. (I.S.)

10. A point is moving in a straight line with S.H.M. about a fixed point O of the line. The point has a velocity v_1 when its displacement from O is x_1, and a velocity v_2 when its distance from O is x_2. Show that the period of the motion is

$$2\pi\sqrt{\frac{x_1{}^2 - x_2{}^2}{v_2{}^2 - v_1{}^2}}. \qquad \text{(I.S.)}$$

11. The velocity of a particle moving in a straight line is given by the equation

$$v = k\sqrt{a^2 - x^2},$$

where k and a are constants, and x is the distance of the particle from a fixed point in the line ; prove that the motion is simple harmonic, and find the amplitude and the periodic time of the motion. (I.E.)

12. A particle is performing a simple harmonic motion of period T about a centre O, and it passes through a point P with velocity v in the direction OP ; prove that the time which elapses before its return to P is

$$\frac{T}{\pi} \tan^{-1} \frac{vT}{2\pi \, OP}.$$ (I.S.)

13. If the speeds of a point moving with S.H.M. at distances x_1 and x_2 from the centre of motion be v_1 and v_2, find the periodic time, the amplitude, and the maximum speed and maximum acceleration. Calculate the numerical values if $x_1 = 2$ feet, $x_2 = 3$ feet, $v_1 = 5$ ft./sec., $v_2 = 4$ ft./sec.   (I.E.)

14. Prove that, in S.H.M., if f is the acceleration and v the velocity at any moment and T is the periodic time, then $f^2 T^2 + 4\pi^2 v^2$ is constant, and find the numerical value of this constant for a motion whose periodic time is 2 seconds and in which the amplitude is 2 feet.   (H.S.D.)

15. A body, moving in a straight line OAB with S.H.M., has zero velocity when at the points A and B whose distances from O are a and b respectively, and has velocity v when halfway between them. Show that the complete period is

$$\frac{\pi(b - a)}{v}.$$ (H.S.D.)

16. A point P describes a circle of radius a and centre O, with uniform angular velocity ω ; show that a point Q which describes a diameter AOB of the circle, so that PQ is always perpendicular to AOB, has an acceleration which is proportional to OQ.

If Q_1, Q_2 are points bisecting OA, OB, find the time the point Q takes to travel from Q_1 to Q_2, and the velocity of the point Q at Q_2 and at Q_1.   (I.S.)

17. In a particular S.H.M. the number of complete oscillations is 45 per minute. The velocity at a point 1 inch away from the mean position is 1 ft./sec. Calculate the greatest distance reached measured from the mean position. If A and B are two points distant 1 inch and 2 inches from the centre of motion respectively, find the time occupied in going from A to B.   (Q.E.)

18. A point moving with S.H.M. is making 3 complete oscillations per second. The extent of the motion on either side of the mean position is 2 inches. Calculate the maximum velocity and maximum acceleration. Find also the velocity and acceleration when the point is 1 inch distant from the centre.   (Q.E.)

19. Show that in S.H.M. the mean velocity (during motion from one end of the path to the other) with respect to the distance is $\frac{\pi}{4} \times$ the maximum velocity, and with respect to the time is $\frac{2}{\pi} \times$ the maximum velocity.   (Q.E.)

20. A particle is moving with S.H.M., and while making an excursion from one position of rest to the other, its distances from the middle point of its path at three consecutive seconds are observed to be x_1, x_2, x_3 ; prove that the time of a complete oscillation is

$$\frac{2\pi}{\cos^{-1}\left(\dfrac{x_1 + x_3}{2x_2}\right)}.$$ (I.C.)

21. A particle moving with acceleration $-\mu x$ has co-ordinates x_1 and x_2, and velocities v_1 and v_2 at any two moments. At the moment midway in time between them its co-ordinate and velocity are $\bar{x}$ and $\bar{v}$; show that

$$\frac{x_1 - x_2}{v_2 - v_1} = \frac{\bar{v}}{\mu\bar{x}},$$

and that

$$\frac{x_1 + x_2}{v_1 + v_2} = \frac{\bar{x}}{\bar{v}}. \qquad \text{(H.C.)}$$

22. If a be the amplitude and n the number of complete oscillations per second in S.H.M., find the velocity in any position in terms of (1) the distance from the centre, and (2) the time that has elapsed since the moving particle was at rest. Show that the time that elapses as the particle moves from the position of maximum velocity to the position in which the velocity is half the maximum is $\frac{1}{6n}$ seconds.

(I.S.)

23. A circle of radius a rolls with uniform angular speed on the inside of a fixed circle of radius $2a$. Prove that any point on the circumference of the moving circle describes a straight line with S.H.M.

(I.E.)

24. A piston weighing 20 lb. has a stroke of 4 feet. Using the line of motion as the axis of x, make graphs to show the value of the velocity and of the accelerating force at any point of the stroke, assuming the motion to be S.H.M. (I.E.)

25. A point P moves in a straight line through a fixed point O in such a manner that its acceleration at each instant is towards O and equal to μ, OP; prove that the velocity is $\sqrt{\mu(OA^2 - OP^2)}$, where A is one of the points where P comes to rest.

If Q is the point on OA such that $2\,OQ^2 = OA^2$, show that the time from O to Q is the same as the time from Q to A. (I.S.)

26. A heavy smoked glass plate is dropped past the end of a vibrating tuning-fork, making n complete simple harmonic oscillations per second, and by means of a light style attached to the fork a rippling trace is obtained on the plate. The vertical length of a certain 10 consecutive ripples is found to be l cm., and of the next 10 is found to be l' cm. Deduce that the value of g is

$$\frac{(l' - l)n^2}{100} \text{ cm./sec.}^2 \qquad \text{(I.A.)}$$

27. A particle performs 150 complete simple harmonic oscillations a minute and its greatest acceleration is 10 ft./sec.^{2}; find (1) its greatest velocity, (2) its mean velocity during the motion from one extreme position to the other. (Q.E.)

28. A point is moving in a straight line with S.H.M. Its velocity has the values 3 ft./sec. and 2 ft./sec. when its distances from the mean position are 1 foot and 2 feet respectively. Find the length of its path and the period of its motion. Find also, correct to the third significant figure, what fraction of the period is occupied in passing between the specified points. (Q.E.)

29. A particle describing S.H.M. does 100 complete vibrations per minute, and its velocity in passing through its mean position is 15 ft./sec. What is the length of its path?

What is its velocity (i) when it is half-way between its mean position and an extremity of its path, (ii) at a time after leaving its mean position equal to half the time required to reach an extremity of its path ?

(Q.E.)

30. If $x = a \sin (\omega t + \epsilon)$, where a, ω, ϵ are constants, prove that $\ddot{x} = -\omega^2 x$. Conversely, if $\ddot{x} = -\omega^2 x$ prove that $x = a \sin (\omega t + \epsilon)$, where a and ϵ are arbitrary constants.

In particular solve $\ddot{x} = -16x$, given that $x = 0$, $\dot{x} = 20$ when $t = 0$.

(I.C.)

31. A point is moving in a straight line with S.H.M. Its velocity has the values 5 ft./sec. and 4 ft./sec. when its distances from the mean position are 2 feet and 3 feet respectively. Find the length of its path and the period of its motion, taking $\pi = 3\cdot1416$.

Determine what fraction of the period is occupied in passing between the two points if they are on opposite sides of the mean position.

(N.U.3)

32. A particle oscillates in S.H.M. on a line 6 inches long with a frequency of 2000 oscillations per minute. Calculate the greatest velocity and the greatest acceleration of the point each in ft./sec. units. [Take $\pi = 3\cdot1416$.]

(N.U.3)

§ 179. Force necessary to produce Simple Harmonic Motion.

Since the force P required to produce an acceleration of f in a mass m is measured by mf, it follows that (if m is constant) P must obey the same law as f. Hence, in the case of simple harmonic motion, the force must be always directed towards the central or equilibrium position, and its magnitude must be proportional to the displacement from that position.

The force tending to restore an elastic body to its natural shape or size is generally of this nature, e.g. the force exerted by a spiral spring when extended or compressed.

§ **180.** The simplest case is that of a particle on a smooth horizontal plane attached by a spring to a fixed point in the plane, the particle being displaced in the direction of the length of the spring.

FIG. 113.

Let A (Fig. 113) be the fixed point, AB the natural length of the spring (l), and λ the modulus of elasticity of the spring.

If a particle of mass m is attached to the end B, then B is the equilibrium position, and if the particle is displaced along the line AB it will oscillate about B.

If P is any displaced position of the particle, where $BP = x$, the tension, acting towards B, is

$$\frac{\lambda}{l}x,$$

and this is the only force acting on m which tends to produce motion along the line AB.

$$\therefore m\frac{d^2x}{dt^2} = -\frac{\lambda}{l}x,$$

$$\therefore \frac{d^2x}{dt^2} = -\frac{\lambda}{ml}x.$$

The motion about B is therefore simple harmonic, and the constant ω^2 in the standard form of the equation is replaced by $\dfrac{\lambda}{ml}$.

The period of oscillation is therefore

$$2\pi\sqrt{\frac{ml}{\lambda}}.$$

It is evident that the constant, and therefore the period of the motion, depends only on the material and length of the spring and the mass of the particle, and not on the amplitude of the oscillation. If the particle is pulled out to a point C($BC = a$) and then let go, it will move through B to a point C′ at an equal distance on the other side of B and then back again to C and so on. The amplitude is equal to the distance from the equilibrium position at which the particle is released from rest.

§ 181. Particle suspended by a Spiral Spring.

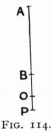

FIG. 114.

Suppose that a particle of mass m is suspended from a fixed point A (Fig. 114) by a spring of natural length l and modulus λ. If $AB = l$, then when the particle is hanging in equilibrium it will extend the spring and be at a point O, where OB ($= d$) is given by

$$mg = \frac{\lambda}{l}d.$$

If the particle is displaced vertically from O it will oscillate in a vertical line about O, and we can show that the motion is simple harmonic. This case is not so simple as that in the last paragraph, since the weight of the particle is acting as well as the force due to the spring.

If P is any displaced position of the particle, and OP $= x$, the tension of the spring is given by

$$T = \frac{\lambda}{l}(d + x).$$

The resultant force acting towards O is

$$T - mg = \frac{\lambda}{l}(d + x) - mg,$$

but
$$mg = \frac{\lambda}{l}d,$$

∴ the restoring force towards O is

$$\frac{\lambda}{l}x,$$

and is therefore proportional to the displacement from O.

Hence the particle moves with S.H.M. about O.

Also
$$m\frac{d^2x}{dt^2} = -\frac{\lambda}{l}x,$$

$$\therefore \frac{d^2x}{dt^2} = -\frac{\lambda}{ml}x.$$

The constant is again $\frac{\lambda}{ml}$, and the period will be

$$2\pi\sqrt{\frac{ml}{\lambda}}.$$

The amplitude will depend on the initial displacement. If the particle is pulled down a distance a below O and released it will rise to this distance above O and then descend again.

Note.—It is most important to notice that the motion is harmonic about the *equilibrium position* O, and not about B.

In the case of a spring it does not matter if the particle rises above B as the law for compression of the spring is the same as that for extension, and the motion is harmonic throughout.

If the particle is suspended by an elastic cord instead of a spring, the working above holds *as long as the particle is below B*, i.e. as long as the string is stretched.

If the particle rises above B the part of the motion above B is simply free vertical motion under gravity.

The particle will rise above B if it is pulled down below O through a distance greater than the permanent extension OB.

§ **182.** EXAMPLE (i).

A spiral spring is found to extend ½ an inch for each additional pound of loading.   It is hung up carrying a mass of 4 lb., and put in vibration. Find the period.   (I.E.)

FIG. 115.

Let AB (Fig. 115) represent the natural length (l) of the spring. The mass of 4 lb. will extend it 2 inches or $\frac{1}{6}$ foot, so that in equilibrium the mass would hang at O where $OB = \frac{1}{6}$ foot.

If λ be the modulus of elasticity,

$$g = \frac{\lambda}{l} \cdot \frac{1}{24},$$

$$\therefore \frac{\lambda}{l} = 24g.$$

If P represent any displaced position of the mass, and $OP = x$, the tension T is given by

$$T = \frac{\lambda}{l}(\tfrac{1}{6} + x)$$

$$= 24g(\tfrac{1}{6} + x),$$

the restoring force is $T - 4g$

$$= 4g + 24gx - 4g$$

$$= 24gx,$$

$\therefore$ the acceleration is

$$\frac{24g}{4}x = 6gx,$$

$\therefore$ the period is

$$2\pi\sqrt{\frac{1}{6g}} = \frac{2\pi}{8\sqrt{3}} = \frac{\sqrt{3}\pi}{12} \text{ seconds.}$$

EXAMPLE (ii).

A light elastic string is stretched by e_0 when a certain weight is suspended by it.   Prove that, if the weight is displaced in a vertical line any distance not greater than e_0, and set free, it will return to the initial position in time

$$2\pi\left(\frac{e_0}{g}\right)^{\frac{1}{2}}.$$ (I.E.)

Let m be the mass attached, λ the modulus and l the natural length of the string. Since the weight mg stretches it a distance e_0,

$$mg = \frac{\lambda}{l}\, e_0,$$

$$\therefore \frac{\lambda}{l} = \frac{mg}{e_0}.$$

For a further extension x, the tension is

$$\frac{\lambda}{l}(e_0 + x) = mg + \frac{mg}{e_0}x,$$

and the restoring force is $\dfrac{mg}{e_0}x,$

$\therefore$ the acceleration is $\dfrac{g}{e_0}x$, and the motion is S.H.M.

The time taken to return to the initial position from which the weight is released is a complete period and is therefore $2\pi\,\sqrt{\dfrac{e_0}{g}}$.

Note.—It is stipulated in the question that the displacement is not greater than e_0, the permanent extension, so that the motion is simple harmonic throughout.

Example (iii).

A particle of mass m on a smooth table is attached to two points A and B of the table by means of two exactly similar stretched elastic strings. Prove that if the particle is displaced in the direction of the line AB, through such a distance that neither string goes slack, and is then released, it will perform simple harmonic oscillations.   (I.E.)

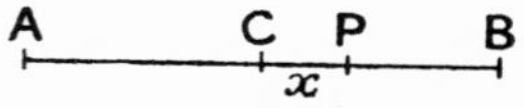

Fig. 116.

Let l_0 be the natural length of each string, λ its modulus, and l the stretched length.

The equilibrium position of the particle is at C (Fig. 116), the middle point of AB, and AC = CB = l.

Suppose the particle in a displaced position P, towards B, where CP = x.

The tension in AP is

$$T_1 = \frac{\lambda}{l_0}(l - l_0 + x),$$

and the tension in PB is

$$T_2 = \frac{\lambda}{l_0}(l - l_0 - x),$$

$\therefore$ the resultant force tending to bring the particle back to C is

$$T_1 - T_2 = 2\frac{\lambda}{l_0}x,$$

$\therefore$ the restoring force is proportional to the displacement, and the motion is simple harmonic.

The acceleration is
$$\frac{2\lambda}{ml_0}x,$$

and the period is
$$2\pi\sqrt{\frac{ml_0}{2\lambda}}.$$

Note.—If the particle is displaced so far that one string goes slack, then for the part of the motion when both strings are tight the acceleration is as above, but for the part of the motion when one string is slack the acceleration is $\frac{\lambda}{ml_0}x$.

The complete motion is then made up of two simple harmonic motions of different periods, the whole of the motion of period $2\pi\sqrt{\frac{ml_0}{2\lambda}}$ being described, but only a portion of the other.

EXAMPLE (iv).

An elastic thread is fixed at one end to a point O in a smooth horizontal table. It passes through a fixed ring C, where OC is the unstretched length of the thread, and is attached to a small mass m which can slide on a fixed smooth horizontal wire. It is held at a point A on this wire and then released. Show that it will perform simple harmonic oscillations and construct the other extremity of the path. (I.S.)

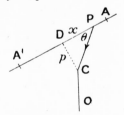

FIG. 117.

Let D (Fig. 117) be the point where the perpendicular from C meets the wire. Then D is the equilibrium position of *m*.

If P is any displaced position of *m*, the extension of the string is CP, and if *l* is the natural length and λ the modulus of the string, the tension *T* is given by
$$T = \frac{\lambda}{l}CP,$$

If DP $= x$, and $\angle$DPC $= \theta$, the component of *T* along the wire is
$$T\cos\theta = \frac{\lambda}{l}CP\cos\theta = \frac{\lambda}{l}x.$$

The force tending to move *m* towards D is therefore proportional to the displacement from D, and the motion is S.H.M. about D. The other extremity of the path will be at A' on the other side of D, where DA' = DA.

EXAMPLES XXXV.

1. A spiral spring supports a carrier weighing 2 lb., and when a 10 lb. weight is placed on the carrier the spring extends 2 inches. The carrier with its load is then pulled down another 3 inches and let go. How high does it rise, and what is the period of its oscillation ? (I.S.)

2. A spring loaded with a certain weight is extended 1 inch when in equilibrium. Find the time of oscillation if the load is pulled vertically downwards through a further distance of half an inch and then let go. Find also the velocity and acceleration when the weight is at a distance of $\frac{1}{4}$ inch below its equilibrium position. (I.S.)

3. A body weighing 12 lb. is suspended by a spring and makes three complete vertical oscillations per second. Find how far the spring would be stretched by a load of 10 lb. hanging at rest. (I.S.)

4. A particle of mass 1 lb. is acted upon by a variable force which makes it move with S.H.M. The maximum speed attained is 5 ft./sec. and the complete period is 2 seconds. Find (a) the amplitude of the motion, and (b) the maximum rate at which the applied force does work (in ft. lb. per sec.). (I.S.)

5. A mass is suspended from a fixed point by a spiral spring and set in vertical oscillation. Show that the period of an oscillation is
$2\pi\sqrt{\dfrac{l}{g}}$, where l feet is the extension of the spring produced by the weight of the attached mass. (I.S.)

6. An elastic string of natural length $2a$ can just support a certain weight when it is stretched till its whole length is $3a$. One end of the string is now attached to a point in a smooth horizontal table, and the same weight is attached to the other end and can move on the table. Prove that, if the weight is pulled out to any distance and then let go, the string will become slack again after a time
$\dfrac{\pi}{2}\sqrt{\dfrac{a}{g}}.$ (I.S.)

7. If a particle describes a harmonic oscillation of amplitude a in complete period T, prove that it will be at a distance x from the centre, from which it started, in a time $\dfrac{\theta T}{2\pi}$, and be moving with a speed $\dfrac{2\pi\sqrt{a^2-x^2}}{T}$, where $a\sin\theta = x$.

An elastic thread is stretched between two points on a smooth horizontal table. A particle of given mass is fastened to the middle point, and after being drawn towards one of the points, the string remaining taut, is set free. Show that it will describe its oscillations in a period independent of the original extent of displacement. (I.S.)

8. A particle is attached to the middle point of an elastic string which is stretched between two points A and B on a smooth table 9 feet apart, and displaced a distance of 1 inch in the direction of the string. If the initial tension of the string is twice the weight of the particle, find the periodic time and the maximum velocity attained by the particle.

9. A spiral spring 2 feet long is hung up at one end. Its length would be doubled by a steady pull of 6 lb. wt. A weight of 3 lb. is hung to

the lower end, and let go. Find how far it falls before first coming to rest and the time of a complete oscillation. (H.S.C.)

10. If two unequal weights are hanging together at one end of an elastic string whose other end is fixed, and one of them falls off, show that the other will perform simple harmonic oscillations or not according as the one which falls off is the lighter or the heavier of the two. (H.S.C.)

11. A weight of 1 lb. suspended by a spring extends it 1 inch when in equilibrium. If a mass of 3 lb. be attached to the spring and released from rest with the spring extended 5 inches, find the number of oscillations per minute and the maximum velocity in the course of an oscillation. (I.C.)

12. A weight of 10 lb. is suspended from a spring, causing an extension of 10 inches. If the weight is pulled down a further distance of 1 inch and then released, find the periodic time of the motion, the velocity when the weight is $\frac{1}{2}$ inch above the lowest point, and the tension in the spring at the top of the path. (Q.E.)

13. A light spiral spring is carrying a weight of 12 lb. ; it extends 2 inches when an extra weight of 3 lb. is placed on it. The extra weight is removed suddenly. Find the period of oscillation of the 12 lb. weight, the tension in the spring and the velocity of the weight when it is 1 inch above its lowest point. (Q.E.)

14. A light helical spring hangs vertically and carries a load of 10 lb. ; it extends 1 inch per extra pound of load. It is extended 2 inches and released. Draw graphs for the kinetic and potential energies at different phases of the subsequent motion. (Q.E.)

15. A certain spring has attached to it a mass of 25 in certain unknown units ; on increasing the load by 6 of these units it extends 1 inch. What is the time of oscillation under the original load ? What will be the velocity and acceleration when it is midway between its lowest and mean positions if it is loaded as at first, pulled down 2 inches and let go ? (Q.E.)

16. A scale pan weighing 1 lb. is attached to a light spiral spring and causes it to extend 2 inches. A 2 lb. weight is then placed in the pan and released. Find to what depth the pan will fall, the tension of the spring when the pan is at its lowest point and the period of the oscillation. (Q.E.)

17. A mass of 5 lb. hangs at rest on a light spring, extending it 2 inches. Another mass of 3 lb. is attached to the first without moving it and the two together are then released. Find the amplitude, period, and maximum velocity of the resulting motion. (Q.E.)

18. A weight of 10 lb. is suspended by means of an elastic string which is extended 2 inches when the weight is hanging at rest. If the upper end is suddenly jerked upwards a distance of 1 inch, and then held fixed, find the greatest velocity attained by the weight and the period of the oscillation set up. (Q.E.)

19. A spring of length 25 cm., whose stiffness is such that a weight of 1 kilogram would double its length, hangs vertically from a fixed point and has attached to its lower end a scale pan of mass 100 gm. Show that, if the pan is pulled downwards from its equilibrium position and then released it will execute simple harmonic oscillations and find their period. Show also that, if the total amplitude of the

oscillations exceeds 5 cm., a small particle in the scale pan will not remain in contact with it during the whole oscillation, but will repeatedly rebound from it.   (H.S.D.)

20. A particle is attached to the middle point of an elastic string stretched between two points A and B on a smooth horizontal table.   If the particle be displaced through a small distance perpendicular to AB, and then released, show that its subsequent motion is approximately a simple harmonic one.   (The displacement is so small that the tension of the string is supposed to be constant.)   If AB = 9 feet, the tension of the string is twice the weight of the particle, and the original displacement is $\frac{1}{2}$ an inch, find the periodic time, and the maximum velocity attained by the particle.   (Ex.)

21. A particle is moving with S.H.M. in a straight line, and takes 3 seconds to perform a complete oscillation.   Its furthest distance from the centre of force is 4 feet.   Find its maximum acceleration and its maximum velocity.   If, when at its furthest point, it receives a blow which drives it in with an initial velocity of u ft./sec., find its new amplitude.   What value of u will make the amplitude 5 feet instead of 4 feet ?   (H.S.C.)

22. A weight is hanging at one end of a light inextensible string, and the uppermost end of the string is made to move vertically up and down with S.H.M. of amplitude 3 inches.   Find the least period for which the string will never become slack.   (H.S.C.)

23. A particle P of mass m is attached to the middle point of an elastic string AB, whose unstretched length is $2a$ and whose modulus of elasticity is equal to the weight of the particle.   A and B are attached to fixed points on a smooth horizontal table at a distance $3a$ apart. AP is initially equal to $2a$, PB is equal to a.   Prove that, when P is let go, it will perform simple harmonic oscillations whose period is $2\pi\sqrt{\dfrac{a}{2g}}$, and will oscillate through a distance a.   (H.S.C.)

24. A mass m hangs from a fixed point by means of a light spring, which obeys Hooke's law.   The mass is given a small vertical displacement, and n is the number of oscillations per second in the resulting harmonic motion.   If l is the length of the spring when the system is in equilibrium, find the natural length of the spring, and show that, when the spring is extended to double its natural length, the tension is $m(4\pi^2n^2l - g)$.   (C.S.)

25. A particle of mass 10 lb. moving with S.H.M. has a maximum velocity of 10 ft./sec., and performs its complete oscillation in $2\frac{1}{2}$ seconds.   Calculate the complete range of the oscillation, and the maximum value of the force applied to the particle.   (Q.E.)

26. A mass m is suspended from a spring causing an extension a.   If a mass M is added to m, find the periodic time of the ensuing motion, and the amplitude of the oscillation.   (C.S.)

27. A fine elastic string OAB, whose modulus of elasticity is λ and unstretched length a, has one end fixed at O, and passes over a smooth pulley fixed at A, where OA = a.   A particle of mass m hangs in equilibrium at B.   Show that if a horizontal impulse I is applied to the particle, it will move in a horizontal line with S.H.M. of amplitude $I\left(\dfrac{a}{\lambda m}\right)^{\frac{1}{2}}$.   (H.C.)

28. A spiral spring supports a carrier weighing 1 lb., and when a 5 lb. weight is placed on the carrier the spring extends 2 inches.   The

carrier with its load is pulled down a further distance of 2 inches and is then let go. How far does it rise, and what is the greatest velocity it attains ? (Q.E.)

29. Given that the amplitude of a S.H.M. is a, and the greatest speed is V, find the period of an oscillation, and the acceleration at distance b from the centre of the oscillation.

A body lies on a horizontal platform which describes a S.H.M. vertically of amplitude 3 inches and complete period 1 second. Compare the greatest and least pressures of the body on the platform. (N.U.3)

30. Prove that if the displacement x of a particle is related to the time t by the formula

$$x = 0 \cdot 1 \cos 3\pi t$$

the motion is simple harmonic.

State the values of (a) the initial velocity, (b) the initial acceleration. If the maximum force on the particle during the motion is 80 dynes, prove that the mass of the particle is nearly equal to 9 grams. (N.U.3)

§ 183. The Simple Pendulum.

This consists of a heavy particle or bob attached to a fixed point by a weightless string and swinging in a vertical plane. It is thus a case of motion in a vertical circle, but we shall now consider more fully the details of the motion when the displacement of the string from the vertical is very small.

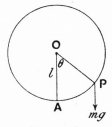

FIG. 118.

Let O (Fig. 118) be the point of suspension, OA the vertical position of the string, l the length of the string, and m the mass of the particle.

If P is any displaced position of the particle, where the angle AOP ($= \theta$) is small, the force tending to bring m back to A along the circle is $mg \sin \theta$.

∴ the acceleration of P along the circle

$$= g \sin \theta = g\theta, \text{ approximately,}$$

$$= g \frac{s}{l},$$

where s is the length of the arc AP.

VOL. I.—18

The acceleration along the circle is therefore proportional to the displacement along the circle measured from A, the equilibrium position.

The motion is therefore simple harmonic, and the period of a complete oscillation is

$$2\pi\sqrt{\frac{l}{g}}.$$

It must be remembered that the motion is only harmonic when the angle of swing is so small that $\sin\theta$ is very nearly equal to θ, and that even then it is only *approximately* harmonic. The approximation is fairly accurate for angles up to about 4°.

§ 184. The Seconds Pendulum.

The period $2\pi\sqrt{\dfrac{l}{g}}$ is the time for a complete oscillation to and fro.

A seconds pendulum is one which vibrates from rest to rest (i.e. makes *half a complete oscillation*) in 1 second.

The period of a seconds pendulum is therefore 2 seconds.

If l is the length of the seconds pendulum,

$$1 = \pi\sqrt{\frac{l}{g}},$$

$$\therefore l = \frac{g}{\pi^2}.$$

The unit of length for l will depend on the units used for g. Taking $g = 32$ ft./sec.^{2} and $\pi = \frac{2\,2}{7}$,

$$l = 3{\cdot}24 \text{ ft.}$$

Taking $g = 981$ cm./sec.^{2} and $\pi = \frac{2\,2}{7}$,

$$l = 99{\cdot}5 \text{ cm.}$$

§ 185.

Since the time of oscillation of a pendulum of given length depends on the value of g, this time will vary in different places, and will also vary with the height above or below the earth's surface.

If the whole pendulum is subject to some other acceleration, such as that due to being in a lift moving with uniform acceleration, or in a train going round a curve, the apparent value of g is altered and so is the time of oscillation.

If T seconds is the period of oscillation of any pendulum, and n the number of oscillations per second, $n = \dfrac{1}{T}$.

A seconds pendulum should beat 86,400 times a day, and the time for a half oscillation is $\dfrac{86400}{86400}$.

If the pendulum gains x seconds a day, the time of a half oscillation is

$$\frac{86400}{86400 + x}.$$

If it loses x seconds a day the time is $\dfrac{86400}{86400 - x}.$

These expressions are useful in problems where the number of seconds lost or gained by a seconds pendulum is required.

The following examples illustrate variations in period due to different causes.

EXAMPLE (i).

If a seconds pendulum be lengthened by $\frac{1}{100}$th of its length, how many seconds will it lose in a day?

If l is the length of the seconds pendulum, the new length is $\dfrac{101}{100}l.$

If x is the number of seconds lost in the day,

$$\frac{86400}{86400} = \pi\sqrt{\frac{l}{g}},$$

and

$$\frac{86400}{86400 - x} = \pi\sqrt{\frac{101}{100}\frac{l}{g}},$$

$$\therefore \frac{86400 - x}{86400} = \sqrt{\frac{100}{101}}.$$

Instead of working out $\sqrt{\dfrac{100}{101}}$, by taking the square root or using logarithms, it is better to write it $\left(\dfrac{101}{100}\right)^{-\frac{1}{2}}$ or $\left(1 + \dfrac{1}{100}\right)^{-\frac{1}{2}}$, and expand by the Binomial Theorem.

We have

$$\left(1 + \frac{1}{100}\right)^{-\frac{1}{2}} = 1 - \frac{1}{200}, \text{ approximately,}$$

$$\therefore \frac{86400 - x}{86400} = 1 - \frac{1}{200},$$

$$\therefore \frac{x}{86400} = \frac{1}{200},$$

$$\therefore x = 432.$$

EXAMPLE (ii).

A seconds pendulum gains 10 seconds a day in one place and loses 10 seconds a day in another; compare the values of g in the two places.

Let l be the length of the seconds pendulum, g_1 and g_2 the values of g at the two planes, then

$$\frac{86400}{86410} = \pi\sqrt{\frac{l}{g_1}},$$

$$\frac{86400}{86390} = \pi\sqrt{\frac{l}{g_2}},$$

$$\therefore \sqrt{\frac{g_1}{g_2}} = \frac{86410}{86390} = 1 + \frac{2}{8639},$$

$$\therefore \frac{g_1}{g_2} = \left(1 + \frac{2}{8639}\right)^2 = 1 + \frac{4}{8639}, \text{ approximately,}$$

$$= \frac{8643}{8639}.$$

EXAMPLE (iii).

A seconds pendulum is in a lift which is ascending with a uniform acceleration of 1 ft./sec.² Show that it will gain at the rate of a little over 56 seconds per hour.

The upward acceleration of the lift increases the effective value of g by 1 ft./sec.²

Hence if x is the number of seconds gained per hour

$$\frac{3600}{3600} = \pi\sqrt{\frac{l}{32}},$$

$$\frac{3600}{3600 + x} = \pi\sqrt{\frac{l}{33}},$$

$$\therefore 1 + \frac{x}{3600} = \sqrt{\frac{33}{32}} = \left(1 + \frac{1}{32}\right)^{\frac{1}{2}} = 1 + \frac{1}{64},$$

$$\therefore \frac{x}{3600} = \frac{1}{64},$$

$$\therefore x = \frac{3600}{64} = 56\tfrac{1}{4}, \text{ approximately.}$$

EXAMPLE (iv).

A pendulum suspended from the roof of a railway carriage travelling at speed V round a curve of radius a makes n oscillations per second. Prove that if n_1 is the number of oscillations per second when the carriage is stationary,

$$V^2 = ag\sqrt{\frac{n^4}{n_1^4} - 1}. \tag{Ex.}$$

Since the point of suspension and the bob of the pendulum are moving in a circle of radius a with speed V, they are subject to a central acceleration equal to $\dfrac{V^2}{a}$. The force necessary to produce this acceleration in the bob must be provided by the tension in the string, which therefore becomes inclined to the vertical as in a conical pendulum. The effect of the circular motion on the bob is therefore the same as if it were at rest (except for its oscillation) and an *outward* force of $\dfrac{mV^2}{a}$ were applied to it, i.e. a horizontal acceleration equal to $\dfrac{V^2}{a}$ outwards.

The resultant of this and the acceleration due to gravity is the effective value of g as far as oscillations of the pendulum are concerned.

If g' is the resultant of these accelerations,

$$g' = \sqrt{g^2 + \frac{V^4}{a^2}}.$$

Also

$$\frac{1}{n_1} = 2\pi\sqrt{\frac{l}{g}}, \quad \text{and} \quad \frac{1}{n} = 2\pi\sqrt{\frac{l}{g'}},$$

$$\therefore \frac{n^2}{n_1^2} = \frac{g'}{g},$$

$$\therefore \frac{n^4}{n_1^4} = \frac{g'^2}{g^2} = 1 + \frac{V^4}{a^2g^2},$$

$$\therefore \frac{V^4}{a^2g^2} = \frac{n^4}{n_1^4} - 1,$$

$$\therefore V^2 = ag\sqrt{\frac{n^4}{n_1^4} - 1}.$$

EXAMPLE (v).

A seconds pendulum at the bottom of a mine, $\frac{1}{2}$ mile deep, loses 10 seconds a day ; at the top of a mountain $\frac{1}{2}$ mile high, show that it will lose about 15·4 seconds a day, assuming that the radius of the earth is 4000 miles.

[Inside the earth the weight of a body varies directly as its distance from the centre ; outside the earth the weight varies inversely as the square of its distance from the centre.] (I.S.)

Let g_1, g, g_2 be the values of the acceleration due to gravity at the bottom of the mine, at the surface, and at the top of the mountain respectively.

Then

$$\frac{g_1}{g} = \frac{4000 - \frac{1}{2}}{4000}, \quad \text{and} \quad \frac{g_2}{g} = \frac{4000^2}{(4000 + \frac{1}{2})^2},$$

$$\therefore \frac{g_2}{g_1} = \frac{4000^3}{(4000 + \frac{1}{2})^2(4000 - \frac{1}{2})} = \frac{1}{\left(1 + \frac{1}{8000}\right)^2\left(1 - \frac{1}{8000}\right)}$$

$$= \left(1 + \frac{1}{8000}\right)^{-2}\left(1 - \frac{1}{8000}\right)^{-1}.$$

Also

$$\frac{86400}{86390} = \pi\sqrt{\frac{l}{g_1}}, \quad \text{and} \quad \frac{86400}{86400 - x} = \pi\sqrt{\frac{l}{g_2}},$$

$$\therefore \frac{86400 - x}{86390} = \sqrt{\frac{g_2}{g_1}} = \left(1 + \frac{1}{8000}\right)^{-1}\left(1 - \frac{1}{8000}\right)^{-\frac{1}{2}}$$

$$= \left(1 - \frac{1}{8000}\right)\left(1 + \frac{1}{16000}\right)$$

$$= 1 - \frac{1}{16000}, \text{ approximately;}$$

$$\therefore 86400 - x = 86390 - \frac{8639}{1600} = 86390 - 5\cdot4,$$

$$\therefore x = 10 + 5\cdot4 = 15\cdot4 \text{ seconds.}$$

EXAMPLES XXXVI.

1. A pendulum beats seconds accurately at a place where the acceleration of gravity is 32 ft./sec.^{2} If taken to a place where the value of this acceleration is 32·2 ft./sec.^{2}, will it gain or lose, and how many seconds in 24 hours ?   (I.S.)

2. Calculate the length of a seconds pendulum at a place where g is 981 cm./sec.^{2} If a pendulum clock loses 9 minutes per week, find in millimetres what change is required in the length of the pendulum in order that the clock may keep correct time.   (I.S.)

3. Show that an incorrect seconds pendulum of a clock which loses x seconds a day must be shortened by $\dfrac{x}{432}$ per cent. of its length in order to keep correct time.   (H.S.C.)

4. A seconds pendulum is correct at a place where the value of g is 32 ft./sec.^{2} How many seconds a day will it gain or lose if taken to a place where the value of g is 32·3 ft./sec.^{2} ?

5. A seconds pendulum is correct at a place where $g = 32\cdot2$ ft./sec.^{2} By what percentage of its length must it be altered in order to keep correct time at a place where $g = 32$ ft./sec.^{2} ?

6. A seconds pendulum is carried down with a lift at a uniform acceleration of 2 ft./sec.^{2} At the rate of how many seconds an hour will it lose ?

7. A pendulum clock gains 20 seconds each day. Calculate the required alteration in the length of the pendulum.
    At what height above the earth's surface would the clock with the uncorrected pendulum give correct time ? (The earth's radius is 4000 miles, and the force of gravity varies inversely as the square of the distance from the earth's centre.)   (H.S.D.)

8. A pendulum, which at the surface of the earth gains 10 seconds a day, loses 10 seconds a day when taken down a mine ; compare the acceleration due to gravity at the top and bottom of the mine and find its depth.

9. Prove that if a pendulum swings from rest to rest n times per second, then $g = n^2\pi^2l$, where l is the length of the pendulum.
    In old French measure the length of the seconds pendulum (for which $n = 1$) at Paris is 3·06 French feet ; calculate the value of g in these units.   (I.A.)

10. A simple pendulum making small oscillations is allowed to swing from a position in which it makes $\alpha°$ with the vertical. If v is the maximum speed, show that the complete period is $\dfrac{45\,v}{4\alpha}$ seconds. $(g = 32$ ft./sec.^{2}).   (H.S.C.)

11. A pendulum bob weighing 1 lb. is hung from the roof of a railway carriage by a 3-foot string. The carriage is moving at 45 m.p.h. round a curve of radius $\frac{1}{2}$ mile. Find the distance of the bob from the vertical through the point of support and the tension in the string. Find also the approximate time of a small oscillation whilst the train is moving round the curve.   (I.E.)

12. Find the formula for the time of a small oscillation of a simple pendulum.
    A simple pendulum is swinging through a small angle and it is

found that when it is vertical the tension of the string is 1 per cent. greater than the weight of the bob. Find the complete angle of swing to the nearest tenth of a degree.   (N.U.3)

13. If the time of oscillation of a simple pendulum is 20 seconds, find the length of the pendulum ; and if the velocity of the bob at its lowest position is 2 ft./sec., find the amplitude of the swing.   (C.W.B.)

§ 186. Composition of two Simple Harmonic Motions of the same Period and in the same straight Line.

Let the displacements for the separate motions be given by

$$a_1 \cos (\omega t + \epsilon_1) \text{ and } a_2 \cos (\omega t + \epsilon_2),$$

then, if x is the resultant displacement,

$$x = a_1 \cos (\omega t + \epsilon_1) + a_2 \cos (\omega t + \epsilon_2)$$
$$= \cos \omega t(a_1 \cos \epsilon_1 + a_2 \cos \epsilon_2) - \sin \omega t(a_1 \sin \epsilon_1 + a_2 \sin \epsilon_2).$$

If
$$a_1 \cos \epsilon_1 + a_2 \cos \epsilon_2 = a \cos \epsilon,$$
$$a_1 \sin \epsilon_1 + a_2 \sin \epsilon_2 = a \sin \epsilon,$$
$$x = a \cos \omega t \cos \epsilon - a \sin \omega t \sin \epsilon,$$
$$= a \cos (\omega t + \epsilon).$$

This represents a simple harmonic motion with amplitude $a = \sqrt{a_1{}^2 + a_2{}^2 + 2a_1a_2 \cos (\epsilon_1 - \epsilon_2)}$, and epoch ϵ such that

$$\tan \epsilon = \frac{a_1 \sin \epsilon_1 + a_2 \sin \epsilon_2}{a_1 \cos \epsilon_1 + a_2 \cos \epsilon_2}.$$

The result is therefore a similar motion of the same period whose amplitude and epoch are known.

Note.—We cannot compound two S.H.M.'s of different periods, i.e. the result is not S.H.M. When the periods are nearly equal, however, we can get an approximate result.

§ 187. Let the displacements be given by

$$a_1 \cot (\omega_1 t + \epsilon_1) \text{ and } a_2 \cos (\omega_2 t + \epsilon_2),$$

where $\omega_2 - \omega_1$ is small and equal to k.

Then $x = a_1 \cos (\omega_1 t + \epsilon_1) + a_2 \cos (\omega_1 t + \epsilon'),$
where $\epsilon' = kt + \epsilon_2.$

From the last paragraph,

$$x = a \cos (\omega t + \epsilon) \quad . \quad . \quad . \quad . \quad (i)$$

where $a^2 = a_1{}^2 + a_2{}^2 + 2a_1a_2 \cos (\epsilon_1 - \epsilon'),$
$$= a_1{}^2 + a_2{}^2 + 2a_1a_2 \cos (\epsilon_1 - \epsilon_2 - kt),$$

and $\tan \epsilon = \dfrac{a_1 \sin \epsilon_1 + a_2 \sin \epsilon'}{a_1 \cos \epsilon_1 + a_2 \cos \epsilon'},$

$$= \frac{a_1 \sin \epsilon_1 + a_2 \sin (\epsilon_2 + kt)}{a_1 \cos \epsilon_1 + a_2 \cos (\epsilon_2 + kt)}.$$

The quantities a and ϵ are now not constant, but vary slowly with the time, since k is very small.

The greatest value of a is when $\epsilon_1 - \epsilon_2 - kt$ is equal to any *even* multiple of π, and the value is then the sum of the amplitudes $(a_1 + a_2)$.

The least value of a is when $\epsilon_1 - \epsilon_2 - kt$ is equal to any *odd* multiple of π, and the value is then the differences of the amplitudes $(a_1 - a_2)$.

The resulting motion may be regarded as S.H.M. of approximately the same period as either of the component motions, but with its amplitude and epoch gradually changing from definite minimum to definite maximum values.

This occurs in the phenomenon known as " beats " in sound.

§ 188. Composition of two Simple Harmonic Motions of the same Period at Right Angles.

Let the displacements of the particles along the axes of x and y be given by

$$x = a \cos \omega t \quad . \quad \quad . \quad \quad . \quad \quad . \quad \quad . \quad \text{(i)}$$
$$y = b \cos (\omega t + \epsilon) \quad . \quad \quad . \quad \quad . \quad \quad . \quad \text{(ii)}$$

The path of the particle is obtained by eliminating t from these equations.

Now (ii) gives

$$\frac{y}{b} = \cos \omega t \cos \epsilon - \sin \omega t \sin \epsilon,$$

$$= \frac{x}{a} \cos \epsilon - \sin \epsilon \sqrt{1 - \frac{x^2}{a^2}}, \text{ using (i)}.$$

$$\therefore \left(\frac{y}{b} - \frac{x}{a} \cos \epsilon \right)^2 = \sin^2 \epsilon - \sin^2 \epsilon \frac{x^2}{a^2},$$

$$\therefore \frac{y^2}{b^2} - \frac{2xy}{ab} \cos \epsilon + \frac{x^2}{a^2} \cos^2 \epsilon + \frac{x^2}{a^2} \sin^2 \epsilon = \sin^2 \epsilon,$$

$$\therefore \frac{x^2}{a^2} - \frac{2xy}{ab} \cos \epsilon + \frac{y^2}{b^2} = \sin^2 \epsilon \quad . \quad \quad . \quad \text{(iii)}$$

This equation always represents an ellipse which is inscribed in the rectangle $x = \pm a$, $y = \pm b$ (ABCD, Fig. 119).

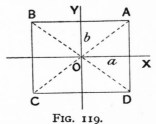

FIG. 119.

If $\epsilon = 0$, the equation (iii) becomes,

$$\frac{x}{a} - \frac{y}{b} = 0,$$

i.e. the straight line AC.

If $\epsilon = \pi$, it becomes $\frac{x}{a} + \frac{y}{b} = 0,$

i.e. the straight line BD.

If $\epsilon = \frac{\pi}{2}$, it becomes $\frac{x^2}{a^2} + \frac{y^2}{b^2} = 1,$

i.e. an ellipse whose axes are in the directions of the component motions.

If, in addition to this, the amplitudes are the same and $b = a$, the path is a circle

$$x^2 + y^2 = a^2.$$

§ 189. Motion of two Particles on a Smooth Horizontal Plane connected by a Spring.

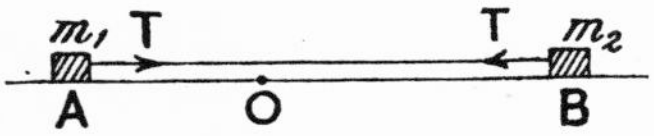

FIG. 121.

Let m_1, m_2 be the masses of the particles, and suppose that they are pulled apart to positions A and B (Fig. 121) so that the spring is elongated, and then released.

Since they are released from rest their centre of mass is initially at rest, and will therefore remain at rest throughout the motion.

If O is the centre of mass, it always divides the spring in the same ratio m_1 to m_2, so that this point of the spring is always at rest.

Let a_1, a_2, be the natural lengths of OA and OB, x_1, x_2, the elongations at time t, so that the total elongation is $x_1 + x_2$ and the tension T is given by

$$T = k(x_1 + x_2), \text{ where } k = \frac{\lambda}{a_1 + a_2}.$$

Now $\dfrac{a_1}{m_2} = \dfrac{a_2}{m_1}$ and $\dfrac{a_1 + x_1}{m_2} = \dfrac{a_2 + x_2}{m_1},$

$$\therefore \frac{x_1}{m_2} = \frac{x_2}{m_1} = \frac{x_1 + x_2}{m_1 + m_2};$$

$$\therefore T = k(x_1 + x_2) = k \frac{m_1 + m_2}{m_2} x_1,$$

$$= k \frac{m_1 + m_2}{m_1} x_2.$$

Hence for m_1 the acceleration is

$$- k \frac{m_1 + m_2}{m_1 m_2} x_1,$$

and for m_2 it is

$$- k \frac{m_1 + m_2}{m_1 m_2} x_2$$

The motions of the two particles are therefore S.H.M.'s of the same period

$$2\pi \sqrt{\frac{m_1 m_2}{k(m_1 + m_2)}}.$$

If one or both the particles be started with any velocity in the line joining them, the centre of mass will move with uniform velocity. The motion of each relative to the centre of mass is, however, exactly the same as if the centre of mass were at rest.

The acceleration of either particle is the resultant of its acceleration relative to the centre of mass and the acceleration of the centre of mass ; and the latter is zero.

This is illustrated in the following example :—

§ **190.** *Two equal particles connected by an elastic string which is just taut lie on a smooth table, the string being such that the weight of either particle would produce in it an extension a. Prove that, if one particle is projected with velocity u directly away from the other, each will have travelled a distance $u\pi\sqrt{\dfrac{a}{8g}}$, when the string first returns to its natural length.* (C.S.)

Let m be the mass of each particle.

The momentum imparted to the system is mu, hence, as the total mass is the same as $2m$ at the centre of mass, the velocity of that point will be a uniform one of $\dfrac{u}{2}$.

As the masses are equal their centre of mass is always midway between them so that the middle point of the string moves with uniform velocity $\dfrac{u}{2}$.

Relative to the centre of mass the motion is the same as if that point were at rest.

If the natural length of the string be $2l$, and x the elongation of each half at time t, the tension T is given by

$$T = k \cdot 2x, \text{ where } k = \frac{\lambda}{2l}.$$

For each particle the acceleration is $-\dfrac{2kx}{m}$,

and the period is $\qquad\qquad 2\pi\sqrt{\dfrac{m}{2k}}.$

But $mg = ka,$ $\qquad\qquad \therefore \dfrac{m}{k} = \dfrac{a}{g},$

$\therefore$ the period $\qquad\qquad = 2\pi\sqrt{\dfrac{a}{2g}},$

and the string will return again to its natural length after half a

period, i.e. after $\qquad\qquad \pi\sqrt{\dfrac{a}{2g}}$ seconds.

Hence the centre of mass, and therefore each particle will have moved a distance

$$\frac{u\pi}{2}\sqrt{\frac{a}{2g}} \text{ or } u\pi\sqrt{\frac{a}{8g}}.$$

§ **191.** The following examples are of a rather more difficult nature :—

EXAMPLE (i).

A light spiral spring is fixed at its lower end with its axis vertical ; a mass, which would compress the spring a distance d when at rest, is dropped on the spring from a height h ; show that it will be shot off on the rebound after remaining on the spring for a time.

$$\sqrt{\frac{d}{g}}\left[\pi + 2\tan^{-1}\sqrt{\frac{d}{2h}}\right]. \qquad\qquad \text{(C.S.)}$$

FIG. 122.

Let AB (Fig. 122) represent the initial position of the spring, and O the point to which the mass would compress it when at rest. When the mass falls on it the spring will be compressed to some point C below O, and will then recover. The mass will leave on the upward journey when the downward acceleration of the spring becomes equal to g.

Let m be the mass, and k the modulus of the spring divided by its natural length, then

$$mg = kd, \text{ or } k = \frac{mg}{d}.$$

The motion is harmonic, and if x is measured from O,

$$m\,\frac{d^2x}{dt^2} = -\,kx,$$

or

$$\frac{d^2x}{dt^2} = -\,\frac{g}{d}\,x \qquad . \qquad . \qquad . \qquad . \qquad . \qquad \text{(i)}$$

Also $\qquad x = a \sin\sqrt{\frac{g}{d}}\,t,$ where a is the amplitude $\qquad .\quad.$ (ii)

It is obvious from (i) that the acceleration is g downwards when $x = -\,d$, i.e. when the mass returns to B.

Now the kinetic energy of m on striking the spring is mgh, and when the spring comes to rest with m at C, the work done in compressing is equal to the loss of kinetic and potential energy of m.

If y is the maximum compression, the final tension is $\dfrac{mgy}{d}$, and the work done is $\frac12\,\dfrac{mgy^2}{d}$,

$$\therefore \tfrac12\,\frac{mgy^2}{d} = mgh + mgy,$$

$$\therefore \frac{y^2 - 2yd}{d} = 2h.$$

The amplitude $a = y - d$.

The time from O to C and back is half a period or $\pi\sqrt{\dfrac{d}{g}}$.

The time from O to B is given by

$$t = \sqrt{\frac{d}{g}}\,\sin^{-1}\frac{d}{y-d}.$$

Now if

$$\sin^{-1}\frac{d}{y-d} = \theta,\ \sin\theta = \frac{d}{y-d},$$

$$\therefore \cot^2\theta = \frac{(y-d)^2}{d^2} - 1 = \frac{y^2 - 2yd}{d^2} = \frac{2dh}{d^2} = \frac{2h}{d},$$

$\therefore$ the time from O to B is $\sqrt{\dfrac{d}{g}}\tan^{-1}\sqrt{\dfrac{d}{2h}}$, and the time from B to O and O to B is $\qquad 2\sqrt{\dfrac{d}{g}}\tan^{-1}\sqrt{\dfrac{d}{2h}}$.

Hence the time the mass remains on the spring is

$$\sqrt{\frac{d}{g}}\Big[\pi + 2\tan^{-1}\sqrt{\frac{d}{2h}}\Big].$$

EXAMPLE (ii).

A railway wagon of mass 21 tons is shunted on to a siding, and reaches a hydraulic buffer at a speed of 8 ft./sec. This buffer is such that it exerts a constant force of 35 tons weight while being pushed in, but exerts only a negligible force while recovering. The wagon buffer springs obey Hooke's law and require a total force of 7 tons weight to compress them 1 inch.

Prove that the wagon moves 9·7 inches after striking the buffer before coming to rest, and that it leaves the buffer at about 4·7 ft./sec.   (C.S.)

Since the force exerted by the hydraulic buffer on compression is 35 tons weight, the wagon springs will have to be compressed 5 inches before the buffer begins to go in.

The work done in compressing the springs is

$$\tfrac{1}{2} \, 35 \times 2240 \times \tfrac{5}{12} \text{ ft. lb.,}$$

and this equals the loss of kinetic energy of the wagon.

Hence, if v is the speed of the wagon when the hydraulic buffer begins to move in,

$$\tfrac{1}{2} \, 21 \times 2240(8^2 - v^2) = \tfrac{1}{2} \times 35 \times 2240 \times \frac{5 \times 32}{12},$$

$$\therefore 8^2 - v^2 = \frac{35 \times 5 \times 32}{12 \times 21} = \frac{200}{9},$$

$$\therefore v^2 = 64 - \frac{200}{9} = \frac{376}{9}.$$

The wagon springs are not compressed any further, and the force retarding the wagon is now a constant one of 35 tons weight.

If x is the distance the hydraulic buffer moves in, the work done by it is $35 \times 2240 \times 32x$ ft. pdls., and this is equal to the further loss of kinetic energy of the wagon,

$$\therefore 35 \times 2240 \times 32x = \tfrac{1}{2} \, 21 \times 2240 \times \frac{376}{9},$$

$$\therefore x = \frac{47}{120} \text{ ft.} = 4\cdot7 \text{ ins.}$$

Hence the total distance moved by the wagon before coming to rest is 9·7 inches.

The wagon rebounds under the force of its own springs, and will leave the buffer when the springs have extended to their natural length, i.e. by 5 inches.

The work done by the springs in recovering is

$$\tfrac{1}{2} \, 35 \times 2240 \times \tfrac{5}{12} \times 32 \text{ ft. pdls.,}$$

and this will equal the kinetic energy of the wagon as it leaves the hydraulic buffer.

Hence, if v is the speed of the wagon on leaving,

$$\tfrac{1}{2} \, 21 \times 2240 v^2 = \tfrac{1}{2} \, 35 \times 2240 \times \tfrac{5}{12} \times 32,$$

$$\therefore v = 4\cdot7 \text{ ft./sec.}$$

EXAMPLE (iii).

An elastic string is stretched between two points A and B in the same vertical line, B being below A. Prove that if a particle is fixed to a point P of the string and released from rest in that position it will oscillate with S.H.M. of period $t\sqrt{\mu}$, and amplitude μa, where t is the period and a the amplitude when P coincides with the middle point of AB, and $\mu = \dfrac{4AP \cdot PB}{AB^2}$.

The string may be considered taut throughout.   (C.S.)

Let m be the mass of the particle, l_0 the natural length of the string, λ its modulus, and l the length of AB.

When the particle is attached to the mid-point of AB, the equilibrium position will be at a depth d below the mid-point given by

$$\lambda \frac{\dfrac{l-l_0}{2}+d}{\dfrac{l_0}{2}} - \lambda \frac{\dfrac{l-l_0}{2}-d}{\dfrac{l_0}{2}} = mg,$$

or

$$4\frac{\lambda}{l_0}d = mg.$$

For a displacement x from the equilibrium position the tension is

$$\lambda \frac{d+x}{\dfrac{l_0}{2}} + \lambda \frac{d+x}{\dfrac{l_0}{2}},$$

and the restoring force is

$$4\frac{\lambda}{l_0}d + 4\frac{\lambda}{l_0}x - mg = 4\frac{\lambda}{l_0}x = \frac{mg}{d}x,$$

$\therefore$ the acceleration is

$$-\frac{g}{d}x,$$

$$\therefore t = 2\pi\sqrt{\frac{d}{g}}.$$

When the particle is released from rest it will descend a distance d below the equilibrium position, so that d is the amplitude, i.e. $d = a$. Now when P is not at the mid-point, the actual and natural lengths of AP and PB are

$$\frac{AP}{AB}l, \frac{PB}{AB}l, \text{ and } \frac{AP}{AB}l_0, \frac{PB}{AB}l_0.$$

Hence the equilibrium position is at a depth d below P given by

$$\lambda \frac{\dfrac{AP}{AB}(l-l_0)+d}{\dfrac{AP}{AB}l_0} - \lambda \frac{\dfrac{PB}{AB}(l-l_0)-d}{\dfrac{PB}{AB}l_0} = mg,$$

$$\therefore \frac{AB}{AP}\frac{\lambda}{l_0}d + \frac{AB}{PB}\frac{\lambda}{l_0}d = mg,$$

$$\therefore \frac{\lambda}{l_0}d\frac{AB^2}{AP.PB} = mg,$$

$$\therefore d = mg\frac{l_0}{\lambda}\cdot\frac{AP.PB}{AB^2} = a\frac{4AP.PB}{AB^2} = \mu a,$$

the new amplitude.

Also for a displacement x from the equilibrium position, the restoring force is

$$\frac{\lambda}{l_0}\cdot\frac{AB^2}{AP.PB}x = \frac{4\lambda}{\mu l_0}x,$$

and the period is,

$$2\pi\sqrt{\frac{l_0\mu m}{4\lambda}} = 2\pi\sqrt{\frac{d\mu}{g}} = t\sqrt{\mu}.$$

EXAMPLES XXXVII.

1. A ring slides on a smooth straight wire. It is attached by an elastic string, of modulus λ and natural length L, to a fixed point in the same horizontal plane as the wire and at distance l from it, where $l > L$. If the ring be drawn along the wire through a small distance from its position of equilibrium and then released, show that it will perform a simple harmonic motion, and find the period. (C.S.)

2. Two masses m_1 and m_2 are connected by a light spring and placed on a smooth horizontal table. When m_1 is held fixed, m_2 makes n complete vibrations per second. Show that if m_2 is held fixed, m_1 will make $n\sqrt{\dfrac{m_2}{m_1}}$, and if both are free they will make $n\sqrt{\dfrac{m_1 + m_2}{m_1}}$ vibrations per second, the vibrations in all cases being in the line of the spring. (C.S.)

3. A heavy particle of mass m is attached to the end of an elastic string of natural length a and modulus λ, the other end of the string being fixed to a point A. The particle is released from rest at A and falls under gravity ; prove that the string will be extended during the interval of time

$$\frac{2\left[\pi - \tan^{-1}\left(\dfrac{2\lambda}{mg}\right)^{\frac{1}{2}}\right]}{\left(\dfrac{\lambda}{ma}\right)^{\frac{1}{2}}}.$$ (C.S.)

4. A particle is suspended from a fixed point by a light elastic string. Show that the period of vertical oscillations is that of a simple pendulum of length $l - l_0$, where l is the equilibrium length of the string and l_0 its natural length.

If the oscillations are of amplitude a and if when the particle is at the lowest point of its path it receives a downward blow which gives it a velocity u, show that the time from the lowest to the highest point of the new path is

$$\frac{u}{g} + \sqrt{\frac{l - l_0}{g}}\left[\pi - \tan^{-1}\left(\frac{u}{a}\sqrt{\frac{l - l_0}{g}}\right)\right].$$ (C.S.)

5. Two equal particles A, B are attached to the ends of a spring which is held by its ends vertically and unstretched, A being uppermost. B is released and at the moment at which it first comes to rest A is also released. Describe fully the subsequent motion, and show that B comes to rest again once. (C.S.)

6. A spring, whose natural length is l_0, is free to vibrate horizontally, one end being fixed. The force required to shorten the spring by an amount x is Ex. The mass of the spring is M, and its centre of gravity may be supposed always at its middle point. The spring is compressed by an amount x_0, a mass m is placed at the end, and that end is released. Find the velocity of the particle when it leaves the spring. (C.S.)

7. An elastic string hangs vertically from a fixed point. To the lower end is attached a heavy particle, which is then allowed to fall. When the particle reaches its lowest point half of it drops off. Show that the other half will rise to a height $2a$ above the starting-point, where a is the extension of the string which the heavy particle would produce when hanging at rest. (C.S.)

8. A heavy particle hangs on the end of a light elastic string which is such that the period of a small vertical oscillation of the particle is $2\pi T$. The string is moving vertically upwards with uniform velocity gT_0 and the particle is in relative equilibrium. Show that, if the upper end of the string is suddenly fixed, the string will become slack if $T_0 > T$, and that in this case the new motion has a period

$$2\left(\pi - \cos^{-1}\frac{T}{T_0}\right)T + 2(T_0{}^2 - T^2)^{\frac{1}{2}}. \qquad \text{(C.S.)}$$

9. Two stationary railway trucks of equal mass m are connected by a spring coupling which is initially just unstressed. For each truck it is assumed that the starting resistance and the running resistance are both equal to R. A constant force $3R$ is applied to the first truck. Prove that the second truck will start after a time $\frac{\pi}{3}\sqrt{\frac{m}{\lambda}}$, where λ is the force in absolute units needed to produce unit extension in the spring. (C.S.)

10. A particle of mass m is moving in the axis of x under a central force $\mu m x$ to the origin. When $t = 2$ seconds it passes through the origin, and when $t = 4$ seconds its velocity is 4 ft./sec. Determine the motion and show that, if the complete period is 16 seconds, the semi-amplitude of the path is $\frac{32\sqrt{2}}{\pi}$ ft. (C.S.)

11. Two masses M and m, connected by a light spring obeying Hooke's law, fall in a vertical line with the spring unstretched until M strikes an inelastic horizontal table. Prove that M will after an interval of time rise from the table if the distance through which M has fallen exceeds $l\left(1 + \frac{M}{2m}\right)$, where l is the extension that would be produced in the spring by a force equal to the weight of M. (C.S.)

12. A spring balance consists of a horizontal disc of mass 4 oz., carried on a light vertical spring which is compressed $\frac{1}{4}$ inch by the weight of the disc. An inelastic mass of 8 oz. is dropped from a height of 2 inches on to the disc; find its velocity when it leaves the disc in the subsequent ascent. (C.S.)

13. A heavy particle is attached to one point of a uniform light elastic string. The ends of the string are attached to two points in a vertical line. Show that the period of a vertical oscillation in which the string remains taut is $2\pi\sqrt{\frac{mh}{2\lambda}}$, where λ is the coefficient of elasticity of the string, and h the harmonic mean of the unstretched lengths of the two parts of the string. (C.S.)

14. A railway truck of mass 10 tons, moving at a speed of 4 ft./sec., collides with a similar stationary truck free to move. The buffer springs, which obey Hooke's law, are such that a force of 5 tons wt. between the trucks decreases their distance apart by 9 inches. Find the greatest compression produced in the springs.

15. Two masses m_1 and m_2 lb. are connected by a light elastic string passing over a smooth pulley. The string stretches 1 foot under a tension of P poundals. The masses are supported so that the two sides of the string are vertical and just slack, and the mass m_1 is

then released. Prove that the mass m_2 will begin to rise after a time

$$\sqrt{\frac{m_1}{P}} \cdot \cos^{-1}\left(1 - \frac{m_2}{m_1}\right).$$ (C.S.)

16. Two light elastic strings are fastened to a particle of mass m and their other ends to fixed points so that the strings are taut. The modulus of each is λ, the tension T, and the lengths a and b. Show that the period of an oscillation along the line of the strings is

$$2\pi\left[\frac{mab}{(T + \lambda)(a + b)}\right]^{\frac{1}{2}}.$$ (C.S.)

17. A light helical spring hanging from a fixed point is such that a force of 10 lb. produces an extension of 1 inch. When the spring is not extended, a mass of 15 lb. is hooked on to the lower end and suddenly released.

Determine (i) the distance the mass will descend; (ii) the force in the spring when the maximum extension is reached; (iii) the time of oscillation of the mass; (iv) the length of the simple equivalent pendulum. (C.S.)

18. A body, of weight W, moves in a straight line under a force always directed to a fixed point O in the straight line and equal to kx, where x is the distance of the body from O at any instant. Prove that the work done on the body as it alters its distance from x_1 to x_2 is $\frac{k(x_1{}^2 - x_2{}^2)}{2}$, and that, if its greatest velocity is v, the body moves to and fro through a distance $2v\sqrt{\frac{W}{gk}}$. (H.S.C.)

19. A particle is moving with S.H.M. of amplitude a and periodic time T; find the velocity and acceleration when at a distance x from the centre.

If, when at the point of greatest velocity, the body collides directly with a stationary body of twice its own mass, what is the amplitude of the ensuing motion of the first body? The law of force is supposed to remain the same and the bodies are perfectly elastic. (H.S.C.)

20. A particle of mass m is attached to two points A and B, distant $12a$ apart on a smooth horizontal table, by two similar elastic strings each of natural length $5a$ and modulus of elasticity λ. If the particle is pulled from its position of equilibrium as far as A and then released, discuss the subsequent motion and find how long it takes to reach B. (H.S.D.)

21. A simple pendulum of length l is at rest in a vertical position. If the point of suspension is made to move horizontally from rest with a small constant acceleration α, describe the subsequent motion of the bob of the pendulum relative to the point of suspension; and find how far the point of suspension moves before the pendulum again becomes vertical. (Ex.)

22. Two inelastic particles, of masses m and m', are attached to the ends of an elastic string of natural length a, whose modulus of elasticity is equal to the sum of the weights of the particles. They are placed on a smooth horizontal plane with the string stretched to double its length and are then let go. Determine the point at which they

meet, and show that the impulse between them when they meet is $(mm'ga)^{\frac{1}{2}}$ units of momentum.   (H.S.D.)

23. An elastic string AB of length l is fixed at A and would be stretched to double its length if a weight W were fastened to B and gently lowered. A weight $\dfrac{W}{10}$ is fastened to B and let fall from A. Find the distance it will fall and prove that the period of the subsequent movement is

$$2\sqrt{\frac{l}{10g}}\left(2\sqrt{5} + \pi - \cos^{-1}\frac{1}{\sqrt{21}}\right).$$ (Ex.)

24. A body of mass m hangs from an elastic spring of negligible mass and, in equilibrium, extends its length by an amount a. If the top of the spring is held fast, prove that the vertical oscillation has a period equal to that of a simple pendulum of length a.

    If the top of the spring is forced to move up and down according to the formula

$$\xi = \epsilon \cos pt,$$

where ξ is the vertical displacement, prove that the forced oscillation of the mass is of amplitude

$$\frac{g\epsilon}{ap^2 - g},$$

when this fraction is positive. Find also the relation between the phases of the forced oscillation of the mass and the oscillation of the top of the spring.   (N.U.4)

25. A particle of mass m is tied to the middle point of an elastic string of natural length l and modulus λ. The string is stretched until its length is a and its ends A, B are then fastened to two points on a smooth table. Show that, for small oscillations of the particle in the line AB, the period is $\dfrac{2\pi}{n}$, where $n^2 = \dfrac{4\lambda}{ml}$.

    The end B is now moved in the direction AB in such a way that at time t the length AB is $a + b \sin 2nt$. If the particle is at rest at the middle point of AB at time $t = 0$, show that its displacement at time t is

$$\tfrac{2}{3} b \sin nt \sin^2 \tfrac{1}{2}nt,$$

it being assumed that the string is always taut.   (N.U.4)

26. In an Attwood's Machine the lighter mass m is tied to the floor by a vertical weightless elastic thread of natural length l and modulus λ. Show that if the inertia and the friction of the pulley can be neglected, the system can oscillate about the equilibrium position with a period

$$2\pi\sqrt{\frac{l(M + m)}{\lambda}},$$

where M is the heavier mass.

    Show also that if the system is released from rest with the elastic thread just not stretched, the amplitude of the oscillations will be $\dfrac{gl(M - m)}{\lambda}$.   (N.U.4)

CHAPTER VII.

MOTION OF A PARTICLE IN TWO DIMENSIONS.

§ **192.** We have dealt with some special cases of motion in two dimensions in the last three chapters, and shall now consider the matter in a more general manner.

To fix the position of a point in a plane we require two co-ordinates, and to determine completely the motion of the point we require its component velocities and accelerations in two different directions. The choice of these directions depends on the nature of the problem, and there are three methods of resolving which are commonly used.

§ 193. Components of Velocity and Acceleration Parallel to two Fixed Axes.

This method has been mentioned already (paras. 21 and 40).

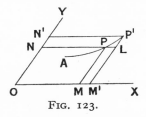

FIG. 123.

Let P, P′ (Fig. 123) be the positions of a point moving in a curve APP′ at times t and $t + \delta t$ respectively.

Take OX, OY as axes, and let OM $= x$, ON $= y$, be the co-ordinates of P; OM′ $= x + \delta x$, ON′ $= y + \delta y$, those of P′

Let PL, parallel to OX, cut P′M′ in L, then

$$PL = \delta x, \ LP' = \delta y.$$

By the triangle of velocities the sides PL, LP′ of the triangle PLP′ will ultimately, when PP′ is very small, represent the components of velocity parallel to the axes on the same scale that PP′ represents the resultant velocity.

Hence the component velocities are the limiting values of

$$\frac{\delta x}{\delta t} \text{ and } \frac{\delta y}{\delta t},$$

i.e. $\dfrac{dx}{dt}$ or $\dot{x}$ parallel to OX,

                         $\dfrac{dy}{dt}$ or $\dot{y}$ parallel to OY.

These are the velocities of M and N along the axes, and the velocity of P is the resultant of the velocities of M and N.

The acceleration of P is the resultant of the accelerations of M and N, and the component accelerations of P are

                         $\dfrac{d^2x}{dt^2}$ or $\ddot{x}$ parallel to OX,

                         $\dfrac{d^2y}{dt^2}$ or $\ddot{y}$ parallel to OY.

Usually the axes OX and OY are at right angles.

This method of resolving is used when we know the components of the forces acting on a particle parallel to two fixed directions, e.g. in the motion of a projectile.

§ 194. Components of Velocity and Acceleration along and perpendicular to the Radius Vector.

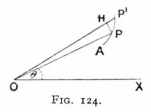

FIG. 124.

Let P, P' (Fig. 124) be the positions of a point moving in a curve APP' at the times t and $t + \delta t$ respectively.

Let OX be the initial line, and r, θ the polar co-ordinates of P, so that OP $= r$, angle XOP $= \theta$; POP' $= \delta\theta$.

If PH is drawn perpendicular to OP',

$$PH = r\delta\theta, \text{ and } HP' = \delta r.$$

The sides PH, HP' of the triangle PHP', when PP' is very small, will ultimately represen⁺ the component velocities of P along and perpendicular to the radius vector OP, PP' representing the resultant velocity.

Hence the component velocities along and perpendicular to the radius vector are the limiting values of

                         $\dfrac{\delta r}{\delta t}$ and $\dfrac{r\delta\theta}{\delta t}$,

or $\dfrac{dr}{dt}$ and $r\dfrac{d\theta}{dt}$.

If we call these u and v, then at P' the components along and perpendicular to OP' are $u + \delta u$, and $v + \delta v$.

Since POP' $= \delta\theta$, the component of velocity at time $t + \delta t$ in the direction OP is

$$(u + \delta u) \cos \delta\theta - (v + \delta v) \sin \delta\theta,$$

hence the acceleration along OP is

$$\underset{\delta t \to 0}{\mathrm{Lt}} \quad \frac{(u + \delta u) \cos \delta\theta - (v + \delta v) \sin \delta\theta - u}{\delta t}$$

$$= \frac{du}{dt} - v\frac{d\theta}{dt} = \frac{d^2r}{dt^2} - r\left(\frac{d\theta}{dt}\right)^2.$$

The component of velocity at time $t + \delta t$ perpendicular to OP is

$$(u + \delta u) \sin \delta\theta + (v + \delta v) \cos \delta\theta,$$

hence the acceleration perpendicular to OP' is

$$\underset{\delta t \to 0}{\mathrm{Lt}} \quad \frac{(u + \delta u) \sin \delta\theta + (v + \delta v) \cos \delta\theta - v}{\delta t},$$

$$= u\frac{d\theta}{dt} + \frac{dv}{dt} = \frac{dr}{dt} \cdot \frac{d\theta}{dt} + \frac{d}{dt}\left(r\frac{d\theta}{dt}\right)$$

$$= \frac{1}{r}\frac{d}{dt}\left(r^2\frac{d\theta}{dt}\right).$$

This method of resolving is used when the acting force is always directed to a fixed point O. Such a force is called a *Central Force*.

§ 195. Components of Velocity and Acceleration along the Tangent and Normal to the Path.

It is obvious that the component of velocity along the normal to the path is zero.

Let P, P' (Fig. 125) be the positions of a point describing a curve APP' at the times t and $t + \delta t$ respectively.

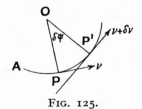

FIG. 125.

Let the arc AP $= s$, then the velocity v at P is along the tangent at P and

$$v = \frac{ds}{dt}.$$

The velocity at P' is equal to $v + \delta v$, and is along the tangent at P'. If PO, P'O are the normals at P and P', then if the angle between the tangents at P and P' is $\delta \psi$, angle POP' $= \delta \psi$.

The components of velocity at time $t + \delta t$ along the tangent and normal at P are

$$(v + \delta v) \cos \delta \psi, \text{ and } (v + \delta v) \sin \delta \psi,$$

Hence the acceleration along the tangent at P is

$$\underset{\delta t \to 0}{\text{Lt}} \quad \frac{(v + \delta v) \cos \delta \psi - v}{\delta t},$$

$$= \frac{dv}{dt}.$$

The acceleration along the normal at P is

$$\underset{\delta t \to 0}{\text{Lt}} \quad \frac{(v + \delta v) \sin \delta \psi}{\delta t} = v \frac{d\psi}{dt},$$

$$= \frac{v^2}{\rho},$$

where ρ is the radius of curvature at P.

$$\left(\frac{d\psi}{dt} = \frac{d\psi}{ds} \cdot \frac{ds}{dt}, \text{ and } \frac{d\psi}{ds} = \frac{1}{\rho}, \frac{ds}{dt} = v \right).$$

This method of resolving is used in cases where a particle is constrained to move along a curve.

Motion in a circle (Chapter V.) is a special case. The radius of curvature is then the radius of the circle and the normal acceleration is $\frac{v^2}{r}$.

§ 196. Angular Momentum.

If a particle of mass m is moving in a plane with velocity v, its linear momentum is mv. If p is the length of the perpendicular from a point O in the plane on the direction of motion of the particle, the product pmv is called the *Moment of Momentum* or *Angular Momentum* of the particle about O.

If we use polar co-ordinates the velocity of the particle perpendicular to the radius vector joining it to O is $r \frac{d\theta}{dt}$, hence its angular momentum about O is $mr^2 \frac{d\theta}{dt}$.

If there is no force acting on the particle perpendicular to the radius vector, then, since the acceleration in this direction is

$$\frac{1}{r} \frac{d}{dt} \left(r^2 \frac{d\theta}{dt} \right),$$

we have
$$m \frac{1}{r}\frac{d}{dt}\left(r^2 \frac{d\theta}{dt}\right) = 0,$$

$$\therefore r^2 \frac{d\theta}{dt} = \text{constant},$$

i.e. *the angular momentum about* O *is constant.*
This corresponds to the Principle of Conservation of Linear Momentum, and is very useful in cases where a particle is moving so that the only external force acting on it is directed towards a fixed point. The force has then no moment about the fixed point and the angular momentum about that point is constant.

The examples in the following paragraphs illustrate the use of the preceding methods.

§ **197.** EXAMPLE (i).
A smooth straight tube rotates in a horizontal plane about a point in itself with uniform angular velocity ω. At time t = 0 a particle is inside the tube, at rest relatively to the tube, and at a distance a from the point of rotation. Show that at time t the distance of the particle from the point of rotation is
$$a \cosh (\omega t).$$

Find the force the tube is then exerting on the particle. (C.S.)
To find the motion along the tube we require only the acceleration along the radius vector.
Now there is no force acting on the particle in this direction,
$$\therefore \frac{d^2r}{dt^2} - r\left(\frac{d\theta}{dt}\right)^2 = 0, \quad \text{and} \quad \frac{d\theta}{dt} = \omega,$$

$$\therefore \frac{d^2r}{dt^2} - r\omega^2 = 0.$$

The solution of this equation is
$$r = Ae^{\omega t} + Be^{-\omega t},$$

where A and B are constants to be determined from the initial conditions.
Now $\qquad r = a$ when $t = 0,$
$$\therefore A + B = a.$$

Also $\qquad \frac{dr}{dt} = 0,$ when $t = 0,$
$$\therefore A - B = 0,$$
$$\therefore A = B = \frac{a}{2};$$

$$\therefore r = \frac{a}{2}(e^{\omega t} + e^{-\omega t}) = a \cosh (\omega t).$$

To find the force R exerted by the tube we require the acceleration perpendicular to the radius vector.

Now this is

$$\frac{1}{r}\frac{d}{dt}\left(r^2\frac{d\theta}{dt}\right) = \frac{1}{r}\frac{d}{dt}(r^2\omega) = 2\omega\frac{dr}{dt},$$

and

$$\frac{dr}{dt} = a\omega \sinh(\omega t),$$

Hence if m is the mass of the particle,

$$R = m \cdot 2\omega\frac{dr}{dt} = 2ma\omega^2 \sinh(\omega t).$$

EXAMPLE (ii).

A light string passing through a smooth ring at O on a smooth hori-
zontal table has particles each of mass m attached to its ends A and B.
Initially the particles lie on the table with the portions of the string OA and
OB straight, and OA = OB. An impulse P is applied to the particle A
in a direction making 60° with OA. Prove that when B reaches O its
velocity is $\dfrac{P}{m} \cdot \dfrac{\sqrt{22}}{8}.$ (C.S.)

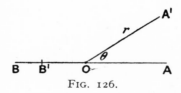

FIG. 126.

The components of the impulse along and perpendicular to the
string are
$$\frac{P}{2} \text{ and } \frac{\sqrt{3}}{2}P.$$

Hence the initial velocities in these directions are
$$\frac{P}{4m} \text{ and } \frac{\sqrt{3}P}{2m}.$$

(In the direction of the string the total mass set in motion is $2m$.)
If r is the distance of the particle A from O at time t, when it has
moved to A' (Fig. 126), θ the angle turned through by OA, and T the
tension in the string at that instant,

$$\frac{d^2r}{dt^2} - r\left(\frac{d\theta}{dt}\right)^2 = -\frac{T}{m} \qquad . \qquad . \qquad . \qquad . \quad \text{(i)}$$

Also the acceleration of B towards O is equal to that of A along
the radius vector. Hence for B we have

$$\frac{d^2r}{dt^2} = \frac{T}{m},$$

∴ using (i),

$$2\frac{d^2r}{dt^2} - r\left(\frac{d\theta}{dt}\right)^2 = 0 \qquad . \qquad . \qquad . \qquad . \quad \text{(ii)}$$

Now the angular momentum about O remains constant,

$$\therefore mr^2\frac{d\theta}{dt} = a\frac{\sqrt{3}}{2}P,$$

$$\therefore \left(\frac{d\theta}{dt}\right)^2 = \frac{3a^2}{4r^4} \cdot \frac{P^2}{m^2},$$

hence from (ii),

$$2\frac{d^2r}{dt^2} = \frac{3a^2P^2}{4m^2}\frac{1}{r^3},$$

$$\therefore \left(\frac{dr}{dt}\right)^2 = -\frac{3a^2P^2}{8m^2} \cdot \frac{1}{r^2} + C,$$

and when

$$r = a, \quad \frac{dr}{dt} = \frac{P}{4m},$$

$$\therefore \frac{P^2}{16m^2} = -\frac{3P^2}{8m^2} + C, \text{ or } C = \frac{7}{16} \cdot \frac{P^2}{m^2};$$

hence when $r = 2a$,

$$\left(\frac{dr}{dt}\right)^2 = \frac{7}{16}\frac{P^2}{m^2} - \frac{3P^2}{32m^2} = \frac{11}{32}\frac{P^2}{m^2},$$

$$\therefore \frac{dr}{dt} = \frac{P}{m}\frac{\sqrt{22}}{8}.$$

EXAMPLE (iii).

A particle of mass m moving in a plane is subject to a constant force mf in the direction of the x-axis and to a force mkv in the direction of the normal to its path, where v is its speed and k is a constant coefficient. Write down the equations of motion and prove that they are satisfied by the special solution

$$x = a(1 - \cos kt), \quad y = a(kt - \sin kt),$$

where a is a constant expressible in terms of f and k.

Determine the solution if $x = 0$, $\dot{x} = 0$, $y = 0$, $\dot{y} = V$, when $t = 0$, where V is any constant value. (N.U.4)

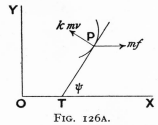

FIG. 126A.

The accelerations produced by the forces are f and kv.

Let x, y be the co-ordinates of the particle P (Fig. 126A) at any instant referred to rectangular axes x and y, PT the tangent to its path

$$v = \sqrt{\dot{x}^2 + \dot{y}^2},$$

$$\tan \psi = \frac{\dot{y}}{\dot{x}},$$

$$\therefore \sec^2 \psi = 1 + \frac{\dot{y}^2}{\dot{x}^2}, \text{ and } \cos \psi = \frac{\dot{x}}{\sqrt{\dot{x}^2 + \dot{y}^2}}, \sin \psi = \frac{\dot{y}}{\sqrt{\dot{x}^2 + \dot{y}^2}}.$$

The accelerations, $\ddot{x}$ and $\ddot{y}$, parallel to OX and OY are given by

$$\ddot{x} = f - k\sqrt{\dot{x}^2 + \dot{y}^2}\sin\psi,$$
$$\ddot{y} = k\sqrt{\dot{x}^2 + \dot{y}^2}\cos\psi,$$
$$\therefore \left.\begin{array}{l}\ddot{x} = f - k\dot{y}\\\ddot{y} = k\dot{x}\end{array}\right\} \qquad . \qquad . \qquad . \qquad . \qquad \text{(i)}$$

With the special solution given in the question,

$x = a[\mathrm{1} - \cos kt]$, $\dot{x} = ak\sin kt$, and $\ddot{x} = ak^2\cos kt$,
$y = a[kt - \sin kt]$, $\dot{y} = ak - ak\cos kt$, and $\ddot{y} = ak^2\sin kt$.

It is clear that these values satisfy equations (i) if

$$ak^2\cos kt = f - ak^2 + ak^2\cos kt,$$

i.e. if
$$a = \frac{f}{k^2}.$$

The special solution satisfies the conditions $x = 0$, $y = 0$, and $\dot{x} = 0$ when $t = 0$.

The condition $\dot{y} = V$ when $t = 0$ is not satisfied by this special solution. We must therefore find the general solution of the equations of motion and determine the constants by using the given conditions.

Integrating the equations once, we have

$$\dot{x} = ft - ky + c_1,$$
$$\dot{y} = kx + c_2.$$

Since $\dot{x} = 0$, and $y = 0$ when $t = 0$,

$$\therefore c_1 = 0,$$

and since $\dot{y} = V$ and $x = 0$ when $t = v$,

$$\therefore c_2 = V.$$

$$\therefore \left.\begin{array}{l}\dot{x} = ft - ky\\\dot{y} = kx + V\end{array}\right\} \qquad . \qquad . \qquad . \qquad \text{(ii)}$$

Also
$$\ddot{y} = k\dot{x} = kft - k^2y,$$
$$\therefore (D^2 + k^2)y = kft,$$
$$\therefore y = A\cos kt + B\sin kt + \frac{ft}{k}.$$

Since $y = 0$ when $t = 0$, $A = 0$,

$$\therefore y = B\sin kt + \frac{ft}{k},$$

and
$$\dot{y} = Bk\cos kt + \frac{f}{k},$$

and since $y = V$ when $t = 0$,

$$Bk = V - \frac{f}{k},$$

$$\therefore y = \frac{\mathrm{1}}{k}\left(V - \frac{f}{k}\right)\sin kt + \frac{ft}{k}.$$

From the second of equations (ii), we have

$$kx = \dot{y} - V,$$

$$\therefore kx = \left(V - \frac{f}{k}\right)\cos kt + \frac{f}{k} - V,$$

$$\therefore x = \frac{1}{k}\left(\frac{f}{k} - V\right)(1 - \cos kt).$$

These values of y and x satisfy all the given conditions.

Note.—We can avoid solving the differential equations by assuming that the solution is of the same form but that the constant a is replaced by three different constants, i.e. we assume

$$x = A(1 - \cos kt) \text{ and } y = Bkt - C \sin kt.$$

From these, we have

$$\dot{x} = Ak \sin kt \text{ and } \ddot{x} = Ak^2 \cos kt,$$

$$\therefore Ak^2 = f - kV, \text{ or } A = \frac{1}{k}\left(\frac{f}{k} - V\right).$$

Also $\qquad \dot{y} = Bk - Ck \cos kt \text{ and } \ddot{y} = Ck^2 \sin kt,$

$$\therefore Ck^2 \sin kt = Ak^2 \cos kt,$$

$$\therefore C = A.$$

Since $\dot{y} = V$ when $t = 0,$

$$Bk = V + Ck = V + Ak,$$

$$\therefore B = \frac{V}{k} + \frac{f}{k^2} - \frac{V}{k} = \frac{f}{k^2},$$

$$\therefore x = \frac{1}{k}\left(\frac{f}{k} - V\right)(1 - \cos kt),$$

$$y = \frac{ft}{k} - \frac{1}{k}\left(\frac{f}{k} - V\right) \sin kt.$$

§ 198. Motion under the Action of a Central Force.

Taking the centre of force as origin, and using polar co-ordinates, let F be the force at any point measured positively towards the origin.

Then

$$\frac{d^2r}{dt^2} - r\left(\frac{d\theta}{dt}\right)^2 = -\frac{F}{m} \qquad \qquad \text{(i)}$$

$$\frac{1}{r}\frac{d}{dt}\left(r^2\frac{d\theta}{dt}\right) = 0 \qquad \qquad \text{(ii)}$$

The second equation gives by integration

$$r^2\frac{d\theta}{dt} = h \qquad \qquad \text{(iii)}$$

where h is a constant whose value depends on the initial conditions.

We have seen that $mr^2\dfrac{d\theta}{dt}$ is the angular momentum so that mh is the angular momentum and is constant throughout the motion.

Let v be the velocity of the particle at any instant, and p the perpendicular from the origin on the direction of motion (i.e. the tangent to the path) at that instant.

The angular momentum is equal to pmv,

$$\therefore pv = h,$$

and
$$v = \frac{h}{p}.$$

Let A be the polar area bounded by the path, the moving radius vector r, and any fixed radius vector.

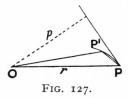

FIG. 127.

Let P, P' (Fig. 127) be the positions of the particle at times t and $t + dt$, and let POP' $= d\theta$.

The area POP' $= \frac{1}{2}r^2 d\theta$ or $\frac{1}{2}pds$, where p is the perpendicular from O on the tangent at P and PP' $= ds$.

$$\therefore r^2 d\theta = 2dA = pds,$$

$$\therefore r^2\frac{d\theta}{dt} = 2\frac{dA}{dt} = p\frac{ds}{dt} = pv \ ;$$

$$\therefore \frac{dA}{dt} = \frac{1}{2}h.$$

This shows, by integration, that *the polar area traced out by the radius vector is proportional to the time of describing it.*

§ **198a.** To find the polar equation of the path we have to eliminate t between equations (i) and (ii) of the last paragraph.

The elimination is simplified by putting $r = \dfrac{1}{u}$,

then
$$\frac{dr}{dt} = -\frac{1}{u^2}\cdot\frac{du}{d\theta}\cdot\frac{d\theta}{dt} = -h\frac{du}{d\theta}, \text{ using } \qquad . \quad \text{(iii)}$$

$$\therefore \frac{d^2r}{dt^2} = -h\frac{d^2u}{d\theta^2}\cdot\frac{d\theta}{dt} = -h^2u^2\frac{d^2u}{d\theta^2}.$$

Substituting this value for $\dfrac{d^2r}{dt^2}$, and the value hu^2 for $\dfrac{d\theta}{dt}$ in equation (i), we have

$$- h^2 u^2 \frac{d^2 u}{d\theta^2} - h^2 u^3 = -\frac{F}{m},$$

or

$$\frac{d^2 u}{d\theta^2} + u = \frac{F}{mh^2 u^2} \quad . \quad . \quad . \quad . \quad \text{(iv)}$$

When given F as a function of r, this differential equation, on integration, will give the equation of the path.

If the polar equation of the path is given, we can find the value of $\frac{d^2 u}{d\theta^2}$ and hence determine F in terms of u and θ.

If we use the tangential and normal components of acceleration we have

$$v \frac{dv}{ds} = -\frac{F}{m}\cos\phi, \quad \frac{v^2}{\rho} = \frac{F}{m}\sin\phi, \quad . \quad . \quad . \quad \text{(v)}$$

where ϕ is the angle between the tangent and radius vector.

Now $\cos\phi = \frac{dr}{ds}$, and the first of these equations becomes

$$v \frac{dv}{ds} = -\frac{F}{m}\frac{dr}{ds},$$

$$\therefore v^2 = C - 2\int\frac{F}{m}\, dr,$$

Putting $v = \frac{h}{p}$, and differentiating with respect to r,

$$h^2 \frac{d}{dr}\left(\frac{1}{p^2}\right) = -2\frac{F}{m},$$

$$\therefore F = -\tfrac{1}{2}mh^2 \frac{d}{dr}\left(\frac{1}{p^2}\right).$$

This expression for the force F is very useful for finding F when we can get the equation of the path in the form $p = f(r)$.

The further treatment of this subject will be found in more advanced books. The most important case is when F is a gravitational force varying as the inverse square.

§ 199. Motion on a Smooth Cycloid under Gravity.

Let the cycloid be placed with its vertex O downwards, and its axis OD vertical (Fig. 128). Let A, A' be the cusps.

Let s be the length of the arc OP measured from O, then it is known that

$$s = 4a \sin \psi, \cdot$$

where a is the radius of the generating circle ($\tfrac{1}{2}$OD), and ψ is the angle made by the tangent at P with the tangent at O.

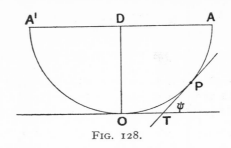

FIG. 128.

If a particle of mass m, free to slide on the cycloid, be at P, its accelerations along the tangent and normal are

$$\frac{d^2s}{dt^2}, \text{ and } \frac{v^2}{\rho},$$

$$\therefore m\frac{d^2s}{dt^2} = -mg \sin \psi = -\frac{mg}{4a}s \qquad . \qquad . \qquad . \text{(i)}$$

and
$$m\frac{v^2}{\rho} = -mg \cos \psi + R, \qquad . \qquad . \qquad . \text{(ii)}$$

where R is the pressure of the curve on the particle.

Equation (i) gives
$$\frac{d^2s}{dt^2} = -\frac{g}{4a}s.$$

The motion is therefore S.H.M. about O, and the period is

$$2\pi\sqrt{\frac{4a}{g}}, \text{ or } 4\pi\sqrt{\frac{a}{g}}.$$

It should be noticed that this is not an approximate S.H.M. as in the case of an ordinary circular pendulum, and it is not necessary for the arc of oscillation to be small.

Also the motion is determined completely by equation (i). Equation (ii) merely gives the pressure on the curve.

If c is the semi-arc of oscillation, then on solving equation (i) we get

$$s = c \sin \left(\sqrt{\frac{g}{4a}}\, t \right).$$

The velocity v at any point can be obtained in terms of s by integrating equation (i) once

$$\tfrac{1}{2}v^2 = -\frac{g}{8a}s^2 + A,$$

and if
$$v = 0 \text{ when } s = c, A = \frac{g}{8a}c^2,$$

$$\therefore v^2 = \frac{g}{4a}(c^2 - s^2).$$

The value of v can also be obtained by the Principle of Energy from the vertical height descended by the particle.

§ **200.** *A bead moves on a smooth parabolic wire whose axis is vertical and vertex upwards. Show that the pressure between the wire and the bead varies inversely as the radius of curvature ρ.*

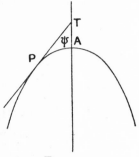

FIG. 129.

Let A (Fig. 129) be the vertex of the parabola, and $y^2 = 4ax$ its equation referred to its axis and the tangent at A, x being measured vertically downwards.

The angle ψ made by the tangent at P with the axis is given by

$$\tan \psi = \frac{2a}{y} = \frac{2a}{\sqrt{4ax}},$$

$$\therefore x = a \cot^2 \psi,$$

and x is the vertical depth of P below A.

If c is the depth below A when the velocity is zero, the velocity v at P is given by

$$v^2 = 2g(a \cot^2 \psi - c).$$

Now

$$\sin \psi = \frac{dy}{ds}, \text{ and } \rho = -\frac{ds}{d\psi} \text{ since } \frac{ds}{d\psi} \text{ is negative.}$$

Also

$$\sec^2 \psi \frac{d\psi}{ds} = -\frac{2a}{y^2} \cdot \frac{dy}{ds} = -\frac{2a}{y^2} \sin \psi,$$

$$\therefore \frac{\sec^2 \psi}{\rho} = \frac{2a}{y^2} \sin \psi,$$

$$\therefore \sin \psi = \frac{y^2 \sec^2 \psi}{2a\rho} = \frac{4a^2 \cot^2 \psi \sec^2 \psi}{2a\rho},$$

$$= \frac{2a \operatorname{cosec}^2 \psi}{\rho}.$$

Resolving along the normal

$$m\frac{v^2}{\rho} = mg\sin\psi - R,$$

$$\therefore \frac{2g(a\cot^2\psi - c)}{\rho} = +\frac{2ag\cosec^2\psi}{\rho} - \frac{R}{m},$$

$$\therefore \frac{R}{m} = \frac{2g}{\rho}(a\cosec^2\psi - a\cot^2\psi + c)$$

$$= \frac{2g(a+c)}{\rho},$$

$$\therefore R = \frac{2mg(a+c)}{\rho},$$

$\therefore R$ varies inversely as ρ.

EXAMPLES XXXVIII.

1. The velocities of a particle along and perpendicular to a radius vector from a fixed origin are λr^2 and $\mu\theta^2$; find the polar equation of the path of the particle and also the component accelerations in terms of r and θ. (C.S.)

2. Masses m, m' are attached to the ends of a weightless inextensible string AOB and rest on a smooth horizontal table. The string is in contact with a smooth fixed peg at O, and the portions OA ($= a$), and OB ($= b$) of the string are in a straight line. The mass m is now projected horizontally with velocity u perpendicular to OA. If the string remains in contact with the peg, and all the motion takes place in a horizontal plane, prove that the mass m' reaches the peg with velocity

$$\frac{u}{a+b}\sqrt{\frac{mb(2a+b)}{m+m'}}. \qquad \text{(C.S.)}$$

3. A particle on a smooth table is attached by a string passing through a small hole in the table and carries an equal particle hanging vertically. The former particle is projected along the table at right angles to the string with velocity $\sqrt{2gh}$ when at a distance a from the hole. If r is the distance from the hole at time t, prove the results

(1) $$2\left(\frac{dr}{dt}\right)^2 = 2gh\left(1 - \frac{a^2}{r^2}\right) + 2g(a - r),$$

(2) the lower particle will be pulled up to the hole if the total length of the string is less than

$$a + \tfrac{1}{2}h + \sqrt{ah + \tfrac{1}{4}h^2},$$

(3) the tension of the string is $\tfrac{1}{2}mg\left(1 + \frac{2a^2h}{r^3}\right)$, m being the mass of each particle. (C.S.)

4. A particle moves on the curve $y = a\log\sec\frac{x}{a}$ in such a way that the tangent to the curve rotates uniformly ; prove that the resultant acceleration of the particle varies as the square of the radius of curvature. (C.S.)

5. A bead threaded on a rough fixed circular wire whose plane is horizontal is projected with velocity V. Show that it will come to rest when the arc traversed is

$$\frac{a}{2\mu} \sinh^{-1}\left(\frac{V^2}{ga}\right),$$

where a is the radius of the wire and μ is the coefficient of friction.

(C.S.)

6. A number of particles lie on the equiangular spiral $r = Ae^{\theta \tan a}$ and are in motion. Prove that, if the particles continue to lie on an equiangular spiral, μ (the component of velocity of a particle normal to the curve) is of the form

$$\mu = r(p + q \log r),$$

where p, q are functions of t only.

If p, q are both constant, find the relations connecting p, q, A and α with t.

(C.S.)

7. A point moves in a circular path of radius a so that its angular velocity about a fixed point in the circumference of the circle is constant and equal to ω ; show that the resultant acceleration of the point at every point of the path is of constant magnitude $4a\omega^2$.

[Use the polar equation of a circle $r = 2a \cos \theta$, and resolve along and perpendicular to the radius vector.] (C.S.)

8. If the co-ordinates x, y of a moving point are given by

$$x = a(\cos \theta + \theta \sin \theta), \quad y = a(\sin \theta - \theta \cos \theta),$$

and θ increases at a uniform rate ω, prove that the velocity of the point is $a\theta\omega$; and find the inclination of the velocity to the axis of x.

9. A smooth horizontal tube OA of length a is movable about a vertical axis OB through the extremity O. A particle placed at the extremity A is suddenly projected towards O with velocity $a\omega$, while at the same time the tube is made to rotate about OB with angular velocity ω. Show that the particle will have travelled half-way down the tube after a time $\frac{1}{\omega} \log_e 2$, and will not reach O in any finite time.

10. The ends of a straight rod move in two straight grooves intersecting at right angles, and one end is constrained to describe its groove with uniform velocity. Show that the acceleration of any definite particle of the rod is perpendicular to this groove and is inversely proportional to the cube of its distance from it.

11. A straight line of constant length moves with its ends on two rectangular axes Ox, Oy, and P is the foot of the perpendicular from O on the straight line. Show that the velocity of P perpendicular to OP is ω . OP and along OP is 2ω . CP, where C is the middle point of the line and ω is the angular velocity of C about O.

12. Two rings, P and Q, each of weight w, are connected by flexible joints to the ends of a light rod of length a, whose weight may be neglected. P moves on a smooth vertical wire OA, and Q on a smooth horizontal wire OB.

At starting, Q is close to O, and P above it ; Q is given a small impulse to enable the rings to begin to slide. Show that, when PQ makes an angle θ with the vertical, the velocity of Q is

$$a \cos \theta \frac{d\theta}{dt},$$

with a similar expression for the velocity of P; and by means of the equation of energy, or otherwise, find the value of $\dfrac{d\theta}{dt}$ in terms of θ, and prove that

$$a\,\frac{d^2\theta}{dt^2} = g \sin \theta.$$

Prove also that the stress in the rod is $w(3\cos\theta - 2)$.   (H.S.C.)

13. A point moves in a plane in such a way that its co-ordinates x, y are given at any time t by

$$x = a \cos \omega t.$$
$$y = b \sin \omega t.$$

Show that the path is an ellipse, and find the acceleration in terms of the distance from the origin; also determine the direction of the acceleration at any time t.   (I.C.)

14. A particle moving in a plane is subject to a force towards the x-axis and proportional to its distance from that axis. If, initially, it is projected from the origin with a velocity V in a direction making an angle α with the x-axis, prove that it will cross the x-axis again at this angle.

Find the time before this occurs and prove that the maximum displacement from the x-axis is proportional to $V \sin \alpha$.   (N.U.4)

15. A particle starting from the origin at time $t = 0$ moves in the parabola $y^2 = 2x$ with a velocity constant in magnitude and equal to unity. Prove that the time it takes to reach the point (x, y) is given by the equation

$$y = \sinh\,[2t - y\sqrt{1 + y^2}],$$

and determine the components of the acceleration as rational functions of the ordinate of its position.   (N.U.4)

16. Two particles of masses m and m', lying on a smooth table, are connected by an elastic string of natural length l and modulus of elasticity $\dfrac{mm'g}{(m + m')}$; they are initially at rest with the string unstretched. By using the principles of conservation of linear momentum and conservation of energy, or otherwise, show that, if m is projected directly away from m' with velocity U, the velocity (R) of m relative to m', when the string is stretched to a length $l + x$, is given by the equation

$$R^2 + \frac{gx^2}{l} = U^2.$$ (N.U.3)

§ 201. We have considered cases of motion in a straight line under a constant force and under a force tending to a fixed point in the straight line and proportional to the distance from that point (S.H.M.).

We shall now consider some cases of other laws of force, and also cases where there is a resistance to the motion, the resistance being some function of the velocity.

The method of working is the same in all cases, we equate $m\dfrac{dv}{dt}$, or $mv\dfrac{dv}{ds}$ to the resultant force acting on the particle and so obtain the equation of motion.

This equation must then be solved, and the main difficulty in problems of this nature is in the solution of the equation of motion.

For this reason we shall only deal with cases involving equations which are more easily solved.

§ **202.** *Motion of a Particle falling Vertically under Gravity in a Medium whose Resistance Varies as the Velocity.*

To simplify the working we will consider the mass m as unity. Let the resistance $= kv$, where k is a constant and v is the velocity. The equation of motion is

$$\frac{dv}{dt} = g - kv.$$

Now when v reaches the value L, where

$$kL = g,$$

the acceleration becomes zero, and the particle continues to descend with uniform velocity L. This velocity is called the *Limiting Velocity*, and it is convenient to use the value $\dfrac{g}{L}$ for k.

The equation of motion then becomes

$$\frac{dv}{dt} = g\left(1 - \frac{v}{L}\right) = \frac{g}{L}(L - v),$$

$$\therefore \frac{dv}{L - v} = \frac{g}{L}\,dt,$$

$$\therefore \log C - \log (L - v) = \frac{gt}{L}.$$

If $v = 0$ when $t = 0$,

$$\log C = \log L,$$

and

$$\log \frac{L}{L - v} = \frac{gt}{L},$$

$$\therefore \frac{L - v}{L} = e^{-\frac{gt}{L}},$$

$$\therefore v = L\left(1 - e^{-\frac{gt}{L}}\right).$$

Notice that $e^{-\frac{gt}{L}}$ gets smaller as t increases, but it only becomes negligible after an infinite time, i.e. v becomes equal to L after an infinite time.

20 *

Writing $\dfrac{ds}{dt}$ for v, we have

$$\frac{ds}{dt} = L\left(1 - e^{-\frac{gt}{L}}\right),$$

$$\therefore s = L\left(t + \frac{L}{g}e^{-\frac{gt}{L}}\right) + C \; ;$$

and if $s = 0$ when $t = 0$,

$$C = -\frac{L^2}{g},$$

$$\therefore s = L\left(t + \frac{L}{g}e^{-\frac{gt}{L}} - \frac{L}{g}\right).$$

§ **203.** *Motion of a Particle falling Vertically in a Medium whose Resistance Varies as the Square of the Velocity.*

If the resistance is kv^2, then, taking the mass as unity,

$$\frac{dv}{dt} = g - kv^2.$$

The limiting velocity L is now given by

$$kL^2 = g.$$

Hence, writing $\dfrac{g}{L^2}$ for k, the equation of motion becomes

$$\frac{dv}{dt} = g\left(1 - \frac{v^2}{L^2}\right) = \frac{g}{L^2}(L^2 - v^2),$$

$$\therefore \frac{dv}{L^2 - v^2} = \frac{g}{L^2}\,dt,$$

$$\therefore \frac{1}{2L}\left(\frac{1}{L + v} + \frac{1}{L - v}\right)dv = \frac{g}{L^2}\,dt,$$

$$\therefore \left(\frac{1}{L + v} + \frac{1}{L - v}\right)dv = \frac{2g}{L}\,dt,$$

$$\therefore \log C + \log (L + v) - \log (L - v) = \frac{2gt}{L} \; ;$$

and if $v = 0$ when $t = 0$, $\log C = 0$,

$$\therefore \log \frac{L + v}{L - v} = \frac{2gt}{L},$$

$$\therefore \frac{L + v}{L - v} = e^{\frac{2gt}{L}},$$

$$\therefore v\left(1 + e^{\frac{2gt}{L}}\right) = L\left(e^{\frac{2gt}{L}} - 1\right),$$

$$\therefore v = L\,\frac{e^{\frac{2gt}{L}} - 1}{1 + e^{\frac{2gt}{L}}}.$$

To find v in terms of s, we have

$$v \frac{dv}{ds} = g \frac{L^2 - v^2}{L^2},$$

$$\therefore \frac{v\,dv}{L^2 - v^2} = \frac{g}{L^2}\,ds,$$

$$\therefore \log C - \tfrac{1}{2} \log (L^2 - v^2) = \frac{gs}{L^2},$$

and if $v = 0$ when $s = 0$,

$$\log C = \tfrac{1}{2} \log L^2,$$

$$\therefore \log \frac{L^2}{L^2 - v^2} = \frac{2gs}{L^2},$$

$$\therefore \frac{L^2 - v^2}{L^2} = e^{-\frac{2gs}{L^2}},$$

$$\therefore v^2 = L^2 \left(1 - e^{-\frac{2gs}{L^2}} \right).$$

§ **204.** EXAMPLE (i).

A particle is moving in a straight line under the action of a force $m\omega^2 x$ towards a fixed point in the line, and subject to a resistance $2kv$ per unit mass, where m is the mass, x the distance from the fixed point, and $k < \omega$. Determine the motion.

The equation of motion is

$$m \frac{d^2x}{dt^2} = - m\omega^2 x - 2mk \frac{dx}{dt},$$

or

$$\frac{d^2x}{dt^2} + 2k \frac{dx}{dt} + \omega^2 x = 0.$$

The solution of this equation is

$$x = A e^{-kt} \sin (pt + B),$$

where $p^2 = \omega^2 - k^2$, and A, B are constants depending on the initial conditions.

It should be noticed that the period of oscillation $\left(\dfrac{2\pi}{p} \right)$ is still constant, but is longer than if there is no resistance.

EXAMPLE (ii).

A particle describes a distance x along a straight line in time t, where $t = ax^2 + bx$, and a, b are positive numbers. Show that the retardation is proportional to the cube of the velocity.

If the initial velocity is 2000 ft./sec., and is reduced to 1975 ft./sec. in 100 feet, show that the initial resistance is about 15·8 times the weight of the particle.

Since $\qquad ax^2 + bx = t,$

differentiating with respect to t,

$$2a\,\frac{dx}{dt} + b\,\frac{dx}{dt} = 1,$$

$$\therefore \frac{dx}{dt} = \frac{1}{b + 2ax}, \text{ giving the velocity } v \qquad . \qquad . \quad \text{(i)}$$

$$\therefore \frac{d^2x}{dt^2} = -\frac{2a}{(b + 2ax)^2} \cdot \frac{dx}{dt},$$

$$= -\frac{2a}{(b + 2ax)^3} = -2av^3 \qquad . \qquad . \qquad . \quad \text{(ii)}$$

$\therefore$ the retardation varies as the cube of the velocity.

If $v = 2000$ when $x = 0$,

$$b = \frac{1}{2000}, \text{ from (i)},$$

and if $v = 1975$ when $x = 100$,

$$b + 200a = \frac{1}{1975},$$

$$\therefore 200a = \frac{1}{1975} - \frac{1}{2000} = \frac{25}{1975 \cdot 2000}.$$

$$\therefore a = \frac{1}{1975 \cdot 2000 \cdot 8}.$$

Hence, from the value of the acceleration in (ii), when $x = 0$,

$$\frac{d^2x}{dt^2} = -2av^3 = -\frac{2 \cdot 2000^3}{1975 \cdot 2000 \cdot 8} = -\frac{10^6}{1975} \text{ ft./sec.}^2$$

Hence the initial retarding force is $m\,\dfrac{10^6}{1975}$,

or $\qquad \dfrac{10^6}{1975 \cdot 32} = 15\cdot8$ of the weight of the particle.

EXAMPLE (iii).

A particle is released from rest at a distance a from a centre of force whose attraction is $\dfrac{\mu m}{x^2}$, where m is the mass of the particle, μ a constant, and x the distance of the particle from the centre. Find the time taken to reach the centre.

The equation of motion is

$$m\,\frac{v\,dv}{dx} = -\frac{\mu m}{x^2},$$

$$\therefore \tfrac{1}{2}v^2 = \frac{\mu}{x} + C,$$

and $v = 0$ when $x = a$, $\qquad C - = \dfrac{\mu}{a}$,

$$\therefore v^2 = 2\mu\left(\frac{1}{x} - \frac{1}{a}\right),$$

$$\therefore \frac{dx}{dt} = \pm\sqrt{2\mu}\,\sqrt{\frac{a - x}{ax}} = \pm\sqrt{\frac{2\mu}{a}}\,\sqrt{\frac{a - x}{x}}.$$

Since $\dfrac{dx}{dt}$ is initially negative we take the negative sign.

The equation is then written

$$dt = - \sqrt{\frac{a}{2\mu}} \sqrt{\frac{x}{a-x}} dx.$$

Putting $x = a \cos^2 \theta$, $dx = -2a \cos \theta \sin \theta \, d\theta$,

and the equation becomes

$$dt = \sqrt{\frac{a^3}{2\mu}} \cdot 2 \cos^2 \theta \, d\theta,$$

$$\therefore t = \sqrt{\frac{a^3}{2\mu}}(\theta + \tfrac{1}{2} \sin 2\theta) \, ;$$

no constant is needed since $x = a$ and $\theta = 0$, when $t = 0$.

When $x = 0$, $\theta = \dfrac{\pi}{2}$, and

$$t = \frac{\pi}{2} \sqrt{\frac{a^3}{2\mu}}.$$

EXAMPLE (iv).

A particle falls from rest at a point A whose altitude above the surface of the earth is equal to the radius. Show that the velocity on arriving at the surface is equal to that acquired by a particle falling from rest through half that distance under a constant force g, where g is the acceleration at the earth's surface.

Let $\dfrac{\mu m}{x^2}$ be the attraction of the earth on a mass m at distance x from the centre of the earth,

Then if the radius of the earth $= a$,

$$\frac{\mu m}{a^2} = mg,$$

$$\therefore \mu = a^2 g.$$

The equation of motion is

$$m \frac{v \, dv}{dx} = - \frac{\mu m}{x^2},$$

$$\therefore \tfrac{1}{2} v^2 = \frac{\mu}{x} + C,$$

and $v = 0$ when $x = 2a$,

$$\therefore C = - \frac{\mu}{2a},$$

$$\therefore \tfrac{1}{2} v^2 = \frac{a^2 g}{x} - \frac{a^2 g}{2a},$$

$$\therefore v^2 = a^2 g \left(\frac{2}{x} - \frac{1}{a} \right).$$

Hence, when $x = a$,

$$v^2 = a^2 g \left(\frac{2}{a} - \frac{1}{a} \right) = ag,$$

and this is the same as the velocity acquired by falling a distance $\dfrac{a}{2}$ with constant acceleration g.

Note.—The expression " a constant force g " used in the question is understood to mean the force which would produce this acceleration. It is the value of the force for unit mass.

EXAMPLES XXXIX.

1. A particle moving in a straight line describes a distance x in time t given by the equation

$$t = ax^2 + bx ;$$

where a and b are constants. Find the velocity v as a function of x, and prove that the retardation of the particle is $2av^3$.

Determine a and b from the following observations ; and find the value of v at the second observation.

x in feet	0	150	300	
t in seconds	0	6	15	(C.S.)

2. A point moves in a straight line so that its distance x feet from an origin in this line is given by

$$x = 2t^3 - 3t^2 - 12t + 18,$$

where t is the time in seconds.

Find the times at which the point is at the origin. Also find the times at which the point is at rest, and its distance from the origin then, and also its acceleration at this time. Give the units throughout. (I.C.)

3. A particle has acceleration at time t seconds given by $\ddot{x} = 2t - 1$. At $t = 4$ seconds the speed is 6 ft./sec., and the displacement at $t = 0$ is 5 feet. Find the displacement at time t. When will the particle be at rest, and what will be the displacement then ? (I.C.)

4. A particle starts from rest at a distance a from a centre of attracting force varying as the direct distance and subject to a resistance per unit mass equal to k times the velocity. Prove that before coming finally to rest at the centre it travels a distance

$$a \coth (\tfrac{1}{8} kT),$$

where T is the period of the damped oscillation. (C.S.)

5. A particle is projected in a medium whose resistance is proportional to the cube of the velocity and no other forces act on the particle ; while the velocity diminishes from v_1 to v_2 the particle traverses a distance d in time t. Show that

$$\frac{d}{t} = \frac{2v_1v_2}{v_1 + v_2}.$$

6. A particle is projected in a medium in which the resistance varies as the cube of the velocity, and the effect of other forces may be neglected ; the time T is observed which the particle takes to travel from P to Q, prove that the velocity at the middle point of PQ is $\dfrac{D}{T}$ where D is the length of PQ.

7. If a particle moves in a straight line towards a centre of force which attracts according to the inverse square of the distance, starting from rest at a distance $2a$ from the centre, show that the time of motion from the distance $2a$ to the distance a is to the time from the distance a to the centre in the ratio $\pi + 2 : \pi - 2$.

8. A smooth circular wire of radius a is fixed in a horizontal position. A small ring, attached to a point of the wire by an elastic string of natural length a, is placed at the point of the wire opposite to the point of attachment and slightly disturbed. Show that the horizontal component of the pressure of the wire on the ring will be outwards until the extension of the string is $\frac{2}{3}a$, and will afterwards be inwards.

9. Form the equation of motion of a particle moving in a straight line against a resistance varying as the cube of the velocity ; and show that the distance described in any time is the same as if the particle moved uniformly with its velocity at the mid-point of that distance. The particle passes three points at distances d_1, d_2 apart at equal intervals of time ; show that its velocities at these points are inversely in the ratios

$$d_3{}^x - 2d_1{}^2 : d_1{}^2 + d_2{}^2 : d_3{}^2 - 2d_2{}^2,$$

where $d_3 \equiv d_1 + d_2$.   (H.C.)

10. The action of a large mass fixed at the origin of co-ordinates on a small particle of mass m free to move along the axis OX is of a twofold character. There is an attractive force whose amount is λm times the distance of m from the origin and a repulsive force varying inversely as the square of the same distance and equal to μm when the distance is unity. Find the position of equilibrium of the particle. Prove that it is a position of stable equilibrium, and that when the particle executes small oscillations about this position it does so in the period in which it would oscillate about the origin if the attractive force were three times its strength and the repulsive force did not exist.   (N.U.4)

11. A particle of mass m is projected in a resisting medium in a direction making an angle α with the horizontal, the horizontal component of its velocity being v. If the resistance is mk times the velocity, where k is small, prove that the equation of the path can be written in the approximate form

$$y = x \tan \alpha - \tfrac{1}{2}\frac{gx^2}{v^2}\left(1 + \frac{2kx}{3v}\right),$$

when squares and higher powers of k are neglected.   (N.U.4)

§ 205. The Hodograph.

Let a point move on any curve and let P (Fig. 130) be its position at time t. From any point O draw a straight line OH to represent in direction and magnitude the velocity of the point, v, at P.

Then OH is parallel to the tangent to the path at P, and its length is kv, where k is a constant depending on the scale on which OH represents v.

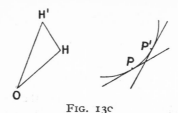

FIG. 13c

If this is done for successive positions of P, then, as P travels along its path, H describes another curve which is called *the hodograph* of the first curve, i.e. of the path of P.

If P' represent the position of the point at time $t + dt$, and H' be the corresponding point on the hodograph, then, since OH' represents the velocity at P', the third side HH' of the triangle OHH' represents the change in velocity during the time dt.

Hence $\dfrac{HH'}{dt}$ represents the rate of change of velocity during this time, and when dt is very small this is the acceleration of the point at P. But when dt is very small HH' becomes the arc of the hodograph and $\dfrac{HH'}{dt}$ represents the velocity of H.

Hence the velocity of H in the hodograph represents, in magnitude and direction, the acceleration of P.

§ **206.** If the speed of the point P is constant the hodograph is a circle with O as centre, and in this case the tangent to the hodograph at H is perpendicular to OH, i.e. it is perpendicular to the tangent to the path of P.

Hence the acceleration of P is along the normal to its path.

Also, if ds' is the length of an element of arc of the hodograph,

$$\text{the acceleration of P} = \frac{ds'}{dt}.$$

But
$$\frac{ds'}{dt} = \frac{ds'}{d\theta} \cdot \frac{d\theta}{dt} = \text{OH} \frac{d\theta}{dt} = v \frac{d\theta}{dt},$$

where $d\theta$ is the angle between two consecutive normals to the path of P; hence, if ds is the element of arc of the path,

$$\frac{d\theta}{dt} = \frac{d\theta}{ds} \cdot \frac{ds}{dt},$$

and $\dfrac{ds}{dt} = v$, $\dfrac{d\theta}{ds} = \dfrac{1}{\rho}$, where ρ is the radius of curvature of the path at P.

Hence the acceleration of P is $\dfrac{v^2}{\rho}$ along the normal to the path at P.

§ 207. If $\dfrac{dx}{dt}$, $\dfrac{dy}{dt}$ are the component velocities of a moving point P, the co-ordinates x', y' of the corresponding point H of the hodograph are

$$x' = k\frac{dx}{dt}, \; y' = k\frac{dy}{dt},$$

where k is an arbitrary constant.

If we know the values of $\dfrac{dx}{dt}$ and $\dfrac{dy}{dt}$ in terms of t, then, by eliminating t we obtain a relation between x' and y' which is the equation of the hodograph.

EXAMPLES XL.

1. What is meant by the hodograph of a moving point ? A truck moves with the·uniform speed of 12 m.p.h. along a horizontal circular track of mean radius 128 feet. Draw the hodograph of its motion over the quadrant beginning due east, and ending due north of the centre.

   Assuming that the track is of 2 feet gauge, find the elevation of the outer rail above the inner in order that lateral thrust on the rails may be avoided. (H.S.D.)

2. A flywheel of radius 4 feet rotates in a vertical plane so that its rim has the uniform linear speed of 8 ft./sec. A small weight is placed on the rim at its highest point ; show that, if there is no slipping, it travels with the wheel through $\frac{1}{6}$ of a revolution, and then leaves the wheel and moves freely under gravity. Draw the hodograph of the motion of the weight and insert the vector line which represents its velocity when it reaches the level of the centre of the wheel.

3. Prove that the hodograph of the path of a projectile is a vertical straight line.

4. Find the hodograph of (i) a uniform circular motion ; (ii) the parabolic motion of a projectile moving under gravity ; (iii) the motion of a point whose rectangular co-ordinates at time t are given by

   $$x = \tfrac{1}{3}t^3, \; y = \tfrac{1}{2}t^2. \qquad \text{(C.W.B.)}$$

5. Find the hodograph of the motion of a point whose rectangular co-ordinates at time t are given by

   $$x = \tfrac{1}{4}t^2 + t, \; y = t^3.$$

6. A line turns round a fixed end O with uniform angular velocity ω, and a point P moves along the line with uniform velocity v away from O. Find the magnitude and direction of the velocity of P when it is at a distance r from O, and prove that the hodograph of its motion is a spiral curve, i.e. a curve in which the polar radius continually increases with the vectorial angle. (C.W.B.)

CHAPTER VIII.

MOTION OF A RIGID BODY ABOUT A FIXED AXIS.

§ 208. A *rigid body* is one whose shape and size are invariable, so that the distance between any two points of it is always the same.

Such a body is said to be moving in two dimensions when all points in the body move in parallel planes, e.g. a cube swinging about one of its edges, or sliding on a horizontal plane with the same face always in contact with the plane.

We shall consider first the case where some line in the body is fixed and the body rotates about this line as axis.

§ 209. Kinetic Energy of a Body Rotating about a Fixed Axis.

Let the Fig. (131) represent a section of the body which is rotating about an axis through O perpendicular to the plane of the paper with angular velocity ω.

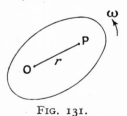

FIG. 131.

Consider a particle of the body of mass m at P, where $OP = r$. The velocity of P is $r\omega$, and the kinetic energy of the particle m is therefore $\frac{1}{2}mr^2\omega^2$.

The kinetic energy of the whole body is the sum of the kinetic energies of all its particles, i.e. $\Sigma\frac{1}{2}mr^2\omega^2$, the Σ denoting summation for the whole of the body, both in the plane shown in the figure and for parallel planes, the value of r for each particle being its perpendicular distance from the axis of rotation.

Now ω is the same for all the particles,

$$\therefore \Sigma\frac{1}{2}mr^2\omega^2 = \frac{1}{2}\omega^2\Sigma mr^2.$$

The quantity Σmr^2 is of great importance, and occurs in all problems involving the rotation of a rigid body. It is called the *Moment of Inertia* of the body about the axis from which r is measured and is usually denoted by I or K.

The moment of inertia of a body about any axis is thus obtained by multiplying the mass of each particle of the body by the square of its distance from that axis, and adding the results for all the particles of the body.

If the body consists of a finite number of particles, the value of Σmr^2 is obtained by ordinary addition. In the case of a rigid body, where the number of particles is infinitely great, the summation is effected by integration.

If a body is rotating with angular velocity ω about a fixed axis, and its moment of inertia about that axis is I, the kinetic energy of the body is

$$\tfrac{1}{2}I\omega^2.$$

This expression corresponds to the $\tfrac{1}{2}mv^2$ for a particle, the moment of inertia I taking the place of the mass m, and the angular velocity ω replacing the linear velocity v.

§ **210.** If the whole mass M of a body be supposed concentrated at a point distant k from the axis such that Mk^2 has the same value as the moment of inertia about that axis, i.e. $Mk^2 = \Sigma mr^2$, the length k is called the *Radius of Gyration* about the axis.

The form Mk^2 is the one in which moments of inertia are usually expressed. For a given body, M is the same for all axes, but the value of k differs for different axes. If M is in pounds and k in feet the moment of inertia is said to be in pound-foot squared or lb./ft.² units.

§ **211. Moment of Inertia of a Thin Uniform Rod about an Axis through its Centre Perpendicular to its Length.**

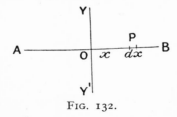

FIG. 132.

Let AB (Fig. 132) be the rod, $2a$ its length, O its middle point, and m the mass per unit length.

The mass of an element of length dx at P is mdx, and if $OP = x$, the moment of inertia of the element about YY' in mx^2dx.

To obtain the moment of inertia of the whole rod we have to

sum this expression by integration for the whole length of the rod,
i.e. we have to evaluate the integral

$$\int_{-a}^{+a} mx^2 dx.$$

Now, m is constant, and $\int x^2 dx = \tfrac{1}{3}x^3$,

$$\therefore \int_{-a}^{+a} mx^2 dx = m\left[\frac{x^3}{3}\right]_{-a}^{a} = \tfrac{2}{3}ma^3.$$

Also, if M is the mass of the rod, $M = 2am$,

$$\therefore \text{ the moment of inertia} = M\frac{a^2}{3}.$$

If the axis is perpendicular to the rod through one end, the
expression $mx^2 dx$ has to be integrated from o to $2a$,

and
$$\int_{0}^{2a} mx^2 dx = m\left[\frac{x^3}{3}\right]_{0}^{2a} = m\frac{8a^3}{3} = M\frac{4a^2}{3}.$$

This is the moment of inertia about a perpendicular axis through
one end.

§ 212. Moment of Inertia of a Rectangular Lamina about an axis through its centre parallel to one of the sides.

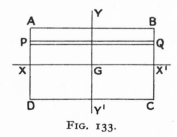

FIG. 133.

Let ABCD (Fig. 133) be the rectangle, AB = $2a$, BC = $2b$, and
G the centre.

To obtain the moment of inertia about YY', parallel to BC,
we divide the rectangle into elementary strips, as PQ, perpendicular
to YY'. From the last paragraph, the moment of inertia of each
strip is equal to its mass multiplied by $\frac{a^2}{3}$.

Hence the moment of inertia of the rectangle, which is the same as the sum of the moments of the strips, is

$$M \frac{a^2}{3},$$

where M is the mass of the whole rectangle.

Similarly the moment of inertia about XX', parallel to AB, is

$$M \frac{b^2}{3}.$$

§ 213. **Moment of Inertia of a Thin Uniform Rod about an axis through its centre inclined at an angle θ to the rod.**

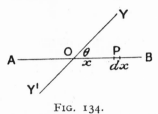

FIG. 134.

Let AB (Fig. 134) be the rod of length $2a$, O its middle point, and YOY' the axis. If m is the mass per unit length, the mass of an element dx at P is mdx, and if OP $= x$, the distance from the axis YOY' is $x \sin \theta$.

Hence the moment of inertia of the element about YOY' is

$$mx^2 \sin^2 \theta \, dx,$$

The moment of inertia of the whole rod is

$$m \sin^2 \theta \int_{-a}^{+a} x^2 dx = m \sin^2 \theta \cdot \frac{2a^3}{3},$$

$$= M \frac{a^2}{3} \sin^2 \theta,$$

where M is the mass of the rod.

§ 214. **Moment of Inertia of a Parallelogram about an axis through its centre parallel to one of the sides.**

Let ABCD (Fig. 135) be the parallelogram, AB $= 2a$, BC $= 2b$, G the centre, and let $\angle$ ADC $= \theta$.

If we divide the parallelogram into elementary strips (as PQ) parallel to AB, the moment of inertia of each strip about YY' is equal to its mass multiplied by $\frac{a^2}{3} \sin^2 \theta$.

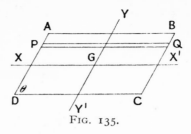

FIG. 135.

Hence the moment of inertia of the parallelogram, which is equal to the sum of the moments of the strips, is

$$M \frac{a^2}{3} \sin^2 \theta.$$

Similarly the moment of inertia about XX' is

$$M \frac{b^2}{3} \sin^2 \theta.$$

§ 215. Moment of Inertia of a Circular Ring about an axis through its centre perpendicular to the plane of the ring.

Let the radius of the ring be a, then each particle of the ring is at the same distance a from the axis,

hence
$$\Sigma m r^2 = \Sigma m a^2 = a^2 \Sigma m$$
$$= M a^2,$$

where M is the mass of the ring.

§ 216. Moment of Inertia of a Circular Disc about an axis through its centre perpendicular to the plane of the disc.

FIG. 136.

Let O (Fig. 136) be the centre of the disc, a its radius, and m the mass per unit area.

Divide the disc into concentric rings of breadth dx.

The mass of a ring of radius x is $2\pi m x dx$, and its moment of inertia is $2\pi m x^3 dx$.

The moment of inertia of the whole disc is obtained by integrating this expression between the limits 0 and a.

Now $$\int_0^a 2\pi m x^3\, dx = 2\pi m \left[\frac{x^4}{4}\right]_0^a = \frac{2\pi m a^4}{4} = \frac{\pi m a^4}{2},$$

and if M is the mass of the disc,

$$\pi m a^2 = M\ ;$$

$$\therefore \text{ the moment of inertia} = M\,\frac{a^2}{2}.$$

The moment of inertia of a circular cylinder about its axis is of the same form, i.e. if M is the mass of the cylinder and a its radius, the moment of inertia is $M\,\dfrac{a^2}{2}$. For if we divide the cylinder into slices perpendicular to the axis, the moment of inertia of each slice is equal to its mass multiplied by $\dfrac{a^2}{2}$. The moment of inertia of the whole cylinder, which is equal to the sum of the moments of the slices, is therefore equal to the total mass multiplied by $\dfrac{a^2}{2}$.

§ 217. Moment of Inertia of a Solid Sphere about a diameter.

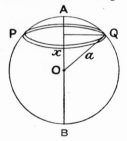

FIG. 137.

Let O (Fig. 137) be the centre of the sphere, a its radius, m the mass per unit volume, and AB any diameter.

Divide the sphere into circular slices of thickness dx perpendicular to AB.

For a slice PQ, distant x from O, the volume is $\pi(a^2 - x^2)dx$, and the moment of inertia about AB is

$$\pi m \frac{(a^2 - x^2)^2}{2} dx.$$

The moment of inertia of the whole sphere is the integral of this between the limits $- a$ and $+ a$, but, as the value of the integral is evidently the same for the upper and lower halves of the sphere, this is the same as twice the integral from o to a.

$$2\frac{\pi m}{2}\int_0^a (a^2 - x^2)^2 dx = \pi m \int_0^a (a^4 - 2a^2x^2 + x^4)dx$$

$$= \pi m \left[a^4x - \tfrac{2}{3}a^2x^3 + \tfrac{1}{5}x^5 \right]_0^a$$

$$= \pi m \tfrac{8}{15}a^5.$$

Now if M is the mass of the sphere,

$$M = \tfrac{4}{3}\pi a^3 m,$$

∴ the moment of inertia $= M\tfrac{2}{5}a^2$.

§ 218. We shall now prove two theorems which are very useful for calculating the moments of inertia of a body about other axes when we know the moments of inertia about certain standard axes. In this way a large amount of integration is avoided.

§ 219. Theorem of Parallel Axes.

If the moment of inertia of a body, of mass M, about an axis through its centre of mass is I, the moment of inertia about a parallel axis at a distance a from the first axis is $I + Ma^2$.

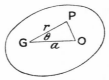

FIG. 138.

Let the Fig. (138) represent a section of the body through its centre of mass G, and let the moment of inertia about an axis through G perpendicular to the plane of the paper be I. We require the moment of inertia about a parallel axis through O where $GO = a$.

Let P be any particle of the body of mass m, $GP = r$, and $\angle OGP = \theta$.

The moment of inertia about the axis through O is

$$\Sigma m \,.\, OP^2 = \Sigma m(r^2 + a^2 - 2ar \cos \theta),$$
$$= \Sigma mr^2 + \Sigma ma^2 - 2a\Sigma mr \cos \theta.$$

Now $\Sigma mr^2 = I$, $\Sigma ma^2 = Ma^2$, and $\Sigma mr \cos \theta = 0$.

The last result follows from the formula for finding the centre of mass of a body. The distance of the centre of mass from a plane through G perpendicular to GO is $\dfrac{\Sigma mr \cos \theta}{\Sigma m}$, and, as G is the centre of mass, this must be zero, so that $\Sigma mr \cos \theta = 0$.

Hence the moment of inertia about the parallel axis through O is

$$I + Ma^2.$$

For example, the moment of inertia of a thin rod, of length $2a$, about a perpendicular axis through its centre is $M \dfrac{a^2}{3}$.

Hence the moment of inertia about a perpendicular axis through one end is

$$M \frac{a^2}{3} + Ma^2 = M \frac{4a^2}{3}.$$

This is the result arrived at by integration in paragraph 211.

§ **220.** *If the moments of inertia of a lamina about two perpendicular axes in its plane which meet at O are A and B, the moment of inertia about an axis through O perpendicular to the plane of the lamina is $A + B$.*

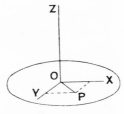

FIG. 139.

Let OX, OY (Fig. 139) be the two perpendicular axes in the plane of the lamina, and OZ an axis perpendicular to the lamina.

If m is the mass of a particle of the lamina at P, where $OP = r$, the moment of inertia about OZ is Σmr^2.

But, if x, y are the co-ordinates of P referred to OX, OY as axes,

$$r^2 = x^2 + y^2,$$
$$\therefore \ \Sigma mr^2 = \Sigma mx^2 + \Sigma my^2.$$

Now Σmx^2 is the moment of inertia about OY ($= B$), and Σmy^2 is the moment of inertia about OX ($= A$), therefore the moment of inertia about OZ $= A + B$.

§ **221.** In § **212** we proved that the moments of inertia of a rectangular lamina of sides $2a$, $2b$ about the axes through its centre parallel to the sides $2b$, $2a$ are $M \dfrac{a^2}{3}$ and $M \dfrac{b^2}{3}$ respectively.

From the theorem of the last paragraph the moment of inertia about an axis through the centre of the rectangle perpendicular to its plane is

$$M \frac{a^2}{3} + M \frac{b^2}{3} = M \frac{a^2 + b^2}{3}.$$

From the theorem of parallel axes the moment of inertia about one of the sides of length $2a$ is

$$M \frac{b^2}{3} + Mb^2 = M \frac{4}{3}b^2.$$

In § **216** we proved that the moment of inertia of a circular disc about an axis through its centre perpendicular to its plane is $M \frac{a^2}{2}$. Now by the theorem of the last paragraph this is equal to the sum of the moments of inertia about two perpendicular diameters. But the moment of inertia is the same about all diameters, hence the moment of inertia about a diameter is half that about the perpendicular axis through the centre,

$$\therefore \text{ the moment of inertia about a diameter} = M \frac{a^2}{4}.$$

From the theorem of parallel axes we see that the moment of inertia about a tangent line is

$$M \frac{a^2}{4} + Ma^2 = M \frac{5a^2}{4}.$$

§ **222. Products of Inertia.**

If we take two axes OX, OY in the plane of a lamina, and multiply the mass of every particle of the lamina by the product of its two co-ordinates x and y, then Σmxy is called the *product of inertia* with respect to these two axes.

If the product of inertia about the two axes OX, OY is zero, the axes are called *Principal Axes* of the lamina at O.

It is evident that the product of inertia will vanish if either axis is an axis of symmetry of the lamina ; for, if it is symmetrical about OX, say, then corresponding to any terms $m_1x_1y_1$ in Σmxy there will be another term $m_1x_1(-y_1)$, and these will cancel on summation.

§ **223.** *To find the relation between the moments and products of inertia of a lamina about different pairs of rectangular axes in its plane drawn through the same point.*

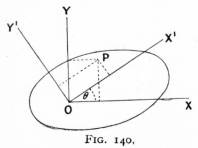

FIG. 140.

Let A, B be the moments of inertia about the rectangular axes OX, OY (Fig. 140), and F the product of inertia about these axes.

$$A = \Sigma my^2, \; B = \Sigma mx^2, \; F = \Sigma mxy.$$

If x', y' are the co-ordinates of a point P referred to new rectangular axes OX', OY', where XOX' $= \theta$, then

$$x' = x \cos \theta + y \sin \theta,$$
$$y' = y \cos \theta - x \sin \theta.$$

Hence the moment of inertia about OX' is

$$\begin{aligned}
\Sigma my'^2 &= \Sigma m (y \cos \theta - x \sin \theta)^2, \\
&= \cos^2 \theta \, \Sigma my^2 + \sin^2 \theta \, \Sigma mx^2 - 2 \sin \theta \cos \theta \, \Sigma mxy, \\
&= A \cos^2 \theta + B \sin^2 \theta - 2F \sin \theta \cos \theta \qquad . \qquad . \quad \text{(i)}
\end{aligned}$$

The moment of inertia about OY' is

$$\begin{aligned}
\Sigma mx'^2 &= \Sigma m (x \cos \theta + y \sin \theta)^2, \\
&= \cos^2 \theta \, \Sigma mx^2 + \sin^2 \theta \, \Sigma my^2 + 2 \sin \theta \cos \theta \, \Sigma mxy, \\
&= A \sin^2 \theta + B \sin^2 \theta + 2F \sin \theta \cos \theta \quad . \qquad . \quad \text{(ii)}
\end{aligned}$$

The product of inertia about OX', OY' is

$$\begin{aligned}
\Sigma mx'y' &= \Sigma m (x \cos \theta + y \sin \theta)(y \cos \theta - x \sin \theta), \\
&= \Sigma m [y^2 \sin \theta \cos \theta - x^2 \sin \theta \cos \theta + xy(\cos^2 \theta - \sin^2 \theta)], \\
&= (A - B) \sin \theta \cos \theta + F \cos 2\theta \qquad . \qquad . \quad \text{(iii)}
\end{aligned}$$

If OX, OY are principal axes, $F = 0$, and these values become

$$A \cos^2 \theta + B \sin^2 \theta,$$
$$A \sin^2 \theta + B \cos^2 \theta,$$
$$(A - B) \sin \theta \cos \theta.$$

EXAMPLE.

Find the moment of inertia of a square of side 2a about a diagonal, and its product of inertia about the two diagonals.

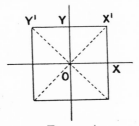

FIG. 141.

The moments of inertia about the axes through the centre O (Fig. 141) parallel to the sides are each equal to $\dfrac{Ma^2}{3}$.

Hence $$A = B = M \frac{a^2}{3}.$$

The angle between the two axes of x is $45°$, so that $\theta = 45°$.
The moment of inertia about the new axis of x is

$$A \cos^2 \theta + B \sin^2 \theta = M\frac{a^2}{3}(\tfrac{1}{2} + \tfrac{1}{2}) = M\frac{a^2}{3}.$$

It is obvious that the moment of inertia is the same about each diagonal.

Since $A = B$, the product of inertia about the diagonals, which is equal to $(A - B) \sin \theta \cos \theta$, is zero.

§ 224. Moment of Inertia of a Rectangular Prism about an axis through its centre perpendicular to a pair of faces.

Let the length of the sides be $2a$, $2b$, $2c$, and the axes Ox, Oy, Oz perpendicular to the faces as shown in Fig. 142, O being the centre of the prism.

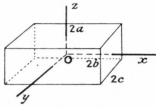

FIG. 142.

To find the moment of inertia about Ox we divide the prism into slices perpendicular to this axis. The edges of each of these rectangular slices are $2b$ and $2c$, and the moment of inertia of each slice about Ox is the product of its mass and $\dfrac{b^2 + c^2}{3}$.

Hence the moment of inertia of the whole prism is

$$M \frac{b^2 + c^2}{3}.$$

Similarly for the axis Oy perpendicular to the faces whose edges are $2a$ and $2b$, the moment of inertia is

$$M \frac{a^2 + b^2}{3}.$$

If the prism is a cube of edge $2a$, then $b = c = a$, and the moment of inertia about any of the three axes through the centre perpendicular to a pair of faces is

$$M \frac{2a^2}{3}.$$

EXAMPLES XLI.

1. Find the moment of inertia of a circular ring of mass M and radius a, about an axis through a point of the ring perpendicular to its plane.

2. Prove that the moment of inertia of a uniform rod of length $2a$ about an axis intersecting the rod at right angles at a distance b from its centre is $M\left(\frac{1}{3}a^2 + b^2\right)$, where M is the mass of the rod. (H.C.)

3. Show that the moment of inertia of a cube, of mass M and edge $2a$, about one of its edges is $\frac{8}{3}Ma^2$.

4. Find the moment of inertia of a square lamina, of mass M and side $2a$, about an axis through one corner perpendicular to the plane of the lamina.

5. Find the moment of inertia of a rectangular lamina, of mass M and sides $2a$, $2b$, about an axis through one corner perpendicular to the plane of the lamina.

6. Find the moment of inertia of a circular ring, of mass M and radius a about a diameter.

7. Prove that the radii of gyration of (i) a circular disc of radius a, (ii) a circular ring of radius a, about a tangent line are respectively $\dfrac{\sqrt{5}}{2}a$ and $\dfrac{\sqrt{6}}{2}a$.

8. Show that the moment of inertia of a square lamina, of mass M and side $2a$, about any line through its centre in the plane of the lamina is $M\dfrac{a^2}{3}$.

9. Show that the moment of inertia of a rectangular lamina, of mass M and sides $2a$ and $2b$, about a diagonal is

$$M\frac{2a^2b^2}{3(a^2 + b^2)}.$$

10. Prove that the moment of inertia of a solid cone about its axis is $\frac{3}{10}Ma^2$, where M is the mass of the cone and a the radius of the base.

11. In a uniform circular plate, of 5 feet diameter, is punched a hole of 1 foot diameter, the centre of the hole being 18 inches from the centre of the plate. Find the moment of inertia of the plate (i) about the diameter which passes through the centre of the hole, (ii) about the diameter which is perpendicular to this. (I.E.)

§ 225. Moment of Inertia of a Thin Hollow Sphere about a diameter.

Let a be the radius of the sphere, m the mass per unit area of surface, and O its centre (Fig. 143).

To find the moment of inertia about a diameter AB we divide the surface into elementary circular bands, such as PQ, perpendicular to AB.

[Care must be taken not to assume that the width of the band is the same as its thickness measured in the direction OA.]

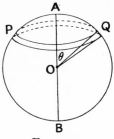

If the angle QOA $= \theta$, the band subtends an angle $d\theta$ at O and its breadth is $ad\theta$.

The radius of the band is $a \sin \theta$, so that its mass is $2\pi ma^2 \sin \theta d\theta$, and its moment of inertia about AB is

$$2\pi ma^2 \sin \theta . d\theta . a^2 \sin^2 \theta,$$
$$= 2\pi ma^4 \sin^3 \theta . d\theta.$$

The moments of inertia of the lower and upper halves of the surface are obviously equal. Hence to obtain the moment of inertia of the whole surface we integrate the above expression from o to $\frac{\pi}{2}$ and double the result.

Now $\displaystyle\int_0^{\frac{\pi}{2}} \sin^3 \theta d\theta = \int_0^{\frac{\pi}{2}} - \sin^2 \theta d(\cos \theta) = \int_0^{\frac{\pi}{2}} (\cos^2 \theta - 1)d(\cos \theta),$

$$= [\tfrac{1}{3} \cos^3 \theta - \cos \theta]_0^{\frac{\pi}{2}} = -\tfrac{1}{3} + 1 = \tfrac{2}{3}.$$

$$\therefore 2 \int_0^{\frac{\pi}{2}} 2\pi ma^4 \sin^3 \theta d\theta = \frac{8}{3}\pi ma^4.$$

But if M is the mass of the sphere, $M = 4\pi ma^2$,

$$\therefore \text{ the moment of inertia} = M\tfrac{2}{3}a^2.$$

§ 226. Moment of Inertia of a Solid Circular Cylinder about a diameter of an end face.

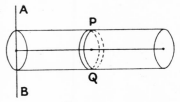

FIG. 144.

Let AB (Fig. 144) be a diameter of an end face, a the radius and l the length of the cylinder, m the mass per unit volume.

Divide the cylinder into circular slices, as PQ, of thickness dx perpendicular to the axis.

The mass of a slice is $\pi ma^2 dx$, and its moment of inertia about *its own diameter* parallel to AB is

$$\pi ma^2 dx \frac{a^2}{4}, \text{ or } \frac{\pi ma^4}{4} dx.$$

If the distance of the slice from AB is x, the moment of inertia about AB (by the Theorem of Parallel Axes) is

$$\frac{\pi ma^4}{4} dx + \pi ma^2 x^2 dx.$$

Hence the moment of inertia of the whole cylinder about AB is obtained by integrating this expression from $x = 0$ to $x = l$.

Now, $$\int_0^l \frac{\pi ma^4}{4} dx + \int_0^l \pi ma^2 x^2 dx,$$

$$= \frac{\pi ma^4 l}{4} + \tfrac{1}{3}\pi ma^2 l^3.$$

The volume of the cylinder is $\pi a^2 l$, and if its mass is M,

$$M = \pi ma^2 l.$$

Hence the moment of inertia about AB is

$$M\frac{a^2}{4} + M\frac{l^2}{3} = M\left(\frac{a^2}{4} + \frac{l^2}{3}\right).$$

The moment of inertia about an axis through the centre of gravity perpendicular to the axis of the cylinder, i.e. parallel to AB is

$$M\left(\frac{a^2}{4} + \frac{l^2}{3}\right) - M\frac{l^2}{4} = M\left(\frac{a^2}{4} + \frac{l^2}{12}\right).$$

EXAMPLES XLII.

1. Show that the moment of inertia of a hollow sphere, whose external and internal radii are a and b, about a diameter is

$$\frac{2M}{5} \cdot \frac{a^5 - b^5}{a^3 - b^3},$$

where M is the mass of the sphere.

2. A solid flywheel of 18 inches diameter and 4 inches thick is keyed on to the end of a shaft of 4 inches diameter whose whole length is 2 feet 4 inches.

Find the moment of inertia of the wheel and shaft about a diameter of the outer face of the flywheel.

3. Show that the moment of inertia of a hollow circular cylinder, whose length is h, and external and internal radii R and r, about an axis through its centre at right angles to its length, is

$$M \frac{R^2 + r^2 + \dfrac{h^2}{3}}{4}. \qquad \text{(Q.E.)}$$

4. Show that the moment of inertia of a paraboloid of revolution about its axis is $\dfrac{M}{3} \times$ the square of the radius of its base.

5. Three rectangular areas, 2 feet by 2 inches, 3 feet by 2 inches, and 1 foot by $1\frac{1}{2}$ inches, are fitted together to form a T figure, the longest and shortest areas forming the cross-pieces. Find the moment of inertia of the figure about the outer edge of the shortest area.   (I.E.)

6. A sledge hammer consists of an iron rectangular block 6 inches × 2 inches × 2 inches. A central circular hole of 1 inch diameter is bored through it at right angles to one of its longer faces and a light shaft 3 feet long of wood is fitted into it. Find the moment of inertia of the hammer about a line drawn through the mid-point of the far end of the shaft normal to the axis of the shaft and parallel to the small face of the block. (Take the density of iron as $437\frac{1}{2}$ lb. per cubic foot.)   (C.S.)

7. Find the moment of inertia of a thin hemispherical bowl (i) about the radius through the centre of gravity ; (ii) about a perpendicular line through the centre of gravity.

§ **227.** A number of results in connection with the motion of a rigid body about a fixed axis can be deduced from the principle of energy. We have seen that if the moment of inertia of a body about the fixed axis is I and ω is its angular velocity, its kinetic energy is $\frac{1}{2}I\omega^2$. Hence if the body is released from rest in any position we can find its angular velocity in any other position by equating $\frac{1}{2}I\omega^2$ to the loss of potential energy. This loss is equal to the product of the mass of the body and the distance the centre of gravity has descended.

Again, if a weight is connected to a fine string wound round a flywheel which is suspended so that it can rotate on a horizontal axis, and the weight is allowed to run down ; the sum of the kinetic energies of the flywheel and the weight in any position must be equal to the loss of potential energy of the weight (assuming that there is no loss of energy due to friction).

This method is illustrated in the following examples :—

EXAMPLE (i).

A uniform rod, of length 2a, can turn freely about one end ; if it be let fall from a horizontal position, find its angular velocity when it first becomes vertical.

Let M be the mass of the rod, AB (Fig. 145) its initial position, A being the fixed end and G the centre of gravity.

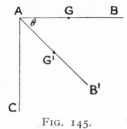

.FIG. 145.

Its moment of inertia about the axis at A is $\frac{4}{3}Ma^2$.

When it has descended to the position A'G'B' where $\angle BAB' = \theta$, the centre of gravity has descended a vertical distance $a \sin \theta$, and the loss of potential energy is $Mga \sin \theta$.

The angular velocity is $\frac{d\theta}{dt}$, and the kinetic energy is $\frac{1}{2} \frac{4}{3}Ma^2 \left(\frac{d\theta}{dt}\right)^2$.

Hence the angular velocity is given by

$$\tfrac{2}{3}Ma^2\left(\frac{d\theta}{dt}\right)^2 = Mga \sin \theta,$$

$$\therefore \left(\frac{d\theta}{dt}\right)^2 = \frac{3g}{2a} \sin \theta.$$

When the rod is in the vertical position AC, $\theta = \dfrac{\pi}{2}$,

and the angular velocity $\qquad = \sqrt{\dfrac{3g}{2a}}.$

EXAMPLE (ii).

The weight of a solid flywheel is 0·45 tons, its diameter is 2 feet, the axle is of diameter 4 inches and weight 0·05 ton. The wheel and axle are set in motion by means of a string wound round the axle and carrying a weight of 20 lb. Find the kinetic energy of the wheel and axle when the weight reaches the floor 10 feet below the starting-point.

The moment of inertia of the wheel = ·45 × 2240 × $\frac{1}{2}$ lb. ft.[2]

,, ,, ,, ,, axle = ·05 × 2240 × $\frac{1}{72}$ lb. ft.[2]

The total moment of inertia

$$I = 2240\left[\frac{\cdot45}{2} + \frac{\cdot05}{72}\right]$$

$$= 2240\frac{18 \times 25}{72} = \frac{10220}{18} \text{ lb. ft.}^2$$

When the 20 lb. mass has descended 10 feet, the loss of potential energy is $200g$ ft. pdls.

If ω is the angular velocity of the wheel and axle when the weight reaches the ground, the velocity of the weight is $\frac{1}{6}\omega$ ft./sec.

The kinetic energy of the wheel and axle is $\frac{1}{2}I\omega^2$ ft. pdls., and that of the weight is

$$\tfrac{1}{2} \cdot 20\frac{\omega^2}{36} = \frac{5}{18}\omega^2 \text{ ft. pdls.,}$$

$$\therefore \frac{5}{18}\omega^2 + \frac{5110}{18}\omega^2 = 200g,$$

$$\therefore \frac{5115}{18}\omega^2 = 200 \times 32,$$

$$\therefore \omega^2 = \frac{200 \times 32 \times 18}{5115}.$$

The kinetic energy of the wheel and axle is

$$\frac{5110}{18}\omega^2 = \frac{5110}{18} \cdot \frac{200 \times 32 \times 18}{5115}, \text{ ft. pdls.}$$

$$= \frac{365}{4092} \text{ ft. tons.}$$

§ **228.** *Determination of the Moment of Inertia of a Flywheel.*
The method of the last example can be modified to determine the moment of inertia of a flywheel.

The axle of the wheel is mounted horizontally on ball bearings to reduce friction. There is usually a small peg on the axle over which a loop in one end of the string, to which the weight is attached, is placed. This peg is also useful in counting the number of revolutions made by the wheel in any time. The height h of the position from which the weight is to be released is measured carefully, and the number of revolutions made by the wheel while the weight is descending is obtained by placing the weight on the ground and counting the number of turns of the wheel required to wind it up to its starting-point, say n_1. The length of the string is adjusted so that the loop comes off the peg as the weight reaches the ground.

The weight is released from rest and the number of revolutions made by the wheel after the weight strikes the ground is measured, and also the time taken for the wheel to come to rest ; let these be n_2 and t.

The friction in the bearings and the rate of retardation of the wheel may be assumed constant, so that the average angular velocity taken over the whole time required to come to rest will be *half* the initial angular velocity ω.

The average angular velocity $= \dfrac{2\pi n_2}{t}$,

$$\therefore \omega = \frac{4\pi n_2}{t}.$$

The velocity v of the weight on reaching the ground is given by

$$v = \omega r,$$

where r is the radius of the axle of the flywheel.

If m is the mass of the weight and I the moment of inertia of the flywheel, their kinetic energies when the weight reaches the ground are $\frac{1}{2}mv^2$ and $\frac{1}{2}I\omega^2$.

The loss of potential energy is mgh.

Now some work has been done against friction. Let f be the amount done in *one* revolution, then in n_1 revolutions the work is $n_1 f$, and this is the amount done while the weight is descending.

$$\therefore mgh = \tfrac{1}{2}mv^2 + \tfrac{1}{2}I\omega^2 + n_1 f.$$

But the kinetic energy of the wheel, $\frac{1}{2}I\omega^2$ is destroyed by the friction in n_2 revolutions.

$$\therefore n_2 f = \tfrac{1}{2}I\omega^2,$$

$$\therefore f = \tfrac{1}{2}\frac{I\omega^2}{n_2},$$

$$\therefore mgh = \tfrac{1}{2}mv^2 + \tfrac{1}{2}I\omega^2\Big(1 + \frac{n_1}{n_2}\Big).$$

All the quantities in this equation, except I, are known, and I can be calculated.

If m is in lb., the radius of the axle r, and the height h must be expressed in feet.

I will then be obtained in lb. ft.² units.

If m is in grams r and h must be measured in centimetres.

I will then be obtained in gm. cm.² units.

EXAMPLES XLIII.

1. A heavy circular disc of mass 20 lb. and radius 1 foot is capable of rotation about its centre in a vertical plane. A mass of 10 lb. is attached to the rim at the highest point, and the whole slightly displaced. Find the angular velocity when the mass of 10 lb. is at the lowest point. (I.E.)

2. A wheel has a cord of length 10 feet coiled round its axle ; the cord is pulled with a constant force of 25 lb. wt. and when the cord leaves the axle, the wheel is rotating 5 times a second. Calculate the moment of inertia of the wheel and axle. (I.E.)

3. A straight uniform rod 4 feet long can turn freely in a vertical plane about a horizontal axis through the rod at a distance of 1 foot from one end. The rod is held in a horizontal position and then let go. Find the velocity of the lower end when the rod is vertical, and the kinetic energy of the rod measured in ft. lb. The mass of the rod is 20 lb. (Q.E.)

4. A circular hoop of small section and 3 feet radius weighs 10 lb. and has a weight of 5 lb. attached to a point on the rim. It is pivoted about a horizontal axis on the rim exactly opposite the weight. If it be turned until the weight is at the highest point and then let go, find the angular velocity with which the weight passes its lowest point. (Q.E.)

5. A uniform circular disc weighs 100 lb. and has a radius of 2 feet ; it is pivoted about a horizontal axis through its centre perpendicular to its plane, and a weight of 100 lb. is fixed to a point on the disc $1\frac{1}{2}$ feet from the axis. The whole is held with that point of attachment level with the axis, and is then let go. What will be the maximum velocity of the rim of the disc in the subsequent motion ?
(Q.E.)

6. The horse-power of a machine is 5, a shearing operation has to be performed every 10 seconds which absorbs 0·8 of the whole energy supplied during that time. If the number of revolutions may only vary between 100 and 130 per minute, find the least moment of inertia of the flywheel. (I.E.)

7. Three equal uniform rods, each of length l and mass m, form the sides of an equilateral triangle ABC. Find the moment of inertia of the frame about the axis through A perpendicular to the plane of the triangle. (Assume that the moment of inertia of each rod about an axis through its middle point perpendicular to the rod is $\frac{1}{12} ml^2$.) The triangular frame is attached to a smooth hinge at A about which it can rotate in a vertical plane. The frame is held, with AB horizontal, and C below AB, and then let go from rest. Find the maximum angular velocity of the triangle in the subsequent motion.
(I.E.)

8. A torpedo is driven by expending the energy stored in a flywheel, initially rotating at 10,000 R.P.M. If the mass of the flywheel is 200 lb. and it is regarded as a uniform circular disc of diameter 2 feet, show that it will be rotating at half the initial rate after about 685 yards run at 30 m.p.h., assuming that the average power necessary for this speed is 50 H.P. (I.E.)

9. Two cog-wheels, having respectively 50 and 100 teeth and moments of inertia 10 and 50 lb. ft.² units, are in gear. The larger wheel is driven by a light spiral spring which exerts a torque of 0·5 lb. feet per revolution through which it is twisted.
If the spring is wound up through 10 turns initially, and the system is then let go, find the maximum speeds which the wheels would attain if they ran smoothly and without friction. (Q.E.)

10. A flywheel, 2 feet in diameter and weighing 20 lb., is keyed on to a shaft of 6 inches diameter, which can turn freely in smooth horizontal bearings ; a long fine string is attached to and wrapped round the axle and carries at its other end a mass of 10 lb. The wheel is turned until it acquires a speed of 480 R.P.M., and is then left running. Prove that it will come to rest after about 33 more revolutions. [Neglect the masses of the axle and string, and assume the mass of the wheel to be concentrated in and uniformly distributed round its rim.] (H.C.)

11. A uniform wire in the form of a circle of radius a swings in a vertical plane about a point A in the circumference. It starts from rest with the diameter AB horizontal. Find its angular velocity when AB is vertical.

12. Calculate the energy in ft. lb. of a disc of 3 feet diameter and $\frac{1}{8}$ inch thick, of material weighing 500 lb. per cu. foot, rotating about an axis through its centre at right angles to its plane and making 2000 R.P.M. (Q.E.)

13. A uniform straight rod 6 feet long swings in a vertical plane about one end ; if V is the velocity of the free end of the rod in its lowest position, find the least value of V consistent with the rod making a complete revolution.

Compare this with the case of a weight hung by a cord of the same length as the rod, and making a complete revolution in a circle.
(Q.E.)

14. A circular disc of uniform thickness, of radius a feet and mass M lb., is rotating with angular velocity ω about a fixed axis at right angles to its plane, at a distance b feet from its centre ; find its kinetic energy in ft. lb.
(Q.E.)

15. A flywheel, of mass 100 lb. and diameter 4 feet, is fixed to the end of a light horizontal axle of 1 foot diameter. A long light cord wound round and fastened to this axle carries at its free end a weight of 20 lb. The flywheel is turning at the rate of two revolutions per second in the direction to wind up the weight, when it is suddenly left to itself. How many revolutions will the wheel make before coming to instantaneous rest ?
(N.U.3)

§ 229. D'Alembert's Principle.

It was mentioned in paragraph 77 that, for a particle of mass m, the quantity $m\frac{d^2x}{dt^2}$ is called the *effective force* acting on the particle in the direction of the x-axis, i.e. this is the force required to give the particle its actual acceleration in that direction. In the same way $m\frac{d^2y}{dt^2}$ is the effective force in the direction of the y-axis, and, if the motion is taking place in three dimensions, $m\frac{d^2z}{dt^2}$ is the effective force parallel to the z-axis.

If f is the resultant acceleration of the particle at any instant, then mf is the resultant effective force at that instant.

Now when the particle is part of a rigid body it is acted on by external impressed forces (such as gravity), and also by the reactions of the neighbouring particles of the body. Let F be the resultant of the impressed forces, R the resultant of the internal forces acting on the particle. Then mf is the resultant of F and R. Hence, if mf be reversed, it will be in equilibrium with F and R. The same reasoning applies to every particle of the body, so that we have a group of forces similar to R, a group similar to F, and a group of effective forces similar to mf, and if all the forces of the last group are reversed they will be in equilibrium with the other two groups. But, by Newton's third law, the forces of group R must be in equilibrium among themselves, since they are internal reactions between the particles.

It follows that the group F, i.e. the impressed forces, must be in equilibrium with the group mf reversed.

This is D'Alembert's Principle, which may be stated as follows :—
The reversed effective forces for all the particles of the body and the external impressed forces are in equilibrium.

This really reduces the solution of a dynamical problem to that of a statical problem.

We resolve the impressed forces into components parallel to the axes and equate each component to the sum of the reversed effective forces in the direction of that axis.

The sum of the moments of the impressed forces about any axis is also equal and opposite to the sum of the moments of the reversed effective forces about that axis.

In the case of a rigid body rotating about a fixed axis, we choose the axis of rotation as the axis about which we take moments. In this way we avoid introducing the impressed forces due to the axis.

We shall now show how to find the moment of the effective forces for all the particles of the body about the axis.

§ 230. *A rigid body is rotating about a fixed axis, to find the moment of the effective forces about the axis of rotation.*

Let any plane fixed in space, and passing through the axis of rotation, be taken as the plane of reference, and let θ be the angle which any other plane through the axis and fixed in the body makes with the first plane. Then $\dot{\theta}$ is the angular velocity of the body about the axis of rotation, and this will also be the angular velocity of any particle m of the body. If r is the distance of a particle m from the axis, the velocity of the particle is $r\dot{\theta}$ perpendicular to the plane containing the axis and the particle.

The moment of momentum is obviously $mr^2\dot{\theta}$.

Hence the moment of the momenta of all the particles is $\Sigma mr^2\dot{\theta}$, i.e. *the moment of inertia of the body about the axis multiplied by the angular velocity.*

The accelerations of the particle m are $r\ddot{\theta}$ and $-r\dot{\theta}^2$ perpendicular to, and along the direction in which r is measured. Hence the moment of the effective force for m about the axis is $mr^2\ddot{\theta}$, and the moment of the effective forces for all the particles is $\Sigma mr^2\ddot{\theta}$, or $(\Sigma mr^2)\ddot{\theta}$, i.e. *the moment of inertia of the body about the axis multiplied by the angular acceleration.*

§ 231. Motion of a Body about a Fixed Axis.

Let L be the moment of the impressed forces about the axis. Taking moments about the axis, we have,

$$\frac{d^2\theta}{dt^2}\,\Sigma mr^2 = L,$$

$$\therefore \frac{d^2\theta}{dt^2} = \frac{\text{moment of forces about axis}}{\text{moment of inertia about axis}}.$$

This equation, when integrated, will give the value of $\dfrac{d\theta}{dt}$ and θ at any time. The constant introduced at each integration is determined from the initial values of $\dfrac{d\theta}{dt}$ and θ.

We shall now consider a special case, the motion of a rigid body about a fixed horizontal axis under the action of gravity. Such a body is often called a Compound Pendulum.

§ 232. The Compound Pendulum.

Take the vertical plane through the axis of rotation as the plane of reference, and the plane through the axis and the centre of gravity of the body as the plane fixed in the body.

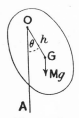

FIG. 146.

Fig. 146 represents a section perpendicular to the axis of rotation through the centre of gravity G, cutting the axis in O.

OA is the vertical through O.

Let $\angle$ AOG $= \theta$, OG $= h$, and let the moment of inertia about an axis through G, parallel to the axis of rotation, be Mk^2.

The moment of inertia about the axis of rotation is therefore $M(k^2 + h^2)$. In the position shown, the moment of the impressed forces about the axis through O is $Mgh \sin \theta$,

$$\therefore \frac{d^2\theta}{dt^2} = - \frac{Mgh \sin \theta}{M(k^2 + h^2)},$$

or
$$\frac{d^2\theta}{dt^2} = - \frac{gh}{k^2 + h^2} \sin \theta \qquad . \qquad . \qquad . \quad \text{(i)}$$

If θ is small we have, approximately, $\sin \theta = \theta$, and the equation becomes

$$\frac{d^2\theta}{dt^2} = - \frac{gh}{k^2 + h^2} \theta \qquad . \qquad . \qquad . \quad \text{(ii)}$$

This represents a simple harmonic motion of period T, where

$$T = 2\pi \sqrt{\frac{k^2 + h^2}{hg}}.$$

In the case of a simple pendulum, of length l, the period is $2\pi\sqrt{\dfrac{l}{g}}$; hence $\dfrac{k^2 + h^2}{h}$ corresponds to l, and a simple pendulum of length $\dfrac{k^2 + h^2}{h}$ would have the same period of oscillation as the compound pendulum. The expression $\dfrac{k^2 + h^2}{h}$ is therefore called the **length of the simple equivalent pendulum.**

Equation (i) can be integrated once and the result is

$$\left(\frac{d\theta}{dt}\right)^2 = \frac{2gh}{k^2 + h^2} \cos \theta + C, \qquad . \qquad . \qquad . \quad \text{(iii)}$$

where C is determined by the initial value of $\dfrac{d\theta}{dt}$.

Equation (iii) gives the value of the angular velocity for any value of θ, but this is obtained more easily from the principle of energy, as explained in § 227.

Equation (iii) cannot be integrated again to give θ in terms of t without introducing what are called Elliptic Functions.

The study of these is a branch of advanced mathematics, and we can only deal here with the connection between θ and the time when θ is small, i.e. we must use equation (ii).

This equation gives

$$\theta = A \cos (\omega t + B),$$

where $\omega = \sqrt{\dfrac{gh}{k^2 + h^2}}$, and A, B are constants depending on the initial values of $\dfrac{d\theta}{dt}$ and θ.

§ 233. Centre of Oscillation.

The point O where the plane through the centre of gravity perpendicular to the axis of rotation cuts this axis is called the centre of suspension.

If l is the length of the simple equivalent pendulum, then, as in the last paragraph,

$$l = \frac{k^2 + h^2}{h}.$$

Produce OG (Fig. 147) to C, so that OC $= l$. Then C is called the *Centre of Oscillation*. If the whole mass were collected at the centre of oscillation and suspended by a thread to the centre of suspension, its angular motion and time of oscillation would be the same as that of the body under the same initial conditions.

FIG. 147.

If the body is suspended at C, then since $CG = l - h$, the length of the simple equivalent pendulum l' is now given by

$$l' = \frac{k^2 + (l - h)^2}{l - h},$$

but

$$k^2 = lh - h^2,$$

$$\therefore l' = \frac{lh - h^2 + l^2 - 2lh + h^2}{l - h} = \frac{l(l - h)}{l - h} = l,$$

$$\therefore l' = l.$$

Hence the period of oscillation about C is the same as that about O, and if we can find two points, on a line through the centre of gravity, about which the periods of oscillation are equal, the distance between these points is the length of the simple equivalent pendulum.

This is made use of in Kater's pendulum, which consists of a bar with two knife edges and a movable mass which slides on the bar. The mass is adjusted so that the times of oscillation about the two knife edges are equal. The distance between the knife edges then gives l, and

$$T = 2\pi\sqrt{\frac{l}{g}},$$

T and l being known, we can calculate g.

This is the most accurate method of determining g.

§ 234. Minimum Time of Oscillation of a Compound Pendulum.

We have seen that the period T is given by

$$T = 2\pi\sqrt{\frac{k^2 + h^2}{hg}}.$$

Now, this will be a minimum when $\dfrac{k^2 + h^2}{h}$ or $h + \dfrac{k^2}{h}$ is a minimum. This is the case when

$$\frac{d}{dh}\left(h + \frac{k^2}{h}\right) = 0,$$

or

$$1 - \frac{k^2}{h^2} = 0,$$

i.e. when

$$h = k.$$

In this case $l = 2k$.

22 *

The period is therefore a minimum when the distance between the axis of suspension and the centre of gravity is equal to the radius of gyration about a parallel axis through the centre of gravity. This only gives the minimum value for axes drawn in a given direction. To get the absolute minimum we should have to find the direction of the axis through the centre of gravity for which the radius of gyration is least.

§ **235.** EXAMPLE (i).

A heavy uniform rod AB of length 2l and mass M has a mass m attached to it at B. The whole oscillates freely about a horizontal axis through A. Prove that the time of a small oscillation is

$$4\pi\sqrt{\frac{(M + 3m)l}{3(M + 2m)g}}.$$ (I.E.)

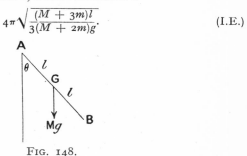

FIG. 148.

Let AB (Fig. 148) represent the rod, G its centre of gravity. The moment of inertia of the rod about A is $\frac{4}{3}Ml^2$, and that of the mass m is $4ml^2$.
The moment of inertia of the rod and mass is therefore

$$4\left(\frac{M + 3m}{3}\right)l^2.$$

The moment of the restoring force about A when the angular displacement from the vertical is θ is

$$Mgl \sin\theta + 2mgl \sin\theta = (M + 2m)gl \sin\theta.$$

Hence $$\frac{d^2\theta}{dt^2} = -\frac{(M + 2m)gl}{\frac{4}{3}(M + 3m)l^2} \sin\theta,$$

$$= -\frac{3(M + 2m)g}{4(M + 3m)l}\theta, \text{ if } \theta \text{ is small.}$$

The period of oscillation is therefore $2\pi\sqrt{\dfrac{4(M + 3m)l}{3(M + 2m)g}}.$

EXAMPLE (ii).

A cylindrical rod 2 feet long and 2 inches in diameter is free to swing about a horizontal axis at right angles to its geometrical axis and intersecting it. Find the position of the axis of suspension if the length of the simple equivalent pendulum is a minimum.   (I.E.)

If k is the radius of gyration about an axis through the centre of gravity parallel to the axis of suspension, h the distance of the centre of gravity from the axis of suspension, and L the length of the simple equivalent pendulum,

$$L = \frac{k^2 + h^2}{h},$$

and L is a minimum when $h = k$ (§ 234).

Now we found (§ 226) that the moment of inertia of a solid cylinder about an axis through its centre of gravity perpendicular to the axis of the cylinder is

$$M\left(\frac{a^2}{4} + \frac{l^2}{12}\right),$$

where a is the radius and l the length of the cylinder. Here $a = \frac{1}{6}$ ft., $l = 2$ ft.,

$$\therefore k^2 = \left(\frac{a^2}{4} + \frac{l^2}{12}\right) = \left(\frac{1}{144} + \frac{4}{12}\right) = \frac{49}{144},$$

$$\therefore k = \tfrac{7}{12} \text{ ft.}$$

Hence the axis of suspension for the minimum period of oscillation must be $\tfrac{7}{12}$ feet, or 7 inches from the centre of gravity.

§ 236. Motion of a Flywheel acted on by a Couple.

If Mk^2 is the moment of inertia of the wheel about its axis, and L is the moment of the couple,

$$\frac{d^2\theta}{dt^2} = \pm \frac{L}{Mk^2},$$

according as L tends to increase or diminish the angular velocity.

Example (i).

A flywheel of weight 1 ton and radius of gyration 3 feet 6 inches is rotating once every second. What is its kinetic energy and how long will it take to come to rest under a frictional torque round the axis of 40 lb. ft.?

The moment of inertia is $2240 \times \frac{49}{4}$ lb. ft.^{2}, and the angular velocity is 2π radians per sec.

The kinetic energy is

$$\tfrac{1}{2} \cdot \frac{2240 \times 49}{4} \cdot 4\pi^2 \text{ ft. pdls.} = 7 \cdot 56 \text{ ft. tons.}$$

The equation of motion is

$$560 \times 49\frac{d^2\theta}{dt^2} = -40 \times 32,$$

$$\therefore \frac{d^2\theta}{dt^2} = -\frac{32}{14 \times 49} = -\frac{16}{343},$$

$$\therefore \frac{d\theta}{dt} = -\frac{16}{343}t + C;$$

and $\dfrac{d\theta}{dt} = 2\pi$ when $t = 0$,

$$\therefore C = 2\pi;$$

$$\therefore \dfrac{d\theta}{dt} = 0 \text{ when}$$

$$\dfrac{16t}{343} = 2\pi,$$

or $t = \dfrac{44}{7} \cdot \dfrac{343}{16} = 134\tfrac{3}{4}$ seconds.

EXAMPLE (ii).

The moment of inertia of a pulley of 6 inches diameter is 0·14 lb. ft.² units. A long cord with a mass of 1 lb. suspended from its end, is wound round the pulley. Through what angle will the pulley turn in 2 seconds from the instant when the weight is released ? What will then be the combined kinetic energy of the pulley and weight ? (Q.E.)

Let θ be the angle turned through by the pulley, x ft. the distance descended by the 1 lb. mass in time t.

Then $x = \tfrac{1}{4}\theta$, $\dot{x} = \tfrac{1}{4}\dot{\theta}$, $\ddot{x} = \tfrac{1}{4}\ddot{\theta}$.

Let T be the tension in the string.

The equations of motion for the pulley and the mass are

$$\cdot 14\ddot{\theta} = \tfrac{1}{4}T \quad . \quad . \quad . \quad . \quad . \quad (i)$$
$$\ddot{x} = g - T \quad . \quad . \quad . \quad . \quad . \quad (ii)$$

Since $\ddot{x} = \tfrac{1}{4}\ddot{\theta}$, the second equation gives

$$\tfrac{1}{4}\ddot{\theta} = g - T,$$
$$\therefore (\cdot 14 + \tfrac{1}{16})\ddot{\theta} = \tfrac{1}{4}g,$$
$$\therefore \cdot 2025\ddot{\theta} = 8,$$
$$\therefore \cdot 2025\dot{\theta} = 8t, \text{ no constant since } \dot{\theta} = 0 \text{ when } t = 0 ;$$
$$\therefore \cdot 2025\theta = 4t^2, \text{ ,, } \quad \text{ ,, } \quad \text{ ,, } \quad \theta = 0 \text{ when } t = 0.$$

Hence, when $t = 2$,

$$\theta = \dfrac{16}{\cdot 2025} = 79 \text{ radians, nearly.}$$

Also $\dot{\theta} = \dfrac{16}{\cdot 2025} = 79$, and the combined kinetic energy is

$$\cdot 07\dot{\theta}^2 + \dfrac{1}{32}\dot{\theta}^2 = \dfrac{3 \cdot 24}{32}\dot{\theta}^2$$

$$= \dfrac{3 \cdot 24(79)^2}{32} \text{ ft. pdls.} = 19 \cdot 7 \text{ ft. lb.}$$

This problem can also be solved by using the principle of energy, if we assume that, since the force producing motion (1 lb. wt.) is constant, the acceleration of the mass is constant.

If $\dot{\theta}$ and $\dot{x}$ are the velocities of the pulley and mass when the latter has descended a distance x, the kinetic energy of the two is

$$\cdot 07\dot{\theta}^2 + \tfrac{1}{2}\dot{x}^2 = 1 \cdot 12\,\dot{x}^2 + \tfrac{1}{2}\dot{x}^2 = 1 \cdot 62\,\dot{x}^2.$$

But the loss of potential energy is gx,

$$\therefore \; 1 \cdot 62 \; \dot{x}^2 = gx.$$

The acceleration, f, is given by

$$\dot{x}^2 = 2fx,$$
$$\therefore \; 3 \cdot 24 fx = gx,$$
$$\therefore f = \frac{g}{3 \cdot 24}.$$

The distance moved by the mass in 2 seconds is therefore

$$\frac{1}{2} \cdot \frac{g}{3 \cdot 24} \cdot 4 = \frac{g}{1 \cdot 62} \text{ ft.}$$

The angle turned through by the pulley is

$$\frac{4g}{1 \cdot 62} = 79 \text{ radians, nearly.}$$

Also, when $t = 2$, the velocity of the mass is $\dfrac{2g}{3 \cdot 24}$ ft./sec.

The total kinetic energy is therefore

$$1 \cdot 62 \; \dot{x}^2 = \frac{g^2}{1 \cdot 62} \text{ ft. pdls.} = \frac{g}{1 \cdot 62} \text{ ft. lb.} = 19 \cdot 7 \text{ ft. lb.}$$

Note.—The assumption mentioned above, although frequently made, really needs justification. It amounts to assuming that a constant force, applied to a rigid body capable of rotation about a fixed axis, will produce in the body a constant angular acceleration.

In the first place, the force will not produce any acceleration at all unless it has a *moment* about the fixed axis. Also, it does not follow that, because a constant force acting on a particle produces a constant acceleration in that particle, a torque of constant moment will produce a constant angular acceleration in a rigid body. This latter fact requires proof, as in § 231, by the aid of D'Alembert's Principle.

EXAMPLES XLIV.

1. A rod AB of length l and negligible weight has two equal weights w attached to the end B and to a point M distant $\frac{1}{3} l$ from B. Find the period of small oscillations about a horizontal axis through A.
   (I.E.)

2. A uniform bar of length $2a$ oscillates about a horizontal axis distant c from the centre of the bar ; prove that the length of the simple equivalent pendulum is $c + \frac{1}{3}\dfrac{a^2}{c}$.

   Assuming that a simple pendulum one metre long beats seconds (in swinging from rest to rest), prove that the least period of complete oscillation for a bar one metre long is about $1\frac{1}{2}$ seconds, and that the horizontal axis is then placed about 29 cm. above the centre.
   (Q.E.)

3. The pendulum of a clock consists of a light rod with a small ball of mass $\frac{1}{2}$ oz. at each end, the distance between the centres of the balls being 3 inches. The axis of oscillation passes through the centre of

the rod at right angles to its length. To disturb the balance a small mass is fixed on the rod at a distance of 1 inch from the axis of oscillation. Find the value of the mass in order that the pendulum may beat seconds. (Q.E).

4. Two equal circular wheels, each of mass 200 lb., and radius $1\frac{1}{2}$ feet, are rotating freely in the same horizontal plane about their centres. A connecting rod of mass 80 lb. is pin-jointed to the rim of each, and is always parallel to the line of centres of the wheels. Show that the angular velocity of the wheels is constant in the absence of friction, and find the kinetic energy of the whole system if each wheel makes 50 R.P.M. and its mass is concentrated in its rim.

If the system is reduced to rest in 60 revolutions by the action of equal retarding torques on each wheel, find the torques, assuming that they are constant. (Q.E.)

5. A solid flywheel of diameter 2 feet, bored for shaft and weighing 0·45 ton, is keyed on to a horizontal shaft of diameter 4 inches and weighing 0·05 ton. What is the kinetic energy of the flywheel and shaft at 1200 R.P.M.? What uniform retarding couple would reduce the flywheel to rest in 2 minutes, and through what angle would it turn in this time ? (Q.E.)

6. A trap door, 4 feet square and of uniform thickness, is hanging vertically by its hinges. If the door is set swinging through a small angle find the periodic time, neglecting the friction of the hinges. (Q.E.)

7. A wheel has a diameter of 2 feet and a mass of 50 lb. which may be regarded as distributed uniformly round the rim. Calculate the number of foot-pounds of energy stored in the wheel when it is making 600 R.P.M. If the wheel is to be stopped in 50 seconds by a brake pressing on the rim, calculate the pressure required, assuming that the coefficient of friction is 0·1 between the brake-block and the rim. (H.C.)

8. A uniform circular disc of radius a has a particle of mass equal to that of the disc fixed to a point of its circumference. The disc can turn freely about a fixed horizontal axis through its centre at right angles to its plane. Assuming that the radius of gyration of the disc about this axis is $\frac{a}{\sqrt{2}}$, show that the length of the simple equivalent pendulum for small oscillations of the system about its position of stable equilibrium is $\frac{3a}{2}$. (H.C.)

9. Calculate the period of small oscillations of a uniform rod, 6 feet long, about a horizontal axis through one end, when a particle of weight equal to that of the rod is attached to its middle point. (H.C.)

10. Two equal solid flywheels, each of mass m and radius a, are in the same vertical plane and free to move in that plane about their centres, which are fixed. A connecting rod, of mass M and length equal to the distance between the centres of the wheels, is smoothly jointed to each wheel at a point on its rim, so that as the wheels revolve it is always parallel to the line of their centres. Show that, as the system moves under gravity, the angular motion of the wheels is the same as that of a simple pendulum of length

$$a\left(1 + \frac{m}{M}\right).$$

(H.C.)

11. A flywheel has a horizontal shaft of radius r, the moment of inertia of the system about the axis of revolution is K. A string of negligible thickness is wound round the shaft and supports a mass M hanging vertically. Find the angular acceleration of the wheel when its motion is opposed by a constant frictional couple G.

If the string is released from the shaft after the wheel has turned through an angle θ from rest, and if the wheel then turns through a further angle ϕ before it is brought to rest by the frictional couple, show that ·

$$G = \frac{KMgr\theta}{K\theta + (K + Mr^2)\phi}.$$

12. A flywheel has a light cord coiled round its axle, and the cord is pulled with a constant force of m lb. wt. until a length l ft. has unwound, when the cord slackens and comes off. It is found that the wheel is then rotating n times a second ; prove that its moment of inertia in foot-pound units is $\dfrac{mlg}{2n^2\pi^2}$. If a constant frictional force is now applied at a distance a feet from the axis equal to the weight of m' lb., show that the wheel will stop after

$$\frac{ml}{m'na\pi} \text{ seconds.} \qquad \text{(B.Sc.)}$$

13. A uniform circular cylinder of mass M, can rotate freely about its axis, which is fixed in a horizontal position ; a light inextensible string is coiled round the cylinder and carries at its free end a particle of mass m. If the system is allowed to move, show that the particle will descend with uniform acceleration

$$\frac{2mg}{M + 2m}. \qquad \text{(B.Sc.)}$$

14. An Attwood's machine has a pulley whose moment of inertia is I, and whose radius is a ; the masses attached at the ends of the string are each M, and the rider is of mass m. Prove that the acceleration of the masses is f, where

$$\frac{g}{f} = 1 + 2\frac{M}{m} + \frac{I}{ma^2},$$

assuming that the string does not slip on the pulley and neglecting axle friction.

15. Show that for a bar equal in length to the seconds pendulum the least time of a beat (from rest to rest), for different points of suspension, is about $\frac{3}{4}$ of a second.

16. A pendulum, of mass M, consists of a heavy bob attached to the end of a light rod, and makes n oscillations per minute when turning about a fixed point O of the rod ; also k is its radius of gyration about O and h is the distance of its centre of inertia from O. On the rod above O slides a small mass m ; when this mass is fixed at a distance x from O, show that the number, n', of oscillations per minute is given by

$$\frac{n'}{n} = 1 - \frac{1}{2}\frac{m}{M}\left(\frac{x}{h} + \frac{x^2}{k^2}\right).$$

17. The mass of a flywheel is 100 lb. and a mass of 10 lb. hangs by a string wrapped round the axle, which is horizontal and has a radius

of 2 inches. If the mass of 10 lb. falls through 20 feet from rest in 16 seconds, show that the radius of gyration of the flywheel is a little over 9 inches.   (B.Sc.)

18. The centre of gravity of a bicycle wheel is in its axis. When a small valve of mass m is fixed to the rim at a distance h from the axis, and the axis is held horizontally, the wheel oscillates in the same period as a simple pendulum of length l. What is the moment of inertia of the wheel (apart from the valve) about the axis ?   (B.Sc.)

19. A bucket of mass m hangs at the end of a light rope which is coiled round a wheel of mass M. If the wheel can rotate freely about its axis, which is horizontal, and if its entire mass is supposed concentrated in its rim, find the speed of the bucket when it has fallen a distance x from rest.   (I.S.)

20. A thin uniform rod of mass m and length $2a$ can turn freely about one end, which is fixed. A uniform bar, whose mass is $\frac{2}{3}m$ and length $3a$, can be clamped to the rod so that its centre occupies any position on the rod. Show that the length of the simple equivalent pendulum for oscillations in which the bar and the rod remain in a vertical plane lies between $\frac{3}{2}a$ and $2a$.   (H.C.)

21. A cylindrical drum weighing 40 lb. and having a radius of 1 foot and a radius of gyration of 9 inches, can turn without friction about its axis, which is horizontal and in fixed bearings. A weight of 10 lb. is attached to one end of a string which is coiled round the drum. The drum is held with the weight hanging freely and is then let go so that the weight falls, causing the string to unwind and the drum to turn. Find the angle through which the drum turns in the first second after the drum is let go.   (Q.E.)

22. A flywheel is mounted on a horizontal axle $1\frac{1}{2}$ inches in diameter. A thin cord wrapped round the axle carries a mass of 5 lb. which is allowed to fall from rest. The mass is observed to fall a distance of 5 feet in 15 seconds. Find its velocity and the angular velocity of the flywheel at the end of this time. Also determine the moment of inertia of the flywheel.   (Q.E.)

23. A thin rod OA, 2 feet in length, is suspended at O and is fixed at A to the rim of a circular disc, of diameter 1 foot, so that OA produced passes through its centre. Find the time of a small oscillation of the pendulum so formed. The motion takes place in the plane of the disc, and the mass of the rod may be neglected in comparison with that of the disc.   (Q.E.)

24. A mass of 10 lb. hangs at the end of a light cord which is wrapped many times round the circumference of a pulley of 3 feet diameter. The pulley is mounted upon a horizontal axis, about which it is free to turn. On starting from rest the mass is found to descend 16 feet in 5 seconds. Show that if there is no friction at the bearing, the moment of inertia of the pulley must be 540 lb. ft.² units.   (Q.E.)

25. A flywheel of weight 200 lb. is rotating about its axis at 150 R.P.M., and it is acted on by a constant frictional couple, so that after 10 seconds it is rotating at 100 R.P.M. Find how many more revolutions it will make before it is brought to rest. If the value of the couple is 40 lb. ft., find the radius of gyration of the wheel.   (N.U.3)

26. A uniform thin magnet of length $2l$ and mass M can turn freely about a smooth vertical axis through its mid-point, and there is a

force F at each end, one to the north and the other to the south. The magnet is placed with its length east and west. Prove that it reaches the north and south direction with angular velocity

$$\left(\frac{12F}{Ml}\right)^{\frac{1}{2}}.$$ (N.U.3)

27. A uniform rod AB of mass m and length $2l$ is hinged about a horizontal axis perpendicular to the rod through its centre and carries at one end, A, a particle of mass m. If the rod is at rest with A vertically below B and A is given a velocity just sufficient to bring the rod to a horizontal position, prove that

$$v^2 = \tfrac{3}{2}gl.$$

Find what horizontal impulsive force acting at A is necessary to give A this initial velocity if $l = 3$ feet, $m = 2$ lb.   (N.U.3)

28. A wheel spins about a fixed axle and a constant frictional couple is exerted on it by the bearings. If the wheel is set spinning at 200 R.P.M. and comes to rest in $1\tfrac{1}{2}$ minutes, find how many revolutions it makes in this time.

If the moment of inertia of the wheel about the axle is 50 cwt. ft.², find in lb. wt. ft. the moment of the frictional couple.   (N.U.3)

§ 237. Pressures on the Axis of Rotation of a Compound Pendulum.

Let O (Fig. 149) be the centre of suspension, G the centre of gravity, and OG $= h$.

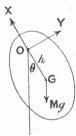

FIG. 149.

Let X, Y be the components of the force exerted by the axis on the body along and perpendicular to GO, Mk^2 the moment of inertia about an axis through G parallel to the axis of suspension. Taking moments about O,

$$\frac{d^2\theta}{dt^2} = -\frac{Mgh}{M(k^2 + h^2)}\sin\theta \qquad . \qquad . \qquad . \qquad (i)$$

The motion of the centre of gravity is the same as if all the forces acted at that point. Since it describes a circle about O, we have, resolving along and perpendicular to GO,

$$Mh\left(\frac{d\theta}{dt}\right)^2 = X - Mg\cos\theta \quad . \quad . \quad . \quad \text{(ii)}$$

$$Mh\frac{d^2\theta}{dt^2} = Y - Mg\sin\theta \quad . \quad . \quad . \quad \text{(iii)}$$

Y is obtained directly by substituting for $\dfrac{d^2\theta}{dt^2}$ in (iii) from (i).

If (i) is integrated once and the resulting constant determined from the initial value of $\dfrac{d\theta}{dt}$, we then, by using (ii), obtain X.

EXAMPLE.

A thin uniform rod of length 2a, attached to a smooth hinge at one end O, is allowed to fall from a horizontal position; show that the horizontal strain on the hinge is greatest when the rod is inclined at an angle of 45° to the vertical, and that the vertical strain is then $\frac{11}{8}$ times the weight of the rod.

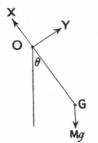

FIG. 150.

Let G (Fig. 150) be the centre of gravity of the rod.

Let M be the mass of the rod, then $k^2 = \dfrac{a^2}{3}$, $h = a$, and the moment of inertia about O is $M\dfrac{4a^2}{3}$. The moment of the weight about O is $Mga\sin\theta$.

Taking moments about O,

$$\frac{d^2\theta}{dt^2} = -\frac{Mga\sin\theta}{M\dfrac{4a^2}{3}} = -\frac{3g}{4a}\sin\theta \quad . \quad . \quad . \quad \text{(i)}$$

Resolving perpendicular to GO,

$$Ma\frac{d^2\theta}{dt^2} = Y - Mg\sin\theta,$$

$$\therefore Y = Mg\sin\theta - \tfrac{3}{4}Mg\sin\theta = \tfrac{1}{4}Mg\sin\theta.$$

Resolving along GO,

$$Ma\left(\frac{d\theta}{dt}\right)^2 = X - Mg\cos\theta \quad . \quad . \quad . \quad \text{(ii)}$$

Integrating (i),

$$\left(\frac{d\theta}{dt}\right)^2 = \frac{3g}{2a}\cos\theta + C,$$

and

$$\frac{d\theta}{dt} = 0, \quad \text{when} \quad \theta = \frac{\pi}{2}, \quad \therefore C = 0,$$

$$\therefore \left(\frac{d\theta}{dt}\right)^2 = \frac{3g}{2a}\cos\theta \; ;$$

∴ from (ii)

$$X = Mg\cos\theta + \tfrac{3}{2}Mg\cos\theta = \tfrac{5}{2}Mg\cos\theta.$$

The horizontal pressure at O is

$$X\sin\theta - Y\cos\theta = \tfrac{5}{2}Mg\cos\theta\sin\theta - \tfrac{1}{4}Mg\sin\theta\cos\theta$$
$$= \tfrac{9}{4}Mg\cos\theta\sin\theta$$
$$= \tfrac{9}{8}Mg\sin 2\theta,$$

and this is obviously a maximum when $2\theta = 90°$, i.e. when $\theta = 45°$. The vertical pressure at O is

$$X\cos\theta + Y\sin\theta = \tfrac{5}{2}Mg\cos^2\theta + \tfrac{1}{4}Mg\sin^2\theta,$$

and when $\theta = 45°$, this becomes

$$\tfrac{5}{4}Mg + \tfrac{1}{8}Mg = \tfrac{11}{8}Mg.$$

§ 238. Impulsive Forces.

In the case of an impulsive force the total change in the moment of momentum about the fixed axis is equal to the moment of the impulsive force about that axis.

If ω, ω' are the angular velocities before and after the blow,

$$\Sigma mr^2 . \omega' - \Sigma mr^2 . \omega = \text{moment of impulse},$$

$$\therefore \omega' - \omega = \frac{\text{moment of impulse about axis}}{\text{moment of inertia about axis}}.$$

Let a rod OA (Fig. 151), of length $2a$ and mass M, be suspended freely from O, and struck a horizontal blow P at a point C, where OC $= x$.

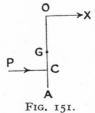

FIG. 151.

Let ω' be the instantaneous angular velocity communicated to the rod, and X the impulsive reaction at O caused by the blow. This reaction will be parallel to the direction of the blow.

The moment of inertia about O is $\frac{4}{3}Ma^2$, and the moment of P about O is Px,

$$\therefore \omega' = \frac{Px}{\frac{4}{3}Ma^2} \qquad . \qquad . \qquad . \qquad . \quad \text{(i)}$$

Also the velocity of the centre of gravity G is $a\omega'$, and this is caused by the two impulses P and X,

$$\therefore Ma\omega' = P + X \qquad . \qquad . \qquad . \qquad . \quad \text{(ii)}$$

From (i) $\qquad\qquad P = \frac{4Ma^2\omega'}{3x}$,

$\therefore$ from (ii) $\qquad X = Ma\omega' - \frac{4}{3}M\frac{a^2}{x}\omega'$,

$$= Ma\omega'\left(1 - \frac{4}{3}\frac{a}{x}\right).$$

If $x = \frac{4}{3}a$, there is no impulsive reaction at O.

In this case the point C is called the *centre of percussion*.

It is easily seen that the length $\frac{4}{3}a$ is the length of the simple equivalent pendulum l, for

$$l = \frac{\frac{a^2}{3} + a^2}{a} = \frac{4a}{3}.$$

If we consider the more general case where OG $= h$, and the moment of inertia about an axis through G parallel to the axis of suspension is Mk^2, equations (i) and (ii) become

$$\omega' = \frac{Px}{M(k^2 + h^2)},$$

and $\qquad\qquad Mh\omega' = P + X,$

$$\therefore X = Mh\omega' - \frac{M(k^2 + h^2)}{x}\omega' = M\omega'\left(h - \frac{k^2 + h^2}{x}\right) ;$$

and if this is zero $\qquad x = \frac{k^2 + h^2}{h}$,

i.e. x is equal to the length of the simple equivalent pendulum.

EXAMPLES XLV.

1. A fine circular hoop of weight W is free to move about a fixed horizontal tangent. It falls over from the position in which it is vertical so that its centre describes a circle in a vertical plane perpendicular to the tangent. Show that, in the positions when the hoop is vertical, the stress on the support is $\frac{11}{3}$W or W. (H.C.)

2. Two lines of shafting with a common axis have moments of inertia 40 and 20 lb. ft.^{2} units respectively. The former is rotating at 250 R.P.M. when it is clutched on to the latter which was previously at rest. Find the amount of energy wasted in the process of clutching. (Q.E.)

3. A thin uniform rod, of length 2 feet and weight 5 lb., is pivoted freely at one end about a horizontal axis. The rod is slightly displaced from the position of unstable equilibrium. With what angular velocity will it reach the horizontal position ? What will be the impulsive blow on a stop which catches the end and prevents the rod moving past that position. (Q.E.)

4. A pendulum consisting of a light rod, of length l, and a heavy bob hangs freely. The point of support is suddenly made to move horizontally with uniform velocity v. Show that the pendulum will describe a complete revolution if $v > 2(gl)^{\frac{1}{2}}$. (C.S.)

5. A uniform solid circular cylinder makes complete revolutions under gravity about a horizontal generator. Show that the supports must be able to bear at least $1\frac{1}{3}$ times the weight of the cylinder. (C.S.)

6. The lock of a railway carriage door will only engage if the angular velocity of the closing door exceeds ω. The door swings about vertical hinges and has a radius of gyration k about a vertical axis through the hinges, whilst the centre of gravity of the door is at a distance a from the line of the hinges. Show that if the door be initially at rest and at right angles to the side of the train, which then commences to move with uniform acceleration f, the door will not close unassisted unless

$$f > \frac{1}{2}\frac{\omega^2 k^2}{a}.$$

7. A rigid pendulum OG swings about a horizontal axis through O, its centre of gravity being at G. The pendulum is released from rest when OG is horizontal. When OG becomes vertical, the pendulum is brought to rest by an inelastic buffer B which is such that the line of the reaction between B and the pendulum is horizontal and at a distance l below O. The mass of the pendulum is m, its moment of inertia about a horizontal axis through G is mk^2, and OG $= h$.

Show that, if the impulse of the force exerted by B upon the pendulum during the impact is P,

$$P = \frac{m}{l}\sqrt{2gh(h^2 + k^2)}.$$

Deduce the impulse Q of the horizontal force exerted on the pendulum during the impact by the axis at O, and show that it vanishes when l is equal to the length of the simple equivalent pendulum.

8. A thin uniform rod of mass m and length $2a$ can turn freely about one end which is fixed, and a circular disc of mass $12m$ and radius $\frac{a}{3}$ can be clamped to the rod so that its centre is on the rod. Show that, for oscillations in which the plane of the disc remains vertical, the length of the simple equivalent pendulum lies between $2a$ and $\frac{2a}{3}$.

9. A uniform cube is free to turn about one edge which is horizontal. Show that the length of the simple equivalent pendulum is $\frac{2}{3}a$, where a is the length of a diagonal of one of the faces. Also show that if the cube starts from rest in its highest position, the vertical component of pressure on the fixed edge vanishes when the cube has turned through an angle $\cos^{-1}(\frac{1}{3})$. (S.)

10. A uniform circular lamina of weight W can turn in a vertical plane about an axis at right angles to its plane through a point in its circumference. If it starts from rest from the position in which the diameter through this point is horizontal, prove that the horizontal and vertical components of the pressure on the axis, when this diameter makes an angle θ with the horizontal are

$$W \sin 2\theta \quad \text{and} \quad \tfrac{1}{3}W(4 - 3\cos 2\theta). \qquad \text{(B.Sc.)}$$

11. A uniform cube swings about one of its edges, which is horizontal, and in the highest position the centroid is level with the axis of rotation. Find the stress on the axis in any position, and show that it varies between $\frac{1}{4}W$ and $\frac{5}{3}W$, where W is the weight of the cube. [The moment of inertia of a cube, of mass M and edge $2a$, about an axis through its centroid parallel to an edge is $\frac{2}{3}Ma^2$.] (B.Sc.)

12. A uniform lamina in the form of a square ABCD of side $2a$, oscillates in its own plane about a horizontal axis through A perpendicular to its plane. In the extreme position a side of the square is directed vertically downwards. Show that the greatest velocity of the corner C is $[6ga(\sqrt{2} - 1)]^{\frac{1}{2}}$. Prove that the stress on the axis, when AC is vertical, is very nearly $1\cdot44$ times the weight of the lamina. (B.Sc.)

13. A uniform rod of weight W, free to turn about a fixed smooth pivot at one end, is held horizontally and released. Prove that when, in the subsequent motion, the rod makes an angle θ with the vertical, the pressure on the pivot is $\frac{1}{4}W\sqrt{1 + 99\cos^2\theta}$.

14. A rifle is fixed to a heavy block which can swing about a fixed horizontal axis, the line of the barrel being at right angles to this axis. The discharge of the rifle produces such recoil that the block swings through an angle θ from its equilibrium position. If in a series of experiments the same bullet is used but different charges of powder, prove that the muzzle velocity of the bullet is proportional to $\sin\frac{\theta}{2}$.

(Q.E.)

15. A mass of 15 lb. is bolted to one of the spokes of a flywheel, its centre of gravity being 3 feet from the centre of the wheel. Another mass of 10 lb. is bolted to another spoke, with its centre of gravity 2 feet from the centre of the wheel. The angle between the two spokes is $120°$. Find the resultant force on the bearings of the flywheel, due to the inertia of these masses, when the wheel is rotating uniformly at 240 R.P.M. (Q.E.)

16. A uniform circular disc of mass M gm. and radius a cm. moves in its own plane about a fixed horizontal axis perpendicular to its plane through its centre O. A small body of mass m gm. is rigidly attached to it at P at a distance x cm. from the centre. The disc is released from rest with OP horizontal. Prove that when P passes through the bottom point of its path it is moving with the speed v cm./sec. given by the formula

$$v^2 = \frac{4mgx^3}{2mx^2 + Ma^2}.$$

An equal disc and particle is free to rotate about the same axis and suddenly becomes connected rigidly with the first disc when both particles are vertically below the axis. Find the height to which the two particles will rise if the second disc were at rest before the connection was made. (N.U.3)

17. Two flywheels in the same plane are free to rotate about horizontal parallel frictionless axles. A light cord has one end attached to the first wheel, is wound round it, passes over to the second wheel, is wound round that, and has its other end attached to the second wheel. A couple of moment G acts on the first wheel so as to make the cord start coiling up on the first wheel and uncoiling from the second. Prove that the angular acceleration of the second wheel is

$$\frac{Gab}{Ib^2 + Ja^2},$$

where a and b are the radii of the wheels, and I and J are their moments of inertia about their respective axles.

Find also the tension of the cord. (N.U.3)

18. Two cog-wheels of radii a, b are spinning about parallel axes with angular velocities ω, ω' in the same sense. If the wheels suddenly become enmeshed, show that the speed of points on their rims becomes

$$\frac{ab(Ib\omega \sim I'a\omega')}{Ib^2 + I'a^2},$$

where I, I' are the moments of inertia of the wheels about their axes. (N.U.4)

19. A lamina of mass M is free to turn in its own plane which is vertical about an axis through a point O at a distance c from its mass-centre G. If the lamina just makes complete revolutions, prove that the greatest reaction at O is

$$\frac{Mg(k^2 + 5c^2)}{k^2 + c^2},$$

where k is the radius of gyration about the axis through G normal to the lamina. Find also the time taken by G in describing the lower half of its path. (N.U.4)

20. If a uniform rectangular lamina ABCD can move about AB as a horizontal axis, and is allowed to fall from rest in a horizontal position, find the velocity at any point in CD when the lamina reaches the vertical position.

If the lamina is brought to rest in the vertical position by an impulse applied to the mid-point of CD, find the resulting impulse on the hinge. (C.W.B.)

CHAPTER IX.

MOTION OF A RIGID BODY IN TWO DIMENSIONS.

§ 239. Instantaneous Centre.

A body can be moved in one plane from any one position into any other by rotation about some point in the plane without any translation.
During any motion let two points A, B (Fig. 152) of the body move into the positions A', B' respectively,

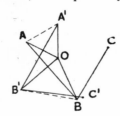

FIG. 152.

Bisect AA', BB' and erect perpendiculars to meet in O, so that OA = OA', and OB = OB'.
Then, since AB = A'B', the triangles AOB, A'OB' are congruent,

$$\therefore \angle AOB = \angle A'OB',$$
$$\therefore \angle AOA' = \angle BOB',$$
and $$\angle OBA = \angle OB'A'.$$

But if any other point C of the body has moved to C',

$$\angle CBA = \angle C'B'A',$$

∴ by subtraction of the third equation above,

$$\angle OBC = \angle OB'C'.$$
Also OB = OB', and BC = B'C',
∴ the triangles OBC, OB'C' are congruent, and we have
$$OC = OC',$$
and $$\angle COB = \angle C'OB',$$
$$\therefore \angle COC' = \angle BOB' = \angle AOA'.$$

Hence the rotation about O, which brings A to A', and B to B', also brings any other point C to its new position C'.

354

The point O always exists unless AA' is parallel to BB', i.e. when the motion is one of pure translation ; the centre of rotation O is then at infinity. When the displacement is very small the point O is called the *Instantaneous Centre*, and in general the body may be moved into the successive positions it occupies by successive instantaneous rotations about some centre or centres.

In the case of a circle rolling along a straight line, the instantaneous centre at any moment is the point of contact of the circle and the straight line.

§ **240.** The instantaneous centre has two loci according to whether we consider its position with regard to the body or in space.

Thus, in the case of the rolling circle, the successive points of contact are the points on the circle, i.e. their locus with regard to the circle is the circle itself. Their locus in space is the straight line on which the circle rolls.

These two loci are called the *Body-Locus* or *Body-Centrode*, and the *Space-Locus* or *Space-Centrode*.

To find the position of the instantaneous centre at any moment we select two points A and B of the body and draw lines at these points perpendicular to the directions in which they are moving at that moment. The point of intersection of these perpendiculars is the instantaneous centre.

EXAMPLE.

A rod AB is sliding with its ends on two perpendicular straight lines CX, CY. Find the instantaneous centre.

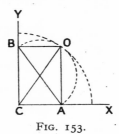

FIG. 153.

A and B are moving along CX and CY, hence we draw perpendiculars to CX and CY at A and B to meet in O (Fig. 153), then O is the instantaneous centre for the position shown.

Since ∠BOA is always a right angle, the locus of O with respect to the rod is the circle on AB as diameter.

Also, since CO = AB, the locus of O in space is a circle with C as centre and radius equal to the length of the rod.

It should be noticed that the instantaneous centre is the point of contact of the space and body centrodes.

23 *

§ **241.** We can find the co-ordinates of the instantaneous centre in terms of the component velocities of the centre of gravity and the angular velocity of the body about the centre of gravity.

Let u, v be the velocities of the centre of gravity G parallel to the axes GX, GY through G, and ω the angular velocity of the body about G (Fig. 154).

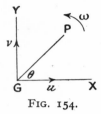

FIG. 154.

Then the velocities of any point P, whose co-ordinates referred to GX, GY are x and y, and such that PG is inclined at an angle θ to GX, are

$$u - \text{PG } \omega \sin \theta = u - y\omega, \text{ parallel to the } x\text{-axis,}$$
$$v + \text{PG } \omega \cos \theta = v + x\omega, \text{ parallel to the } y\text{-axis.}$$

Now these are zero if $\quad x = -\dfrac{v}{\omega}, \; y = \dfrac{u}{\omega},$

and these are the co-ordinates of the instantaneous centre referred to G as origin.

§ **242. Centre of no acceleration.**

With the notation of the last paragraph the accelerations of P relative to G are PG . ω^2 along GP, and PG . $\dot{\omega}$ perpendicular to PG.

Hence the component acceleration of P parallel to the axis of x is

$$\dot{u} - \text{PG} . \omega^2 \cos \theta - \text{PG} . \dot{\omega} \sin \theta = \dot{u} - x\omega^2 - y\dot{\omega},$$

and its acceleration parallel to the axis of y is

$$\dot{v} - \text{PG} . \omega^2 \sin \theta + \text{PG} . \dot{\omega} \cos \theta = \dot{v} - y\omega^2 + x\dot{\omega}.$$

If these are both zero,

$$x\omega^2 + y\dot{\omega} = \dot{u},$$
$$- x\dot{\omega} + y\omega^2 = \dot{v},$$
$$\therefore x(\omega^4 + \dot{\omega}^2) = \dot{u}\omega^2 - \dot{v}\dot{\omega},$$
$$\therefore x = \frac{\dot{u}\omega^2 - \dot{v}\dot{\omega}}{\omega^4 + \dot{\omega}^2}, \quad \text{and} \quad y = \frac{\dot{v}\omega^2 + \dot{u}\dot{\omega}}{\omega^4 + \dot{\omega}^2}.$$

EXAMPLES XLVI.

1. The centre of a disc falls vertically with constant acceleration, while the disc rotates in its own plane (which is vertical) with constant angular velocity. Prove that the locus in space of the instantaneous centre is a parabola.

2. Prove that if ω be the angular velocity of a lamina, the angular velocity of a point P of the lamina about a fixed point O is $\omega\frac{PN}{PO}$, where N is the foot of the perpendicular from the instantaneous centre upon PO.

3. A rod AB moves with its ends on two fixed lines OA, OB; show that if the rod turns with uniform angular velocity ω the velocity of any point P of the rod is equal to ω . IP perpendicular to IP, where IA, IB are drawn perpendicular to the fixed lines. Prove also that the acceleration of P is equal to ω^2 . OP towards O.

4. A disc moves in a plane in such a way that a point O on it describes a straight line in this plane with an acceleration f, whilst the disc itself is rotating about O with a constant angular velocity ω. Find the acceleration in magnitude and direction of any point of the disc. Hence prove that the locus of points whose accelerations have the same magnitude is a circle. (N.U.3)

5. A large sheet of paper lies on a table. The paper is moved without rotation so that a point in the paper which lies above a point A in the table takes up its position above a point B in the table ; the paper is then rotated about B through an angle θ. Show that there is a point C of the paper (if the sheet is large enough) whose position on the table is unaltered, and show how to find this point.

Show also that the paper might have been brought into its new position by a rotation about C through an angle θ. (N.U.3)

6. A bar AB slides with its ends one on each of two perpendicular lines OX, OY. Show that the speeds of A and B are in the ratio OB : OA. Prove that at any instant there is one point P on the rod which is moving in the direction AB, and that AP : PB=OB^2 : OA.^{2} (N.U.4)

§ **243.** In dealing with the motion of a body in one plane, when no point in the body is fixed, it is clear that the body can be brought from any one position to any other position by first moving some chosen point of it (say its centre of gravity) to its new position without any rotation, and then rotating the body about that point. This is also true for motion in three dimensions.

The working of problems is much simplified by considering the motion of a body to be made up of two parts in this manner, i.e. as a motion of translation of the centre of mass and a motion of rotation about the centre of mass.

We shall now prove two theorems which enable us to treat these motions separately.

I. *The motion of the centre of mass of a rigid body, acted on by any forces, is the same as if all the mass were collected at the centre of mass, and all the forces were applied at that point parallel to their former directions.*

II. *The motion of a rigid body, acted on by any forces, about its centre of mass is the same as if this point were fixed and the same forces acted on the body.*

§ **244.** Let x, y, z be the co-ordinates of a particle m of a body at time t referred to any set of fixed rectangular axes, and X, Y, Z the components of the impressed forces on this particle parallel to the axes.

Then, by D'Alembert's Principle, the forces

$$\left(X - m\frac{d^2x}{dt^2}\right), \quad \left(Y - m\frac{d^2y}{dt^2}\right), \quad \left(Z - m\frac{d^2z}{dt^2}\right),$$

together with similar forces for every other particle of the body, will be in equilibrium

Hence

$$\Sigma m \frac{d^2x}{dt^2} = \Sigma X \quad . \qquad . \qquad . \qquad . \qquad . \quad \text{(i)}$$

and two similar equations for y and z.

If $\bar{x}$, $\bar{y}$, $\bar{z}$ are the co-ordinates of the centre of mass, and M the mass of the body, then $M\bar{x} = \Sigma mx$, $M\bar{y} = \Sigma my$, and $M\bar{z} = \Sigma mz$, so that

$$M \frac{d^2\bar{x}}{dt^2} = \Sigma m \frac{d^2x}{dt^2},$$

$$M \frac{d^2\bar{y}}{dt^2} = \Sigma m \frac{d^2y}{dt^2},$$

$$M \frac{d^2\bar{z}}{dt^2} = \Sigma m \frac{d^2z}{dt^2}.$$

For motion in two dimensions we are only concerned with the equations in x and y, so that we have

$$M \frac{d^2\bar{x}}{dt^2} = \Sigma X,$$

$$M \frac{d^2\bar{y}}{dt^2} = \Sigma Y \quad . \qquad . \qquad . \qquad . \qquad . \quad \text{(ii)}$$

But these are the equations giving the motion of a mass M acted on by forces ΣX, ΣY, parallel to the axes.

This proves Theorem I.

Let (x', y') be the co-ordinates, relative to the centre of mass, of a particle m whose co-ordinates referred to the original axes were (x, y).

Then
$$x = \bar{x} + x', \quad y = \bar{y} + y',$$
$$\frac{d^2x}{dt^2} = \frac{d^2\bar{x}}{dt^2} + \frac{d^2x'}{dt^2}, \quad \frac{d^2y}{dt^2} = \frac{d^2\bar{y}}{dt^2} + \frac{d^2y'}{dt^2}.$$

Taking moments about the axis of z, D'Alembert's Principle gives

$$\Sigma m\left[(\bar{x} + x')\left(\frac{d^2\bar{y}}{dt^2} + \frac{d^2y'}{dt^2}\right) - (\bar{y} + y')\left(\frac{d^2\bar{x}}{dt^2} + \frac{d^2x'}{dt^2}\right)\right]$$

$$= \left[\Sigma(\bar{x} + x')Y - (\bar{y} + y')X\right],$$

or $\quad \Sigma m\left(\bar{x}\frac{d^2\bar{y}}{dt^2} - \bar{y}\frac{d^2\bar{x}}{dt^2}\right) + \Sigma m\left(x'\frac{d^2y'}{dt^2} - y'\frac{d^2x'}{dt^2}\right)$

$$+ \Sigma m\left(\bar{x}\frac{d^2y'}{dt^2} + x'\frac{d^2\bar{y}}{dt^2} - \bar{y}\frac{d^2x'}{dt^2} - y'\frac{d^2\bar{x}}{dt^2}\right) = \Sigma(\bar{x}Y - \bar{y}X) + \Sigma(x'Y - y'X).$$

Now the first expressions on the left and right-hand sides of this equation are equal from equations (ii) above.

The third expression on the left is zero since $\Sigma mx'$, $\Sigma m\frac{d^2x'}{dt^2}$, etc., are zero.

Hence $\quad \Sigma m\left(x'\frac{d^2y'}{dt^2} - y'\frac{d^2x'}{dt^2}\right) = \Sigma(x'Y - y'X)$ . . (iii)

But this is the equation we should get if the centre of mass were fixed.

This proves Theorem II.

§ **245.** In dealing with the motion of a rigid body in two dimensions we therefore write down the equations of motion for the centre of mass by considering all the impressed forces to act on the whole mass concentrated at that point. We then write down the equations for the motion about the centre of mass by taking moments about it as if it were a fixed point.

§ 246. Angular Momentum and Kinetic Energy of a Rigid Body moving in Two Dimensions.

If x, y be the co-ordinates of a particle m, then the moment of momentum, or angular momentum, about the axis of z for this

particle is $\quad\quad\quad m\left(x\frac{dy}{dt} - y\frac{dx}{dt}\right)$,

and for the whole body $\quad \Sigma m\left(x\frac{dy}{dt} - y\frac{dx}{dt}\right)$ . . . . (i)

Now, if $\bar{x}$, $\bar{y}$ are the co-ordinates of the centre of mass, and x', y' the co-ordinates of m referred to parallel axes with the centre of mass as origin,

$$x = \bar{x} + x', y = \bar{y} + y'.$$

Also,

$$\Sigma mx' = 0, \text{ and } \Sigma my' = 0,$$

$$\therefore \Sigma m\frac{dx'}{dt} = 0, \text{ and } \Sigma m\frac{dy'}{dt} = 0.$$

On substituting for x and y in (i) we get

$$\Sigma m\left(x'\frac{dy'}{dt} - y'\frac{dx'}{dt}\right) + M\left(\bar{x}\frac{d\bar{y}}{dt} - \bar{y}\frac{d\bar{x}}{dt}\right)$$

$$+ \bar{x}\Sigma m\frac{dy'}{dt} - \bar{y}\Sigma m\frac{dx'}{dt} + \frac{d\bar{y}}{dt}\Sigma mx' - \frac{d\bar{x}}{dt}\Sigma my'.$$

Now the four quantities in the second line are each zero.

The first term is the angular momentum about the centre of mass, and the second is the angular momentum about the origin of the whole mass collected at the centre of mass.

The kinetic energy of the body is equal to

$$\tfrac{1}{2}\Sigma m\left[\left(\frac{dx}{dt}\right)^2 + \left(\frac{dy}{dt}\right)^2\right].$$

Substituting $x = \bar{x} + x'$, $y = \bar{y} + y'$, this becomes

$$\tfrac{1}{2}\Sigma m\left[\left(\frac{dx'}{dt}\right)^2 + \left(\frac{dy'}{dt}\right)^2\right] + \tfrac{1}{2}\Sigma m\left[\left(\frac{d\bar{x}}{dt}\right)^2 + \left(\frac{d\bar{y}^2}{dt}\right)^2\right]$$

$$+ \frac{d\bar{x}}{dt}\Sigma m\frac{dx'}{dt} + \frac{d\bar{y}}{dt}\Sigma m\frac{dy'}{dt}.$$

Now the terms in the second line vanish.

The first term is the kinetic energy due to motion about the centre of mass. The second term is the kinetic energy of the whole mass Σm collected at the centre of mass.

We see therefore that—

The angular momentum about the origin is equal to the angular momentum about the centre of mass, together with the angular momentum about the origin of the whole mass collected at the centre of mass,
and also that—

The kinetic energy is equal to the kinetic energy due to motion about the centre of mass, together with the kinetic energy of the whole mass collected at the centre of mass.

§ **247.** Let M be the mass of the body, V the velocity of its centre of mass, ω the angular velocity about an axis through its centre of mass, and Mk^2 the moment of inertia about that axis.

The angular momentum about a point O is

$$MVp + Mk^2\omega,$$

where p is the length of the perpendicular from O on the direction of motion of the centre of mass.

The kinetic energy of the body is

$$\tfrac{1}{2}MV^2 + \tfrac{1}{2}Mk^2\omega^2.$$

§ 248. EXAMPLE (i).

A wheel with a diameter of 3 feet, and a mass of 70 lb., which may be regarded as distributed uniformly round the rim, is rolling along a horizontal road at a speed of 10 m.p.h. Calculate the number of ft. lb. of energy stored in the wheel.

If it comes to a hill rising 1 in 5 along the road, how far will it go before it stops ? (In a rolling motion no work is done against friction.)

(H.C.)

The moment of inertia of the wheel about its centre is

$$\frac{70 \times 9}{4} \text{ lb. ft.}^2$$

Since the centre is moving at $\frac{44}{3}$ ft./sec., the angular velocity is $\frac{44}{3} \div \frac{3}{2} = \frac{88}{9}$ radians per second.

The kinetic energy due to rotation $= \frac{1}{2} \cdot \frac{70 \times 9}{4} \cdot \frac{88^2}{9^2}$ ft. pdls.

The kinetic energy due to translation $= \frac{1}{2} \cdot 70 \cdot \frac{44^2}{9}$ ft. pdls.

The total kinetic energy $= \frac{35 \times 44^2}{9}\left[\frac{4}{4} + 1\right]$ ft. pdls.

$$= \frac{35 \times 44^2 \times 2}{9 \times 32} \text{ ft. lb.} = 470\tfrac{5}{9} \text{ ft. lb.}$$

It will run up the hill until the gain of potential energy is equal to the kinetic energy on the level (assuming that no change in speed occurs when it begins to mount the hill).

Hence, if x is the vertical height it rises,

$$70x = \frac{35 \times 44^2}{9 \times 16} = \frac{35 \times 121}{9},$$

$$\therefore x = \frac{35 \times 121}{9 \times 70} = \frac{121}{18} \text{ ft.}$$

The distance it goes up the slope is

$$\frac{5 \times 121}{18} = 33\tfrac{11}{18} \text{ ft.}$$

EXAMPLE (ii).

A uniform solid sphere of mass M and radius a rolls down an inclined plane, rough enough to prevent sliding ; find the motion.

Let α be the inclination of the plane, O (Fig. 155) the point of contact when the sphere was initially at rest, C the centre of the sphere, A the point on the sphere which was originally in contact with O, and N the point of contact at time t.

Take O as origin, ON as axis of x, CA as the line fixed in the body, and the normal to the plane as the line fixed in space for measuring the angular velocity, and let $\angle ACN = \theta$.

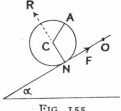

FIG. 155.

The external forces acting on the sphere are the friction F up the plane, the reaction R perpendicular to the plane, and the weight of the sphere vertically downwards.

Considering the motion of the centre of mass parallel and perpendicular to the plane,

$$M\ddot{x} = Mg \sin \alpha - F \qquad . \qquad . \qquad . \qquad . \quad \text{(i)}$$

$$M\ddot{y} = R - Mg \cos \alpha \qquad . \qquad . \qquad . \qquad . \quad \text{(ii)}$$

Taking moments about the centre of mass C,

$$Mk^2\ddot{\theta} = Fa \qquad . \qquad . \qquad . \qquad . \qquad . \quad \text{(iii)}$$

Now since the sphere remains in contact with the plane

$$\ddot{y} = 0,$$

$$\therefore R = Mg \cos \alpha.$$

Since there is no slipping,

$$x = a\theta,$$

$$\therefore \ddot{x} = a\ddot{\theta} \qquad . \qquad . \qquad . \qquad . \qquad . \quad \text{(iv)}$$

Also $k^2 = \tfrac{2}{5}a^2$, and from (iii) and (iv)

$$F = \tfrac{2}{5}Ma\ddot{\theta} = \tfrac{2}{5}M\ddot{x},$$

$\therefore$ from (i) $\tfrac{7}{5}M\ddot{x} = Mg \sin \alpha,$

$$\therefore \ddot{x} = \tfrac{5}{7}g \sin \alpha.$$

From (i) $F = \tfrac{2}{7}Mg \sin \alpha,$

and $R = Mg \cos \alpha,$

$$\therefore \frac{F}{R} = \tfrac{2}{7} \tan \alpha.$$

The coefficient of friction necessary to prevent sliding is therefore not less than $\tfrac{2}{7} \tan \alpha$.

EXAMPLES XLVII.

1. Show that the acceleration of a uniform circular disc, rolling down a plane of inclination α which is rough enough to prevent sliding, is $\tfrac{2}{3}g \sin \alpha$.

2. Show that the acceleration of a thin uniform circular ring, rolling down a plane of inclination α which is rough enough to prevent sliding, is $\tfrac{1}{2}g \sin \alpha$. Show also that the least coefficient of friction necessary to prevent sliding is $\tfrac{1}{2} \tan \alpha$.

3. One end of a thread, which is wound on to a reel, is fixed, and the reel falls in a vertical line, its axis being horizontal and the unwound part of the thread vertical. If the reel is a solid cylinder of radius a and mass M, show that the acceleration of the centre of the reel is $\frac{2}{3}g$ and that the tension of the thread is $\frac{1}{3}Mg$.

4. A girder is being pushed horizontally on three rollers at a speed of $\frac{1}{8}$ m.p.h., the diameter of each roller being 6 inches ; find the speed of their forward motion if there is no slipping. If the girder weighs 1 ton, and each roller 2 cwt., find the kinetic energy of the system in foot-pounds. (I.E.)

5. The total weight of a railway truck was 2 tons. It had two pairs of wheels, each pair weighing with the attached axle 0·24 ton. The radius of gyration of each wheel was 0·84 foot, and the distance from the centre of the axle to the rail was 1·2 feet. Calculate the kinetic energy of the truck when travelling at 60 ft./sec. If it can be brought to rest by the brakes in 80 seconds, without slipping of the wheels on the rails, find the retarding force, supposed constant, exerted by the rails. (I.E.)

6. Prove that the moment of inertia of a uniform cylindrical tube of mass M, about its axis, is equal to $\frac{1}{2}M(a^2 + b^2)$, where a and b are the internal and external radii of the tube.

    The tube starts from rest and rolls, with its axis horizontal, down an inclined plane of inclination α. Show that T, the time occupied in travelling a distance l along the plane, is given by

$$l\left(3 + \frac{a^2}{b^2}\right) = gT^2 \sin \alpha.$$

7. A wheel of radius a is formed of a thin uniform rim of mass M and n uniform spokes of length $a - b$, each of mass m, which are fastened to the rim and to an axle of radius b and mass m'. The wheel rolls down an inclined plane of inclination α. Find the acceleration of its centre. (H.C.)

8. Find the moment of inertia of a uniform circular cylinder 3 feet long, 1 foot in diameter, and weighing 40 lb., about (1) its axis, (2) a diameter of one of its ends. A roller of the above dimensions and mass rolls down a plane inclined at 30° to the horizontal, and rough enough to prevent slipping. The handle of the roller, whose mass may be neglected, is parallel to the plane and is attached to a cord also parallel to the plane, which passes over a smooth fixed pulley attached to the highest point of the plane and carries a weight of 10 lb. at its other end. Find the acceleration of the weight as the roller rolls down the plane. (H.C.)

9. At a point P of a uniform circular hoop there is attached a particle of mass equal to that of the hoop. The hoop rolls, in a vertical plane, on a perfectly rough horizontal table. Prove that if the system starts from rest when P is at the highest point, the angular velocity ω, when the radius to P makes an angle θ with the downward vertical, is given by

$$\omega^2 = \frac{g}{a} \cdot \frac{1 + \cos \theta}{2 - \cos \theta}.$$

10. A heavy particle of mass m is attached to the highest point of a uniform sphere of mass M and radius a, which rests on a perfectly

rough horizontal plane. If the equilibrium is just disturbed, find the angular velocity of the sphere in terms of the angle through which it will have rolled at any time, and the direction of the .plane's reaction when it has rolled through 90°. (S.)

11. A plane lamina of mass M in the form of a square of side $2a$ is placed with a diagonal almost vertical and its lowest point in contact with a *smooth* horizontal plane, and falls from this position, remaining in a vertical plane. Find its angular velocity when the diagonal that was vertical makes an angle θ with the vertical.

12. A uniform rod of length $2a$ is swinging as a pendulum about one end, its greatest angular deviation from the downward vertical being α. At an instant when the rod is vertical its fixed end is suddenly released ; find how far the centre of the rod descends before it is again vertical.

13. A uniform rod, of length $2a$, hinged at one end to a fixed point O, is let fall from the horizontal position ; when it becomes vertical the hinge breaks. Prove that, when the rod is next horizontal, the horizontal and vertical distances of its middle point from O are $\dfrac{\pi a}{2}$ and $a + \dfrac{\pi^2 a}{12}$ respectively.

14. A small ring of mass M can slide on a fixed smooth horizontal wire, and a particle of mass m is attached to the ring by a light rod of length l. The particle is held in contact with the wire and is let fall. What is the path described by the centre of gravity of the ring and the particle ? Also show that the path of the particle m is a semi-ellipse, and that, if ω denotes the greatest angular velocity attained by the rod,

$$Ml\omega^2 = 2(M + m)g. \qquad \text{(H.S.D.)}$$

15. A circular cylinder of radius r has its centre of mass in its axis, and has a radius of gyration k about this axis. Prove that, when it rolls down a plane of inclination α, the acceleration is

$$\frac{r^2 g \sin \alpha}{r^2 + k^2}. \qquad \text{(N.U.3)}$$

16. Prove that if the rotational velocity of a rigid body is zero the sum of the moments of the forces acting on it about its centre of mass must be zero, even if the body has an acceleration of translation.
    The centre of gravity of a table is 4 feet above a smooth horizontal floor and midway between the front and back pair of legs which are 5 feet apart. The table, which weighs W lb., is being accelerated by a force $\frac{1}{4}W$ lb. wt., acting horizontally 3 feet above the floor in a direction from the middle of the back to the middle of the front pair of legs. Find the upward thrust of the floor on each pair of legs. (N.U.3.)

§ 249. Impulsive Forces.

When a rigid body, free to move in a plane, is struck by a blow in that plane, we can obtain the resulting motion from the following considerations. The change in the linear momentum is in the direction of the blow, and equal to the impulse of the blow.

The change in the angular momentum about the centre of mass is equal to the moment of the blow about the centre of mass. Instead of considering the angular momentum about the centre of mass, it is often convenient to use the fact that the change of angular momentum about any point in the line of action of the impulse is zero.

These principles are illustrated in the following examples :—

EXAMPLE (i).

A uniform rod AB, of length 2a, is lying on a smooth horizontal plane and is struck by a horizontal blow, of impulse P, perpendicular to the length of the rod at a distance x from the centre. Find the motion and the point about which the rod begins to turn.

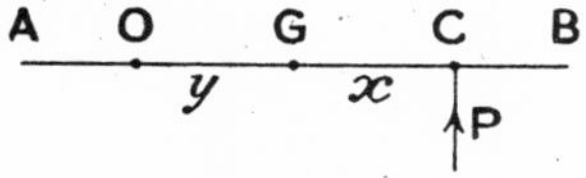

FIG. 156.

The centre of mass G (Fig. 156) will begin to move in the direction of *P*, and the rod will begin to turn about G.

Let *u* be the velocity of G, *M* the mass of the rod, and *ω* the angular velocity, then

$$Mu = P \qquad . \qquad . \qquad . \qquad . \qquad (i)$$

and

$$M \frac{a^2}{3} \omega = Px \qquad . \qquad . \qquad . \qquad . \qquad (ii)$$

These equations give *u* and *ω*.

Let O be the point about which the rod begins to turn, where GO = *y*. The velocity of O relative to G is *yω* in the opposite direction to that in which G moves, hence the velocity of O is

$$y\omega - u,$$

and this is zero if

$$y = \frac{u}{\omega} = \frac{a^2}{3x}, \text{ from (i) and (ii).}$$

The distance between O and the line of action of *P* is

$$\frac{a^2}{3x} + x = \frac{a^2 + 3x^2}{3x}.$$

This is the length of the simple equivalent pendulum when the rod is suspended at C or O.

The points O and C are the same as those in § 233, where O was called the centre of suspension and C the centre of oscillation.

EXAMPLE (ii).

A light rigid rod has particles, each of mass m, attached at A, B and C, where AB = a, BC = b. A blow P perpendicular to the rod is applied at the middle point of AC; show that the angular velocity acquired is

$$\frac{P}{4m} \cdot \frac{a \sim b}{a^2 + ab + b^2}.$$ (C.S.)

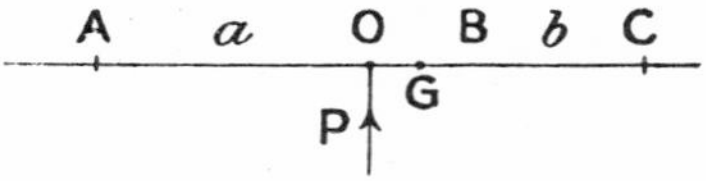

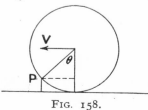

FIG. 157.

Let O (Fig. 157) be the middle point of AC, G the centre of mass of the three particles.
Then

$$OB = a - \frac{a+b}{2} = \frac{a-b}{2}, \; OG = \frac{a-b}{6}, \; GB = \frac{a-b}{3}.$$

$$\therefore AG = \frac{a+b}{2} + \frac{a-b}{6} = \frac{2a+b}{3}, \; GC = \frac{a-b}{3} + b = \frac{a+2b}{3}.$$

Hence the moment of inertia about G is $m(AG^2 + GB^2 + GC^2)$

$$= m\left[\frac{4a^2 + 4ab + b^2}{9} + \frac{a^2 - 2ab + b^2}{9} + \frac{a^2 + 4ab + 4b^2}{9}\right]$$

$$= \tfrac{2}{3}m(a^2 + ab + b^2).$$

The centre of mass G moves parallel to P, and taking moments about G, if ω is the angular velocity,

$$\tfrac{2}{3}m(a^2 + ab + b^2)\omega = P\frac{a-b}{6}, \;\cdot$$

$$\therefore \omega = \frac{P}{4m} \cdot \frac{a-b}{a^2 + ab + b^2}.$$

EXAMPLE (iii).

A circular hoop of radius a, rolling on a rough horizontal plane, impinges on a rough peg of height $\tfrac{1}{2}a$ fixed in the plane. Find the angular velocity with which the hoop begins to turn about the peg. If V be the velocity of the centre before the impact, prove that if $81V^2 < 8oga$, the hoop leaves the peg immediately.   (H.C.)

FIG. 158.

Since V is the velocity of the centre, the angular velocity is $\dfrac{V}{a}$.

Let C (Fig. 158) be the centre, P the point of contact with the peg. The angular momentum about P is unaltered by the impact. Now the angular momentum about P before impact is

$$Ma^2\frac{V}{a} + \tfrac{4}{5}MaV = \tfrac{9}{5}MaV,$$

and if ω is the angular velocity after impact, the angular momentum about P is $2Ma^2\omega$.

$$\therefore 2Ma^2\omega = \tfrac{9}{5}MaV,$$
$$\therefore \omega = \frac{9V}{10a}.$$

Resolving along CP after the impact, since the velocity of C is $a\omega$ perpendicular to CP, we have, if R is the pressure on the peg,

$$Mg\cos\theta - R = M\frac{a^2\omega^2}{a},$$
$$\therefore R = \tfrac{4}{5}Mg - Ma\omega^2,$$
$$= \tfrac{4}{5}Mg - Ma\frac{81}{100}\cdot\frac{V^2}{a^2},$$

and R becomes negative, i.e. the hoop leaves the peg immediately, unless

$$Ma\frac{81V^2}{100a^2} < \tfrac{4}{5}Mg,$$
or $81V^2 < 80ga.$

EXAMPLES XLVIII.

1. Two masses m, m', connected by a weightless rod, lie on a smooth horizontal table. The rod is struck at right angles to its length by an impulsive force F ; find the velocities of the masses, and show that the kinetic energy is least if F is applied at the centre of gravity of the masses. (C.S.)

2. Two particles A, B, each of mass m, are attached to the ends of a light rod of length a. The rod is horizontal and instantaneously at rest when A receives an upward vertical impulse mv. Prove that, in the subsequent motion, the vertical component of B's velocity will always be downwards if $\dfrac{v^2}{2ga}$ is less than the least positive root of the equation
$$x\sin(x + \sqrt{x^2 - 1}) = 1. \qquad\text{(C.S.)}$$

3. Two particles A, B of masses $2m$ and m respectively are connected by a light rod and lie on a smooth horizontal table. If the mass A is struck a blow in a direction $\tan^{-1}\tfrac{4}{3}$ with AB, prove that the initial velocity of A is $\sqrt{5}$ times that of B. (C.S.)

4. Two equal heavy particles A, B are connected by a light wire, and lie on a smooth table. If A is struck a blow at right angles to AB, so that it starts with velocity V, determine the subsequent motion. (H.S.C.)

5. A uniform heavy rod, of length $2l$, has attached to it at one end a small ring which is free to move on a smooth horizontal wire. If the rod is let go from a horizontal position in which it lies along and under the wire, prove that when it becomes vertical the velocity of either end is $\sqrt{6lg}$. (H.S.C.)

6. A cube of side $2a$ slides down a smooth plane inclined at an angle $2\tan^{-1}\frac{1}{5}$ to the horizontal, and meets a fixed horizontal bar placed perpendicular to the plane of the motion and at a perpendicular distance $\frac{a}{4}$ from the plane. Show that, if the cube is to have sufficient velocity to surmount the obstacle when it reaches it, it must be allowed first to slide down the plane through a distance $\frac{107}{60}a$. The obstacle may be taken to be inelastic and so rough that the cube does not slip on it.

7. A uniform rod of mass m and length $2a$ is lying on a smooth horizontal table and is struck a blow P perpendicular to its length at one extremity. Find the velocities with which the two ends begin to move.

8. A four-wheeled railway truck has a total mass M, the mass and radius of gyration of each pair of wheels and axle are m and k respectively, and the radius of each wheel is r. Prove that, if the truck is propelled along a level track by a force P, the acceleration is

$$\frac{P}{M + \dfrac{2mk^2}{r^2}},$$

and find the horizontal force exerted on each axle by the truck. (Axle friction and wind resistance are to be neglected.) (M.T.)

9. A solid uniform circular cylinder of mass m and radius r rolls (under the action of gravity) inside a fixed hollow cylinder of radius R, the axes of the cylinders being parallel to each other and also horizontal. At any time t during the motion the plane containing the axes of the cylinders makes an angle θ with the vertical. Show that the potential energy of the moving cylinder is

$$mg(R - r)\,(1 - \cos\theta),$$

and that its kinetic energy is

$$\frac{3m}{4}(R - r)^2\left(\frac{d\theta}{dt}\right)^2.$$

Hence, or otherwise, show that the time T of a small oscillation is

$$T = 2\pi\sqrt{\frac{3(R - r)}{2g}}. \qquad \text{(M.T.)}$$

10. An impulse is applied at a point P in the rim of a uniform circular disc in such a manner that P starts to move along the tangent to the rim at P. Prove that the initial velocity of the centre of the disc is $\frac{1}{3}$ that of P.

11. A uniform circular hoop lying on a smooth table receives a blow at a point P, the direction of the blow lying in the plane of the hoop and making an angle α with the radius through P. Show that P begins to move in a direction inclined to the radius through P at an angle $\tan^{-1}(2\tan\alpha)$.

12. A uniform square lamina of mass M lying on a smooth horizontal table has a particle of mass m attached to one corner by an inextensible string. The particle is projected with velocity V along the table in a direction along one of the sides through the point of attachment. Prove that the loss of energy of the system when the string becomes taut is

$$\tfrac{1}{2}mV^2 \Big/ \left(1 + \frac{5m}{2M}\right).$$

13. A uniform rod AB hangs vertically from a fixed point A. At B is attached freely an equal rod BC which also hangs vertically. At a point D in BC a horizontal blow of given magnitude is applied. Prove that if BD is $\frac{3}{5}$ of BC, then the initial angular velocity of BC is zero.
(S.)

14. Two uniform rods AB, BC, alike in all respects, are freely jointed at B and lie on a smooth horizontal plane with AB and BC in one straight line. AB receives a horizontal blow at its middle point at right angles to its length. Show that the two rods begin to move with the same angular velocity.

15. A lamina at rest on a smooth horizontal table receives a horizontal blow at a given point. Prove that, whatever be the magnitude and direction of the blow, the instantaneous centre of rotation lies upon a fixed straight line.

16. A billiard ball, whose diameter is 2 inches, moving with a velocity of 10 ft./sec. and having an angular velocity about a vertical axis through the centre of 100 radians a second, is made to rebound off the side cushion of the table in such a way as will ensure its path being deflected through a right angle. The sense of the spin and disposition of the cushion are shown in Fig. 159, and it may

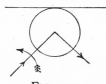

FIG. 159.

be assumed (i) that there is no slip at the impact, (ii) that the impulsive reaction is in a horizontal plane passing through the centre of the ball, and (iii) that the coefficient of restitution is 0·75. Find the angle that the initial path must make with the cushion. (N.U.4)

17. A lamina of mass M moving in its own plane has angular velocity ω, and its mass-centre G has a velocity V. Prove that its momentum can be represented by a vector MV at a distance $\dfrac{k^2\omega}{V}$ from G.

Two equal uniform rods AB, BC, each of length $2a$, are smoothly jointed at B and rest in a straight line on a smooth table. The rod AB is smoothly pivoted to the table at a point distant x from B. If a blow is given to C in a horizontal direction perpendicular to the rods, prove that their initial angular velocities are in the ratio

$$2ax : 12ax - 9x^2 - 8a^2 \qquad\text{(N.U.4)}$$

ANSWERS TO THE EXAMPLES.

EXAMPLES I.

(1) 19 ft./sec.
(2) 12·16 ft./sec.
(3) 34 ft./sec.

(4) $6\sqrt{3}$ or 10·39 ft./sec.
(5) 30 ft./sec. ; 51·96 ft./sec.

EXAMPLES II.

(1) 300 ft.
(2) At $\cos^{-1}\frac{1}{3}$ with the bank up stream.
(3) At 131° 48' with his direction of motion.
(4) The one who swims north ; $\frac{1}{2}$ min. sooner.
(5) 80° 25'.

(6) 12 nearly ; about 79° N. of E.
(9) (i) straight across ; 2 mins. ; $\frac{1}{6}$ mile ;
   (ii) at $\tan^{-1}\frac{1}{3}$ with bank up stream ; $2\frac{1}{2}$ mins. ; 704 ft.
(10) 16° 41' E. of N. ; 43° 19' E. of N.

EXAMPLES III.

(1) 64·03 m.p.h. at 38° 40' with direction of second.
(2) 18·03 m.p.h. at 33° 41' with direction of 'bus.
(3) $\tan^{-1}\frac{6}{11}$ with horizontal ; 24·17 ft./sec.
(4) $\tan^{-1}\frac{2+\sqrt{2}}{2}$ S. of W.
(5) 20 m.p.h. ; $\tan^{-1}\frac{3}{4}$ W. of N.
(6) After 0·55 hour ; 6·9 miles.
(7) $\sin^{-1}\frac{1}{35}$ in front of ship.
(8) 5 m.p.h. ; $\tan^{-1}\frac{4}{3}$ with A's direction.
(9) $17\frac{1}{2}$ m.p.h. ; 202 yds. and 36·7 yds.
(10) $11\frac{1}{3}$ m.p.h. ; $\tan^{-1}\frac{4\sqrt{2}-3}{3}$ W. of N. ; $\frac{\sqrt{2}}{2}$ miles.

(11) 26° 9' E. of N.
(12) 31° 5' N. of E. ; 20·55 knots.
(13) 56·35 m.p.h. ; 27° 28' N. of E. ; about $4\frac{1}{2}$ mins.
(14) 0·13 mile.
(15) 12·8 m.p.h. ; nearly 5 mins.
(16) 4·92 mins.
(17) 48° 36' with FW.
(18) 15·4 nautical miles ; 47° E. of N.
(19) 10·1 knots ; 12° 7' E. of N. ; 10° 11' W. of N. ; 9·7 knots.
(21) 147 and 96 nautical miles nearly.
(22) $\frac{1}{20}$ mile.
(23) 10·36 m.p.h.
(24) 24·97 m.p.h.
(25) (i) 0·19 mile ; (ii) $\frac{1}{4}$ mile.

EXAMPLES IV.

(1) 10π ; 62·8 ft./sec.
(3) 71·55 m.p.h. at 26° 33' above and below the horizontal.
(4) Nearly 109 ft./sec.
(5) 18 : 1.
(6) 5 ; 28·28 ft./sec. at 45° above and below the horizontal.

(7) $12\frac{1}{2}$ m.p.h. ; $7\frac{1}{2}$ m.p.h. ; 20 m.p.h.; zero.
(8) $u+v$; $\sqrt{u^2+v^2+\sqrt{2uv}}$; $\sqrt{u^2+v^2}$; where u is the velocity of the wheel and v that of the point.
(9) $\frac{1}{3}\sqrt{1813+588\cos\theta}$ m.p.h.

24 *

EXAMPLES V.

(1) 25 yds. per sec.
(2) 0·264 ft./sec.^{2} ; 0·528 ft./sec.^{2}
(3) 5 ft./sec.^{2}
(4) $2b = a + c$; $f = \dfrac{c-b}{t^2}$; $u = \dfrac{3a-b}{2t}$.
(6) $u = 3$ ft./sec. ; $f = \frac{1}{2}$ ft./sec.^{2} ; 720 ft.
(7) $\frac{29}{105}$ mile ; $44\sqrt{2} = 62\cdot2$ ft./sec.
(8) $\frac{121}{625}$ ft./sec.^{2}
(11) 300 ft.
(14) $\dfrac{3u+v}{4(u+v)}$.

(15) $u = \dfrac{4b - c - 3a}{2n}$.
(16) $8\frac{1}{4}$ miles.
(18) $\frac{2}{3}$ ft./sec.^{2} ; $\frac{3}{4}$ ft./sec.^{2}
(19) 3 secs. more.
(20) $\frac{6}{7}$.
(21) $10\sqrt{7}$ m.p.h. ;   4 mins. ;   2·58 mins.
(22) $\frac{1}{11}$ ft./sec.^{2}
(23) 176 secs. ; $1\frac{43}{44}$ mile.
(24) 20 ft./sec. ; $82\frac{1}{2}$ secs.
(25) 120 ft. W. of O.
(26) $43\frac{1}{2}$ m.p.h.

EXAMPLES VI.

(1) Uniform speed for the first 10 secs., then an acceleration of $\frac{3}{4}$ ft./sec.^{2} ; 275 ft.
(2) 40 ft./sec. ; 2 ft./sec.^{2}
(4) $37\frac{1}{2}$ ft./sec.
(5) The increase in $\frac{1}{2}v^2$.
(6) $\frac{9}{8}$ ft./sec.^{2} ; 81 ft./sec. ; 3240 yds.
(7) 66 ft./sec.
(8) 1571 ft. ; 38 secs.

(9) 2·8 ft./sec.^{2}
(11) 23·2 ft./sec. ; 25 ft./sec.
(12) 2·7 miles ; $\frac{1}{3}$ ft./sec.^{2}
(13) 57 ft. ; 9 ft./sec.^{2}
(14) 0·975 ft./sec.^{2} ; 1 ft./sec.^{2}
(15) $14\frac{2}{3}$, 20, 30, 30 ft./sec.
(16) About 1·9 sec.
(17) $\frac{11}{12}$ mile ; 35 m.p.h. ; 1 min.

EXAMPLES VII.

(1) $3\frac{67}{80}$ mins.
(2) 81·24 secs.
(3) (i) The foot of the perpendicular from B on OA ;
   (ii) the centre O.
(4) He cannot swim up stream.
(6) B, in direction CB ; C at $\tan^{-1}\frac{4}{3}$ with CB ; $\tan^{-1}\frac{3}{4}$ with AB.
(7) $\dfrac{b}{a} = \dfrac{\sin OPQ}{\sin OQP}$; $\dfrac{v}{u} = -\dfrac{\cos OPQ}{\cos OQP}$.

(8) $\theta = \dfrac{\pi}{2}$.
(9) $1\frac{1}{21}$; $\frac{7}{13}$; 440 ft.
(10) 34° 48′ E. of N. ; 3 hrs. 6 mins. ; 31·5 miles to N.
(11) 11·1 mins.
(12) $\cos^{-1}\frac{39}{40}$ or 12° 49′ ; 28° 17′.
(13) $11\frac{1}{4}$ knots ; $21\frac{1}{2}$ mins. nearly.
(14) $2\frac{68}{87}$ mins.
(15) 2 secs. nearly ; $8\frac{1}{15}$ ft./sec.^{2}
(16) $54\frac{6}{11}$ m.p.h. ; $49\frac{1}{11}$ m.p.h.

EXAMPLES VIII.

(1) (i) $56\frac{1}{4}$ ft. ; (ii) $\frac{3}{4}$ sec. and 3 secs.
(2) (i) After 2 secs. ; (ii) 5 secs. ; (iii) 1 sec. and 4 secs.
(3) (i) 1600 ft. ; (ii) $2\frac{1}{2}$ secs. ; (iii) 80 ft./sec.
(4) 264 ft.
(5) (i) 3 secs. ; (ii) 16 ft.

(6) 400 ft.
(7) 320 ft./sec. ; 20 secs.
(8) 49·17 ft.
(12) 1 ft. above the top of the window.
(13) 24 ft. ; $2\frac{1}{2}$ sec.
(16) 240 ft. ; 272 ft. ; 8·8 secs.

EXAMPLES IX.

(1) $112\frac{1}{2}$ ft. ; $3\frac{3}{4}$ secs.
(2) 30°.
(3) 24 ft./sec. ; $3\frac{1}{3}$ secs.
(5) $\sqrt{\dfrac{g}{2h}}\dfrac{l^2 - h^2}{l}$.

(6) $\frac{1}{2}gt^2 \sin \alpha \cos \beta$.
   A circle of diameter $\frac{1}{4}gt^2 \sin \alpha$ with A as highest point.

EXAMPLE X.

(1) Let the bisector of $\angle$BCA cut BA in D, and let the circle with centre D and radius B touch CA at E, then BE is the required line.

EXAMPLES XI.

(1) $\frac{1}{2}$ ft./sec.² ;   16 ft./sec.²

(2) $\frac{77}{25}$ lb. wt.

(3) $36\frac{2}{3}$ mins.

(4) $53\frac{31}{648}$ tons wt.

(5) $188\frac{2}{5}$ ft.

(6) $102\frac{2}{3}$ lb. wt. per ton ; 1 min.

(7) 225 cm./sec. ; $562\frac{1}{2}$ cm.

(8) 80,000 dynes.

(9) 1·23 mile.

(11) 6150 dynes.

(12) $11\frac{13}{80}$ lb. wt. per ton.

(13) $19\frac{1}{5}$ ft./sec. ; $28\frac{4}{5}$ ft.

(14) (i) 10 lb. ; (ii) $11\frac{9}{16}$ lb. wt.

(15) (i) $192\frac{1}{2}$ lb. wt. ; (ii) $87\frac{1}{2}$ lb. wt.

(16) 19 cm./sec.².

(17) $\frac{g}{13}$ downwards.

(18) (i) 110 secs. ; (ii) 22 secs. ; (iii) 546 secs.

(19) $220\sqrt{3}$ secs.

(20) 9 lb. ; $\frac{g}{9}$.

(21) 2 : 1.

(22) $250\sqrt{2}$ ft./sec.

(23) 1323×10^5 dynes ; 134862·4 gm. wt.

EXAMPLES XII.

(1) (i) 8 ft./sec.² ; (ii) $7\frac{1}{2}$ lb. wt. ; (iii) 15 lb. wt.

(2) (i) $5\frac{1}{3}$ ft./sec.² (ii) $5\frac{5}{6}$ lb. wt.

(3) (i) 4 ft./sec.² ; (ii) $7\frac{7}{8}$ oz. wt.

(4) (i) $196\frac{1}{4}$ cm./sec.² ; (ii) 24 gm. wt.

(5) (i) 14 ft./sec.² ; (ii) $3\frac{15}{16}$ lb. wt. ; (iii) $\frac{63\sqrt{2}}{16}$ lb. wt.

(6) (i) 1 sec. ; (ii) $\frac{1}{2}$ sec.

(7) (i) 1 sec. ; (ii) 1 sec.

(8) (i) 8 ft./sec.² ; (ii) $2\frac{1}{4}$ lb. wt.

(9) (i) 1 sec. ; (ii) $2\frac{1}{2}$ secs.

(10) (i) $\sqrt{5}$ secs. ; (ii) $\frac{\sqrt{5}}{2}$ secs.

(11) $13\frac{1}{3}$ ft.

(12) $2\frac{2}{7}$ ft./sec.² ; $2\frac{1}{4}$ lb. wt.

(13) 8 ft./sec.² ; $2\frac{1}{4}$ lb. wt.

(14) 32 ft./sec. ; 112 ft.

(16) 7·32 ft./sec.²

(17) $8\sqrt{10}$ ft./sec. ; $\frac{5\sqrt{10}}{4}$ secs.

(18) 6·4 ft./sec.² ; $3\frac{1}{2}$ ins.

(19) 16 ft./sec.² ; 0·79 sec.

(20) 17920 and 15360 ; 16 ft./sec.

(21) $4\sqrt{55}$ ft./sec.

(22) $o = V - \frac{F}{M}t$; $o = V^2 - \frac{2F}{M}s$.   8 : 1 and 1 : 4.

(23) $\dfrac{W_1W_2(1 + \mu)g}{W_1 + nW_2}$; $\dfrac{nW_1W_2(1 + \mu)g}{W_1 + nW_2}$; $\dfrac{W_1 - \mu nW_2}{W_1 + W_2n}g$; $W_1 : W_2 = n : \mu$.

(24) $1\frac{1}{21}$ kilo ; $\frac{g}{21}$; 42 cm./sec.²

EXAMPLES XIII.

(1) $21\frac{1}{3}$ ft./sec.² ; $\frac{5}{3}m$ lb. wt.

(2) 12 lb. ; 20 lb. wt.

(3) $5\frac{5}{7}$ lb. ; $13\frac{5}{7}$ ft./sec.² ; $2\frac{6}{7}$ lb. wt.

(4) For M, $\dfrac{4m_1m_2 - M(m_1 + m_2)}{4m_1m_2 + M(m_1 + m_2)}g$;

for m_1 $\dfrac{4m_1m_2 + M(m_1 - 3m_2)}{4m_1m_2 + M(m_1 + m_2)}g$;

for m_2 $\dfrac{M(3m_1 - m_2) - 4m_1m_2}{4m_1m_2 + M(m_1 + m_2)}g$.

(5) $\dfrac{2Mmg}{(m+4M)(m+M)}$, $\dfrac{m^2g}{(m+4M)(m+M)}$.

(6) $\frac{9}{13}mg$ pdls. ; A, $\frac{5}{13}g$; B, $\frac{10}{13}g$.

(7) $\dfrac{wg}{3W + 2w}$ for $(W + w)$; $\dfrac{wg}{3W + 2w}$ for $2W$.

(8) $\frac{g}{4}$.

(9) (i) 2 oz. wt. ; (ii) $1\frac{5}{7}$ oz. wt. ; (iii) $1\frac{1}{7}$ oz. wt.

(11) 2 : 1.

(12) $\dfrac{mg \sin \alpha \cos \alpha}{M + m \sin^2 \alpha}$, $\dfrac{Mg \sin \alpha \cos \alpha}{M + m \sin^2 \alpha}$, $\dfrac{(M + m) \sin^2 \alpha}{M + m \sin^2 \alpha}g$.

(14) $\frac{g}{23}$ downwards.

(15) Acceleration of m, $\dfrac{3Mm'g}{M(m + m') + 4mm'}$;

Acceleration of m', $\dfrac{M(m' - 2m) + 4mm'}{M(m + m') + 4mm'}g$;

Acceleration of M, $\dfrac{M(m + m') - 2mm'}{M(m + m') + 4mm'}g$;

Tension, $\dfrac{3Mmm'g}{M(m + m') + 4mm'}$.

(16) $\dfrac{3Mmm'g}{M(m + m') + 4mm'}$.

(17) $\dfrac{M(M + m)g\cos\alpha}{M + m\sin^2\alpha}$.

(18) $8\frac{3}{4}$ secs. ; $17\frac{17}{24}$ secs. ; 10 cwt.

(19) $1\frac{1}{4}$ ft./sec.^{2}

(20) 966 lb. wt.

(23) $\frac{1}{8}g$; 24 lb. wt. ; 48 lb. wt.

(26) $Mg\dfrac{n^2g}{n^2g - 2b}$.

(29) $\frac{13}{17}g$; $\frac{1}{8}g$.

(30) 13 ft./sec.^{2}

(32) $\dfrac{g}{5}$; $\dfrac{4g}{101}$; $\dfrac{21g}{101}$.

(35) $\dfrac{5m_1m_2g}{16m_2 + m_1}$; $\dfrac{20m_1m_2g}{16m_2 + m_1}$.

EXAMPLES XIV.

(1) 25 lb. wt. per ton.
(2) 168 lb. wt. ; 13·44 H.P.
(3) $507\frac{11}{16}$ H.P.
(4) $6346\frac{2}{3}$ lb. wt. ; $507\frac{11}{16}$ H.P.
(5) 15 m.p.h.
(6) $\frac{9}{77}$.
(7) 618 lb. wt. ; 16·48 H.P.
(8) $86826\frac{2}{3}$.
(9) (i) 0·46 ; (ii) 9·2.
(10) 28·64 H.P.
(11) $230\frac{10}{21}$ ft. ; $201\frac{2}{3}$ ft.
(12) $\tan\alpha < \mu$.
(13) 677·6 ft. lb. ; 45 m.p.h.
(14) 2 pdls. ; $18\frac{3}{4}$ ft. lb. ; $\dfrac{\sqrt3}{440}$ H.P.
(15) $170\frac{1}{2}$ ft.
(16) 436 ft. lb. ; 8 H.P.
(17) $8\frac{1}{6}$ ft. lb. ; $\frac{13}{2400}$ H.P.
(18) (a) 68·4.   (b) 5·7 m.p.h.
(19) 1 in $\dfrac{mV}{550H - VR}$; $\dfrac{550Hn}{V}$;
1 in $34\frac{2}{7}$; $93\frac{3}{4}$ lb. wt.
(20) (i) $11\frac{2}{7}$ m.p.h. ; (ii) $8\frac{9}{7}$ m.p.h. ; $18\frac{3}{4}$ lb. wt.
(21) $606\frac{6}{11}$ H.P.
(22) 768 H.P. ; 72 m.p.h.
(23) $7\frac{1}{2}$ secs. ; $244\frac{4}{11}$ H.P.
(24) $2462\frac{22}{49}$ H.P.
(25) 256 H.P. ; $23\frac{9}{17}$ m.p.h.
(26) $\frac{2}{9}$ ft./sec.^{2} ; $56\frac{1}{4}$ m.p.h.
(27) (i) 537·6 H.P. ; (ii) 1075·2 H.P.
(29) $266\frac{2}{3}$ ft. ; $1333\frac{1}{3}$ ft. lb.
(30) 16·9 H.P.
(31) 1·9 H.P.
(32) 8800 ft. lb. ; 4840 ft. lb. ; 24·8 H.P.

(33) $1339\frac{11}{16}$ H.P.
(34) 300 lb. wt. ; $85\frac{3}{7}$ mins. ; $17\frac{89}{108}$ miles ; 78 miles.
(35) 14,525 lb. wt.
(36) $11\frac{6}{17}$ H.P.
(37) 5·98 H.P.
(38) $11\frac{1}{6}$ lb. wt. per ton ; $1\frac{12}{125}$ H.P.
(39) $\frac{11}{30}$ ft./sec.^{2} ; $4106\frac{2}{3}$ lb. wt. ; $657\frac{1}{15}$ H.P.
(40) $266\frac{2}{3}$ H.P.
(41) $37\frac{1}{2}$ m.p.h.
(42) $34\frac{6}{17}$ H.P.
(44) $658\frac{14}{15}$ H.P.
(45) $4·45 \times 10^5$; $835\frac{1}{2}$ H.P.
(46) $46\frac{11}{18}$ m.p.h. ; 22·73 m.p.h. ; 1 in 160.
(47) $62\frac{1}{4}$ m.p.h. ; 3000 lb. wt.
(48) 29·96 H.P.
(49) 12 m.p.h. ; $1\frac{11}{14}$ ft./sec.^{2}
(51) $2\frac{34}{55}$ H.P.
(52) $272\frac{8}{11}$ H.P.
(53) 121 : 225 ; $\frac{9688}{17113}$; 6·1 H.P.
(54) 35·96 secs. ; 11·99 H.P.
(55) 48·5 H.P.
(57) $32\frac{8}{11}$ H.P. ; 8 ; 2250 lb. wt. ft.
(58) $648\frac{4}{27}$ lb. wt. ; 3·9 ins.
(60) 1·136 cm.
(63) $128\frac{4}{7}$ ft. ; $\frac{94}{77}$ H.P. ; $7\frac{1}{3}$ ft./sec.
(64) 5° 8′.
(65) 42·6 H.P. ; $94\frac{7}{17}$ m.p.h.
(67) $1\frac{87}{88}$ H.P.
(68) 550 ; $13\frac{3}{4}$ secs.
(69) $583\frac{1}{3}$ ft.
(70) $17,562\frac{1}{2}$ lb. wt. ; $8781\frac{1}{4}$ lb. wt.
(71) 8125 lb. wt. ; $25\frac{25}{77}$ m.p.h.
(72) $\frac{1}{6}$ ft./sec.^{2} ; $23\frac{7}{10}$ m.p.h.

EXAMPLES XV.

(1) $4\frac{9}{5}$ H.P.
(2) 1 in 56.
(3) $\frac{1}{8}$ ft./sec.^{2}
(4) 1000 lb. wt. ; $698\frac{9}{8}$ H.P. ; $\frac{127}{2800}$ ft./sec.^{2}
(5) 165 lb. wt.
(6) $\dfrac{55H}{224R}$ ft./sec.
(7) 5·35 tons wt.
(8) 40 m.p.h. nearly.
(9) 7500 lb. wt. ; $\frac{313}{8400}$ ft./sec.^{2}

(10) 103 ; 800 H.P.
(12) 14 H.P.
(14) 375,000 lb. wt. ; $56,953\frac{1}{3}$ H.P.
(15) 11·3 nearly.
(16) 0·12 ft./sec.^{2} ; 2160 lb. wt.
(17) $28\frac{4}{5}$ H.P. ; 24·8 m.p.h.
(18) 0·644 H.P.
(19) 18 H.P.
(20) 1289.
(21) 51·8 m.p.h.
(22) $627\frac{1}{4}$ H.P. ; 45 m.p.h. nearly.

EXAMPLES XVI.

(2) 25·6 m.p.h. ; 1584 ft.

(5) $v = \dfrac{Pg}{2240m}\left(t - \dfrac{1}{2}\dfrac{t^2}{a}\right)$ ft./sec. ;

$\dfrac{P^2gt}{2240m}\left(1 - \dfrac{t}{2a}\right)\left(2 - \dfrac{t}{a}\right)$ ft. lb. per sec.

(7) $\dfrac{M}{2bg}\log\dfrac{a + bv_1{}^2}{a + bv_0{}^2}$ ft.

(8) 180 ft./sec.

(9) 3·68.

(12) 5·6 m.p.h. ; 14·84 H.P.

(13) 2 ft./sec.^{2}

(14) 1·7 mile.

(15) 55·3 m.p.h. ; $7260\displaystyle\int_0^V \dfrac{dv}{1936 - v^2}$.

(16) $2\frac{1}{7}$ ft./sec.

(17) 41 secs. ; $\frac{13}{800}$.

(18) $20\sqrt{2}$ ft./sec.

(19) 20·7 ft./sec.

(20) 1·7 miles ; 603·4 H.P.

(21) 2·2 ft./sec.^{2} ; 5·6 H.P.

(22) 2·5 × 10^7 pdls. ; 2 × 10^7 pdls.

(23) 33 m.p.h.

(24) 506 H.P.

(25) 27·4 ft./sec.

(26) (i) 8·3 ft. tons ; (ii) 6 ft./sec.
(iii) 18·5 ft. tons.

(27) Nearly 25 ft./sec.

(28) Nearly 32 ft./sec.

(29) $16\frac{2}{3}$ ft.

EXAMPLES XVII.

(1) 1 pdl. ; 100 ft. pdls.

(2) 741·6.

(3) 8 pdls.

(4) $1028\frac{4}{7}$ ft.

(6) (i) 1·382 × 10^4 ; (ii) 981^2 × 10^3.

(7) Ft. pdls. (i) × 1000 ; (ii) × 10^5 ;
(iii) × 10^4 ; (iv) × 10^6.

(10) 2,319,000.

(11) $\dfrac{L^3}{MT^2}$; 6·482 × 10^{-8}.

(12) $32M$ pdls. ; $\dfrac{M}{V}$ lb. per cu. ft. ;

$\dfrac{M}{62\cdot3V}$

443,100M dynes ; $\dfrac{\cdot016M}{V}$ gm. per

c.c. ; $\dfrac{M}{62\cdot3V}$.

EXAMPLES XVIII.

(1) 8 ft./sec.

(2) 20 cm./sec.

(3) $12\frac{1}{2}$ ft./sec. ; nearly 58·6 tons wt.

(4) $\dfrac{75\sqrt{3}}{8} = 16\cdot2$ ft./sec. ; 8·2 ft.

(5) $\frac{25}{288}$ pdls.

(6) 156 tons wt.

(8) 19·4 ft./sec. ; $3\frac{1}{88}$ per cent. ; $\frac{11}{1280}$
sec. ; $145\frac{5}{11}$ lb. wt.

(9) $\dfrac{R - 2W + \sqrt{R^2 + 48RW - 48W^2}}{26}$;
7·47 ft./tons.

(10) $\dfrac{m}{M}$; 31·15 tons wt.

(12) 30 ft./sec. ; 361 ft. tons ; $\frac{7}{57}$ ft.

(13) $\dfrac{M}{M + m}v$; $\dfrac{m}{M}\sqrt{\dfrac{M}{M + m}}v$;
$\dfrac{m^2v^2}{2Mg(M + m)}$.

(14) 19,400 lb. wt.

(15) $360\sqrt{97}$ lb. ft. units of impulse.

(17) (i) 30 ft./sec. ; (ii) 35·3 ft. ;
(iii) 16 : 1.

(20) 575·8 ft./sec.

(21) 715·8 lb. wt.

(22) 100·2 H.P.

(23) Nearly 22 lb. wt.

(24) $8\frac{1}{15}$ ft.

(25) $4\frac{1}{6}$ tons wt. ; $\dfrac{3\sqrt{2}}{32}$ sec.

(28) 834·5 H.P.

(29) $\dfrac{MV}{mv}$; $\dfrac{1}{2}\cdot\dfrac{Mm(V + v)^2}{(M + m)}$.

(30) 27,300 lb. ft. units.

(31) 307,700 ft. lb. ; 51,270 lb. wt.

(32) $65\frac{5}{48}$ lb. wt.

(33) 3 ft./sec. ; 72,090 ft. pdls.

(34) $\frac{1}{2}m(v - u)\left[v + u - 2V - \dfrac{m(v - u)}{M}\right]$;
$\frac{1}{2}m\dfrac{(v - u)}{a}\left[v + u - 2V - m\dfrac{(v - u)}{M}\right]$.

(37) $1\frac{3}{28}$ tons wt.

EXAMPLES XIX.

(2) $2\sqrt{\dfrac{2a(m_1 - m_2)}{g(m_1 + m_2)}}$ sec. ;

$\dfrac{m_2}{m_1 + m_2}\sqrt{\dfrac{2ga(m_1 - m_2)}{m_1 + m_2}}$.

(3) $\frac{16}{17}$ ft. ;   2 secs.

(5) $2\frac{13}{14}$ ft. ; $\dfrac{3\sqrt{5}}{4}$ secs.

(7) 6 ft./sec. ; $\frac{3}{4}$ sec.
(8) 0·96 sec., assuming that edge of table is rectangular. If the edge is assumed to be rounded the time is 0·870.

(11) $\sqrt{\dfrac{2awg}{W + w}}$;   B, $\dfrac{w}{W + w}\sqrt{\dfrac{2awg}{W + w}}$ vertical ; A has a vertical component velocity equal to that of B and a horizontal component of $\sqrt{\dfrac{2awg}{W + w}}$.

(12) Perpendicular to the original direction of the first particle at $\dfrac{10\sqrt{3}}{9}$ ft./sec.; 10 ft./sec. at 60° to its direction before the blow.

(16) A, $\dfrac{2\sqrt{13}I}{15m}$; B, $\dfrac{7I}{15m}$; C, $\dfrac{2I}{15m}$.

(17) $\dfrac{1}{2}\dfrac{P^2[m + (m' + m'')\sin^2\alpha]}{[m^2 + m(m' + m'') + 4m'm''\sin^2\alpha\cos^2}$

(18) $\dfrac{P}{2\sqrt{2m}}$; $\dfrac{P}{2\sqrt{2m}}$; zero.

(20) A, $\dfrac{m_2 I\cos\alpha}{m_2(m_1 + m_2 + m_3) + m_1 m_3\sin^2\alpha}$;

B, $\dfrac{I\sqrt{m_2{}^2 + m_1{}^2\sin^2\alpha} + 2m_1 m_2\sin^2\alpha}{m_2(m_1 + m_2 + m_3) + m_1 m_3\sin^2\alpha}$;

C, $\dfrac{(m_2 + m_1\sin^2\alpha)I}{m_2(m_1 + m_2 + m_3) + m_1 m_3\sin^2\alpha}$.

(21) $\frac{17}{60}$ sec. ;   6 ft./sec. ; $\frac{405}{512}$ ft. lb.

(22) $\dfrac{n(n - 1)}{2}\dfrac{S}{V}$; $\dfrac{V}{n}$.

(23) 32 ft./sec. ;   168 ft. lb. ;   2 lb.
(24) 2·4 ft./sec. ;   94 ft. pdls. ;   2·12 ft./sec.

EXAMPLES XX.

(1) 3 ft./sec. ; $3\frac{1}{2}$ ft./sec.
(2) 6 ft./sec. ; $7\frac{1}{2}$ ft./sec.
(3) $\frac{5}{9}$ ft./sec. ; $4\frac{8}{9}$ ft./sec. reversed.
(7) $\dfrac{v_1(m_1 - em_2)}{m_1 + m_2}$. $\dfrac{m_1 v_1(m_2 - m_3 e')(1 + e)}{(m_1 + m_2)(m_2 + m_3)}$; $\dfrac{m_1 m_2 v_1(1 + e)(1 + e')}{(m_1 + m_2)(m_2 + m_3)}$.

(8) 32·7 ft./sec. and 7·8 ft./sec., both reversed ;   47·8 ft. pdls.
(11) $\frac{3}{5}$ secs.
(12) 7000 ft. lb.
(13) 2 ft./sec. ;   3 ft./sec. ;   45 ft. pdls.

(15) 2 ft./sec. ;   5 ft./sec. ;   1050 ft. lb.
(17) $\frac{13}{64}u$; $\frac{15}{64}u$; $\frac{36}{64}u$.
(18) 1 ft./sec. ;   2800 ft. lb.
(24) Three.
(25) 160 ft. ;   360 ft.
(26) $\frac{5}{22}$; $2\frac{1}{2}$ ft./sec.
(30) $\dfrac{ab(1 + e)^2}{(a + b)(b + c)}u$; $\dfrac{a}{b} = \dfrac{b}{c} = e$.
(31) 38 ft./sec. ;   22 ft./sec., both reversed ;   42·07 per cent.
(32) $\dfrac{m_1 m_2(1 + e)(v_1 - v_2)}{m_1 + m_2}$.

EXAMPLES XXI.

(1) 1 ft. ; $\frac{1}{2}$ sec. ;   1·6 ft./sec.
(2) $\frac{4}{5}$.
(3) $10\sqrt{13}$ ft./sec. at $\tan^{-1}\left(\dfrac{1}{2\sqrt{3}}\right)$ with the plane.

(4) (i) $8\sqrt{13}$ ft./sec. at $\tan^{-1}$ $(\frac{2}{3})$ below the horizontal ;

(ii) $8\sqrt{19}$ ft./sec. at $\tan^{-1}\left(\dfrac{7\sqrt{3}}{9}\right)$ below the horizontal.

(5) 0·0256 ft. lb.
(6) 0·91.

(7) $1\frac{1}{5}$ ft. from the corner at $\tan^{-1}(\frac{3}{2})$.
(8) (i) $u\sqrt{\cos^2\alpha + e^2\sin^2\alpha}$ at $\tan^{-1}$ $(e\tan\alpha)$;
   (ii) $mu(1 - \sqrt{\cos^2\alpha + e^2\sin^2\alpha})$
   (iii) $\frac{1}{2}mu^2\sin^2\alpha(1 - e^2)$.
(10) 2·3 ins.
(11) $\dfrac{u(1 - e)}{2}$ towards the wall ;
   $\dfrac{u(1 + e)e'}{2}$ away from the wall.
(12) 5625 lb. wt. ; $2559\frac{3}{8}$ ft. lb.

EXAMPLES XXII.

(1) 8·66 ft./sec. perpendicular to the line of centres ; $2\frac{1}{2}$ ft./sec. along the line of centres.

(2) 3·7 ft./sec. at $\cot^{-1} \dfrac{5\sqrt{3}}{12}$ to line of centres ; 6·1 ft./sec. along the line of centres.

(3) 4·62 ft./sec. at 60° to the line of centres ; 4·16 ft./sec. at $\tan^{-1}$ $\left(\dfrac{\sqrt{3}}{7}\right)$ to the line of centres.

(4) 4·07 ft./sec. at $\tan^{-1}(-3\sqrt{3})$ to the line of centres ; 6·43 ft./sec. at $\tan^{-1}\left(\dfrac{3\sqrt{3}}{11}\right)$ to the line of centres.

(5) $\dfrac{\sqrt{2}}{2}u$ and $\dfrac{\sqrt{6}}{2}u$, each at 45° to the line of centres.

(6) 0·8u ft./sec. and 1·16u ft./sec. at 40° 12′ and 48° 12′ to the line of centres.

(10) $\dfrac{u\sqrt{4\sin^2\alpha + \cos^2\alpha(1-e)^2}}{2}$; $\dfrac{u\cos\alpha(1+e)}{2}$; at $\tan^{-1}\left[\dfrac{2\tan\alpha}{1-e}\right]$ to, and along the line of centres.

(13) Along the line of centres ; at $\tan^{-1}\left(\dfrac{10\sqrt{3}}{3}\right)$ to the line of centre.

EXAMPLES XXIII.

(4) A and B, $\dfrac{\sqrt{3}u}{5}(1+e)$; C, $\dfrac{u}{5}(2-3e)$.

(9) $V\sin\phi$ and $V\cos\phi$.

(15) 5 ft./sec. : 20 gm. cm. units of impulse.

(16) The impulsive friction is greater than the momentum down the plane, and the bodies will remain at rest.

EXAMPLES XXIV.

(1) (i) 36 ft. ; (ii) 3 secs., 144$\sqrt{3}$ ft. ; (iii) 92·24 ft./sec. at $\tan^{-1}\left(\dfrac{5\sqrt{3}}{18}\right)$ to the horizontal.

(2) (i) 128 ft. ; (ii) $112\frac{1}{2}$ ft. ; (iii) 288 ft.

(3) 80 ft./sec. ; $\dfrac{5\sqrt{2}}{2}$ sec.

(4) 5000$\sqrt{2}$ ft.

(5) 9600$\sqrt{3}$ ft.

(6) 80 ft./sec. at $\tan^{-1}(\frac{3}{4})$ to the horizontal.

(7) 1088 yds.

(8) 97,96 ft./sec. ; 4·33 secs.

(10) 277·12 ft.

(11) 1115·6 yds. ; $9\frac{1}{2}$° to the horizontal.

(12) 18·13 miles.

(13) 394·7 ft.

(14) 13·4 ft.

(15) $\tan^{-1}(\frac{4}{3})$; 200 ft./sec. ; 10 secs.

(16) $2\frac{1}{8}$ secs.

(18) 29·14 ft./sec.

(19) 64$\sqrt{660}$ ft./sec.

(20) Horizontal and vertical distances from O are 1152 ft., 1152 ft. ; 1440 ft., 720 ft.

(21) $\tan^{-1}(\frac{16}{33})$; 366·7 ft./sec.

(24) 4110 ft./sec. ; 25 miles.

(26) $\dfrac{a}{2}\sqrt{\dfrac{g}{2b}}$; $\sqrt{2gb}$.

(28) $110\frac{11}{15}$ ft. ; 60$\sqrt{3}$ ft.

(29) $a\tan\alpha - \dfrac{ga^2}{2V^2\cos^2\alpha} - b$.

(30) $\tan^{-1}(1\cdot05)$ to horizontal.

(32) $\dfrac{\sqrt{3}}{16}R$.

(33) $\tan^{-1}\left(\dfrac{11\sqrt{30}}{60}\right)$.

(34) $3\frac{21}{80}$ ft. ; 0·45 sec.

EXAMPLES XXV.

(1) $\dfrac{25\sqrt{3}}{4}$ sec. ; 1875 ft.

(2) (i) Nearly 8834 yds. ; (ii) nearly 15,300 yds.

(3) 217·5 metres.

(4) 2000 metres ; 6000 metres.

(5) 27,777$\frac{7}{9}$ yds. ; 21,566$\frac{2}{3}$ yds. 27,777$\frac{7}{9}$ yds. ; 24,408 yds.

(12) 64,030 ft. ; 1887 ft./sec. at $\tan^{-1}$ (1·6) to the horizontal.

(13) 160,000 ft. ; 100 secs.

EXAMPLES XXVI.

(3) $\tan^{-1}\left[\dfrac{bc}{a(c-a)}\right]$; $\dfrac{bc^2}{4a(c-a)}$.

(4) A little over $1°$; $2\cdot6$ ft.

(5) $15°$ and $75°$; $\dfrac{2-\sqrt{3}}{2+\sqrt{3}}$.

EXAMPLES XXVII.

(3) $\alpha-\tfrac12\sin^{-1}\left(\dfrac{a\sin 2\alpha}{a+b}\right)$; $\alpha\dfrac{b}{a+b}$; $15'$.

(4) $\dfrac{2\cos^2\alpha(u^2-2gl\sin\alpha)}{g}$;

$y=x\tan\alpha-\dfrac{gx^2}{2\cos^2\alpha(u^2-2gl\sin\alpha)}$;

$1+\dfrac{2gl\cos^2\alpha}{u^2\sin\alpha}$ times as great.

(12) $a\left(\sqrt{\dfrac{l+h}{h}}-1\right)$ from foot of wall ;

$\sqrt{\dfrac{g(a^2+4hl+4h^2)}{2h}}$.

(16) $31{,}200$ ft. ; $\tan^{-1}(1\tfrac32)$.

(17) $63\cdot24$ ft./sec. at $\tan^{-1}(2)$; $1\cdot09$ sec.

EXAMPLES XXVIII.

(1) $\dfrac{9v^2\sin\alpha\cos\alpha}{256}$; $\dfrac{v\sin\alpha}{64}$.

(4) 160 ft. horizontally from A.

(6) $\tfrac13$.

(8) $8h\sin\alpha$, where α is the inclination of the plane.

(9) $\dfrac{V^2(1+e)\tan\theta}{g\cos\alpha}$, where V is the velocity of projection, and $\cot 2\theta=(1+e)\tan\alpha$.

EXAMPLES XXIX.

(1) $2\tfrac12$ lb. wt.

(2) 120.

(3) $18\cdot15$ tons wt.

(4) $410\tfrac23$ lb. wt.

(5) $0\cdot45$ ft.

(6) $2\pi\sqrt{\dfrac{l}{g}}$.

(7) $\dfrac{240}{\pi}$.

(10) $36\cdot4$ ft./sec. ; $61\tfrac{1}{25}$ ft./sec.²

EXAMPLES XXX.

(1) $\dfrac{\pi^2n^2a}{900g}$.

(4) $\dfrac{18}{7\pi^2}$ ft.

(5) $4\cdot98$ ft. ; $10\cdot96$ lb. wt.

(6) $\dfrac{g(\lambda-ma\omega^2)}{\lambda a\omega^2}$.

(7) $\tfrac56\pi^2$ lb. wt.

(11) $\cos^{-1}\left(\dfrac{m}{M}\right)$; $\dfrac{1}{2\pi}\sqrt{\dfrac{Mg}{m(l-a)}}$.

(14) $ma\left(4\pi^2n^2-\dfrac{g}{b}\right)$.

(15) 12 lb. wt.

EXAMPLES XXXI.

(1) $2\cdot92$ ins.

(2) 40 ft./sec.

(3) $\dfrac{bv^2}{gr}$.

(4) $1\cdot15$ in.

(5) $50\cdot1$ m.p.h. ; $\tfrac98$.

(6) $48°\,54'$; $2\cdot28$ tons wt.

(7) 51 m.p.h.

(8) 8 ins.

(9) $7°\,40'$; $0\cdot1345$.

(10) $11°\,24'$; $0\cdot52$.

(11) $38\cdot5$ m.p.h.

(12) $38°\,27'$.

(13) $31\cdot87$ tons wt.

(15) $0\cdot06$ of wt.

(16) $0\cdot15$ ton wt. nearly.

(18) 1047 lb. wt.

(19) $18\cdot1$ m.p.h.

(20) $47\cdot36$ ft./sec.

(21) $\tan^{-1}\left(\dfrac{v^2}{gR}\right)$.

EXAMPLES XXXII.

(3) $\dfrac{Wa\omega^2}{g}$.

EXAMPLES XXXIII.

(1) 25·3 ft./sec. ; 9 oz. wt.

(3) 239 cm./sec.^{2} ; 1·24 gm. wt.

(4) 10·12 ft./sec.

(5) $8\sqrt{3}\sin\theta$ ft./sec. ; $1\frac{1}{2}$ lb. wt. ; $\frac{4}{3}$ ft. ; $\frac{3\sqrt{3}}{4}$ lb. wt.

(6) 6·3 ft. ; 6·8 ft.

(7) $3\frac{1}{3}$ ft.

(8) $1\frac{81}{20}$ tons wt.

(9) $27\frac{3}{11}$ m.p.h.

(11) $W\left(1+\dfrac{v^2}{ag}\right)$; 16 ft./sec. ; 4 ft. ; $\dfrac{W}{2}$.

(13) $16\sqrt{3}$ ft./sec. ; $\dfrac{8\sqrt{3}}{3\pi}$; $12\sqrt{2}$ ft./sec.

(14) 300 lb. wt. ; just.

(15) $mg(3\cos\theta-2)$ outwards ; $\dfrac{3g}{4}$.

(18) 3 lb. wt. ; 1 ft.

(20) 0·43 of its wt.

(24) $12\sqrt{2}$ ft./sec. ; $1\frac{1}{2}$ ft.

(26) 6 ins.

(28) $\sqrt{5ag}$; $\dfrac{a}{2}$ vertically below top of semicircle.

(29) (i) The particle describes complete circles.
  (ii) The particle does not reach the level of the point of suspension.

EXAMPLES XXXIV.

(1) $\sqrt{2\pi}$; $\dfrac{\pi}{2}$.

(2) $5\sqrt{2}$ ft./sec. ; $3\sqrt{2}$ ft./sec.

(3) 3 ft. ; π sec.

(4) 2π sec. ; 5 ft./sec.^{2}

(5) 4 ft. ; $2\sqrt{7}$ ft./sec.

(6) 3π ft./sec. ; $3\pi^2$ ft./sec.^{2}

(8) 8 secs. ; $\dfrac{11\sqrt{2}}{12}$ ft. or $11\sqrt{2}$ ins.

(9) $\dfrac{2}{\pi}$ ft./sec. ; $\dfrac{4}{5\pi^2}$ ft.

(11) a ; $\dfrac{2\pi}{k}$.

(13) $2\pi\sqrt{\dfrac{x_2{}^2-x_1{}^2}{v_1{}^2-v_2{}^2}}$; $\sqrt{\dfrac{v_1{}^2x_2{}^2-v_2{}^2x_1{}^2}{v_1{}^2-v_2{}^2}}$;

$\sqrt{\dfrac{v_1{}^2x_2{}^2-v_2{}^2x_1{}^2}{x_2{}^2-x_1{}^2}}$;

$\dfrac{\sqrt{v_1{}^2-v_2{}^2}}{x_2{}^2-x_1{}^2}\sqrt{v_1{}^2x_2{}^2-v_2{}^2x_1{}^2}$.

$\dfrac{2\pi\sqrt{5}}{3}$; $\dfrac{\sqrt{161}}{3}$; $\sqrt{\dfrac{161}{5}}$; $\dfrac{3\sqrt{161}}{5}$.

(14) Nearly 1600.

(16) $\dfrac{\pi}{3\omega}$ sec. ; $\dfrac{\sqrt{3}}{2}a\omega$.

(17) 2·72 ins. ; 0·095 sec.

(18) π ft./sec. ; 60 ft./sec.^{2} ; $\dfrac{\sqrt{3}\pi}{2}$ ft./sec. ; 30 ft./sec.^{2}

(22) (i) $2\pi n\sqrt{a^2-x^2}$; (ii) $2\pi na\sin 2\pi nt$.

(27) (i) $\dfrac{2}{\pi}$ ft./sec. ; (ii) $\dfrac{4}{\pi^2}$ ft./sec.

(28) $\dfrac{8\sqrt{10}}{5}$ ft. ; $2\pi\sqrt{\tfrac{2}{5}}$ sec. ; 0·080 sec.

(29) $\dfrac{9}{\pi}$ ft. ; (i) $\dfrac{15\sqrt{3}}{2}$ ft./sec. ; (ii) $\dfrac{15\sqrt{2}}{2}$ ft./sec.

(30) $x=5\sin 4t$.

(31) 8·4 ft. ; 4·683 secs. ; 0·204.

(32) 52·36 ft./sec. ; 10966 ft./sec.^{2}

EXAMPLES XXXV.

(1) 6 ins. ; $\dfrac{\pi\sqrt{10}}{20}$ sec.

(2) $\dfrac{\pi\sqrt{6}}{24}$ sec. ; $\dfrac{\sqrt{2}}{2}$ ft./sec. ; 8 ft./sec.^{2}

(3) About $\frac{8}{9}$ in.

(4) (i) $\dfrac{5}{\pi}$ ft. ; (ii) $\dfrac{25\pi}{64}$ ft. lb. per sec.

(8) $\dfrac{\pi}{8}\sqrt{9-2l}$; $\dfrac{4}{3\sqrt{9-2l}}$ ft./sec.

(9) 2 ft. ; $\dfrac{\sqrt{2}\pi}{4}$.

(11) $\dfrac{240\sqrt{2}}{\pi}$ per min. ; $\dfrac{4\sqrt{2}}{3}$ ft./sec.

(12) $\dfrac{\pi}{4}\sqrt{\dfrac{5}{3}}$ sec. ; $\dfrac{\sqrt{5}}{5}$ ft./sec. ; 9 lb. wt.

(13) $\dfrac{\pi\sqrt{3}}{6}$ sec. ; $13\frac{1}{2}$ lb. wt. ; 1 ft./sec.

(15) $\frac{5\pi}{24}$ sec.; $\frac{4\sqrt{3}}{5}$ ft./sec.; $\frac{192}{25}$ ft./ sec.²

(16) 8 ins.; 5 lb. wt.; $\frac{\pi}{4}$ sec.

(17) $1\frac{1}{5}$ in.; $\frac{\pi\sqrt{30}}{30}$ sec.; $\frac{\sqrt{30}}{5}$ ft./sec.

(18) $\frac{2\sqrt{3}}{3}$ ft./sec.; $\frac{\pi\sqrt{3}}{12}$ sec.

(19) $\frac{\pi\sqrt{2}}{14}$ sec., taking $g = 980$.

(20) $\frac{3\pi}{8}$ sec.; $\frac{2}{5}$ ft./sec.

(21) $\frac{16\pi^2}{9}$ ft./sec.²; $\frac{8\pi}{3}$ ft./sec.
$$\sqrt{16 + \frac{9u^2}{4\pi^2}};\ 2\pi.$$

(22) $\frac{\pi\sqrt{2}}{8}$ sec.

(25) $\frac{25}{\pi}$ ft.; $\frac{5\pi}{2}$ lb. wt.

(26) $2\pi\sqrt{\dfrac{a(M+m)}{mg}}$ sec.; $\frac{aM}{m}$.

(28) 4 ins.; $\frac{3}{5}\sqrt{10}$ ft./sec.

(29) $T = \frac{2\pi a}{V}$; $\frac{V^2 b}{a^2}$; $\frac{9}{11}$ nearly.

(30) zero; 9·0 nearly.

EXAMPLES XXXVI.

(1) Gains 270 secs.
(2) 99·4 cm.; 1·775 mm. shorter.
(4) 405 secs.
(5) $\frac{100}{101}$.
(6) 120 secs.
(7) $\frac{9}{500}$ in.; $4888\frac{8}{9}$ ft.

(8) 1·0005 : 1; 1·852 mile.
(9) 30·2.
(11) 1·86 in.; 1 lb. wt.; 1·92 sec.
(12) 11·4°.
(13) Nearly 320 ft.; 1°.

EXAMPLES XXXVII.

(1) $2\pi\sqrt{\dfrac{ml\,L}{\lambda(l-L)}}$.

(6) $2x_0\sqrt{\dfrac{E}{M+4m}}$.

(12) 1·9 ft./sec.
(14) 7·35 ins.
(17) (i) 3 ins.; (ii) 30 lb. wt.;
(iii) $\frac{\pi}{8}$ sec.; (iv) $1\frac{1}{2}$ ins.

(19) $\frac{1}{3}a$.

(20) $\sqrt{\dfrac{5am}{\lambda}}\left[\pi - 2\sin^{-1}\frac{2}{7} + \sqrt{2}\sin^{-1}\sqrt{\frac{2}{47}}\right]$.

(21) $\frac{2\pi^2\alpha l}{g}$.

(22) At a point $a\,\dfrac{m-m'}{m+m'}$ from the middle point of the string.

(23) $\dfrac{(11+\sqrt{21})l}{10}$.

EXAMPLES XXXVIII.

(1) $\frac{\lambda}{\theta} = \frac{\mu}{2r^2} + c$; $2\lambda^2 r^3 - \frac{u^2\theta^4}{r}$;
$$\lambda\mu r\theta^2 + \frac{2\mu^2\theta^3}{r}.$$

(8) θ.

(12) $\frac{d\theta}{dt} = \sqrt{\dfrac{2g(1-\cos\theta)}{a}}$.

(13) $\omega^2 r$; $\tan^{-1}\left(\dfrac{b}{a}\tan\omega t\right)$ with x-axis.

(14) $\frac{\pi}{\sqrt{\mu}}$.

(15) $\dfrac{1}{(y^2+1)^2}$; $-\dfrac{y}{(y^2+1)^2}$.

EXAMPLES XXXIX.

(1) $\dfrac{1}{2ax+b}$; $a = \dfrac{1}{15,000}$, $b = \dfrac{3}{100}$; $v = 20$.

(2) $\frac{3}{2}$ sec.; $\pm\sqrt{6}$ secs.: 2 secs., -1 sec.; -2 ft., 25 ft.; 18 ft./sec.², -18 ft./sec.²

(3) 3 secs. or -2 secs.; $8\frac{1}{2}$ ft. or $12\frac{1}{3}$ ft.

(10) $\sqrt[3]{\dfrac{\mu}{\lambda}}$ from O.

EXAMPLES XL.

(1) The hodograph is a quadrant of a circle beginning due N. and ending due W. of the origin, and of radius proportional to $\frac{8g}{8}$. About 1·8 in.

(2) Velocity $= 8\sqrt{3}$ ft./sec. The vector makes an angle $\cos^{-1}\left(\dfrac{1}{2\sqrt{3}}\right)$ with the horizontal.

(4) (i) a circle ; (ii) a vertical straight line ; (iii) the parabola $y^2 = x$.

(5) The parabola $y = 12(x - 1)^2$.

EXAMPLES XLI.

(1) $2Ma^2$.
(4) $\frac{8}{3}Ma^2$.
(5) $\frac{1}{3}M(a^2 + b^2)$.

(6) $\frac{1}{2}Ma^2$.
(11) (i) $\frac{13}{18}M$, where $M =$ mass of remainder of plate ; (ii) $\frac{19}{32}M$.

EXAMPLES XLII.

(2) $\frac{1780}{2488}M$, where M is the mass of wheel and shaft.
(5) $\frac{1787}{5776}M$, where M is the total mass.

(6) 48·4 lb./ft.^{2}
(7) (i) $\frac{2}{3}Ma^2$; (ii) $\frac{5}{12}Ma^2$.

EXAMPLES XLIII.

(1) 8 radians per sec.
(2) 16 lb./ft.^{2} nearly.
(3) $24\sqrt{\frac{5}{7}}$ ft./sec. ; 20 ft. lb.
(4) $\frac{8}{3}\sqrt{3}$ radians per sec.
(5) $\frac{16}{17}\sqrt{102}$ ft./sec.
(6) 18,365 lb./ft.^{2}
(7) $\frac{3}{2}ml^2$; $\sqrt{\dfrac{2\sqrt{3}g}{3l}}$.

(9) 101 and 202 R.P.M. nearly.
(11) $\sqrt{\dfrac{g}{a}}$ radians per sec.
(12) 28,380 ft. lb.
(13) $6\sqrt{g}$; $\sqrt{30g}$.
(14) $M\dfrac{a^2 + 2b^2}{128}\omega^2$ ft. lb.
(15) 8·05.

EXAMPLES XLIV.

(1) $2\pi\sqrt{\dfrac{13l}{15g}}$.
(3) 0·06 oz.
(4) $\frac{375}{8}\pi^2$ ft. lb. ; 0·614 lb. ft.
(5) 57·9 ft./tons ; 17 lb. wt./ft. ; 1200 revolutions.
(6) $\dfrac{\sqrt{3}\pi}{3}$ sec.
(7) 3125 ft. lb. nearly ; $\dfrac{25\pi}{4}$ lb. wt.
(9) $\dfrac{\pi}{4}\sqrt{7}$ sec.

(11) $\dfrac{Mgr - G}{k + Mr^2}$.
(18) $mh(l - h)$.
(19) $\sqrt{\dfrac{2mgx}{M + m}}$.
(21) $\frac{64}{13}$ radians.
(22) $\frac{2}{3}$ ft./sec. ; $\frac{32}{3}$ radians per sec. ; $\frac{3695}{256}$ lb./ft.^{2}
(23) $\pi\sqrt{\dfrac{51}{5g}}$.
(25) $16\frac{2}{3}$ revolutions ; 3·49 ft.
(27) 32 lb. ft. units of impulse.
(28) 150 revolutions ; $40\frac{20}{27}$ lb. wt./ft.

EXAMPLES XLV.

(2) 142·8 ft. lb.
(3) $4\sqrt{3}$; $\dfrac{40\sqrt{3}}{3}$ lb. ft. units.
(7) $m\sqrt{\dfrac{2gh}{k^2 + h^2}}\left[h - \dfrac{h^2 + k^2}{l}\right]$.
(15) 781 lb. wt.
(16) $\dfrac{x}{4}$.

(17) $\dfrac{aGJ}{Ib^2 + Ja^2}$.
(19) $2\sqrt{\dfrac{k^2 + c^2}{gc}}\log_e(\sqrt{2} + 1)$.
(20) $\sqrt{6ag}$, where $2a$ is the length of BC. $\dfrac{M}{6}\sqrt{6ag}$.

EXAMPLES XLVI.

(4) Accel. $= \sqrt{f^2 - 2fx\omega^2 + (x^2 + y^2)\omega^4}$, where x, y are the co-ordinates of the point referred to O as origin and the given lines as axis of x. The circle $(x^2 + y^2)\omega^4 - 2fx\omega^2 + f^2 - F^2 = 0$, where F is the given magnitude. This is a circle fixed relatively to the disc, and not a circle in space.

(5) C is the point $x = \dfrac{a}{2}$, $y = \dfrac{a \sin \theta}{2(1 - \cos \theta)}$, referred to A as origin and AB as x-axis, and $a = AB$.

EXAMPLES XLVII.

(4) 1·3 ft. lb.

(5) 281,635·2 ft. lb. ;   117·3 lb. wt.

(7) $\dfrac{a^2 g(M + nm + m') \sin \alpha}{2Ma^2 + nm\left(\dfrac{4a^2 + ab + b^2}{3}\right) + \dfrac{m'}{2}(2a^2 + b^2)}.$

(8) (i) 5 lb./ft.² ;   (ii) 122½ lb./ft.² ; $\dfrac{g}{7}$.

(10) $\sqrt{\dfrac{10mg(1 - \cos \theta)}{(7M + 10m + 10m \cos \theta)a}}$;

$\tan^{-1}\left[\dfrac{49M^2 + 189Mm + 205m^2}{5m(7M + 13m)}\right]$ to the horizontal.

(11) $\sqrt{\dfrac{3\sqrt{2}g(1 - \cos \theta)}{a(1 + 3\sin^2 \theta)}}$.

(12) $\dfrac{\pi^2 \alpha}{3(1 - \cos \alpha)}$.

(14) A vertical straight line.

(16) $\frac{11}{20}$ W lb. wt. on back ; $\frac{9}{20}$ W lb. wt. on front.

EXAMPLES XLVIII.

(1) $\left(\dfrac{Fx}{m'l} + \dfrac{F}{m+m'}\right)$ and $\left(\dfrac{Fx}{ml} - \dfrac{F}{m+m'}\right)$, where x is the distance of F from the centre of gravity.

(4) The mid-point of the wire moves with uniform velocity $\dfrac{V}{2}$, and the wire rotates with angular velocity.

$\dfrac{V}{2a}$, where $2a$ is the length of the wire.

(7) $\dfrac{4P}{m}$ and $\dfrac{2P}{m}$.

(8) $\dfrac{m(k^2 + r^2)P}{Mr^2 + 2mk^2}$.

(16) $\cos^{-1}(\frac{2}{3})$, approximately.

Printed in Great Britain by Lowe & Brydone Printers Ltd., London, N.W.1